Lessons
in
Humiliation

Lessons
in
Humiliation

Timothy Edward

With illustrations by the author

Dear Vanse and Tony,
Thanks for waiting,
Happy reading!

Tim
x

I'd understand if you
built a 10 foot wall
along our boundary
x

Matador
9 Priory Business Park,
Wistow Road, Kibworth Beauchamp,
Leicestershire. LE8 0RX
Tel: (+44) 116 279 2299
Fax: (+44) 116 279 2277
Email: books@troubador.co.uk
Web: www.troubador.co.uk/matador

ISBN 978 1784620 110

British Library Cataloguing in Publication Data.
A catalogue record for this book is available from the British Library.

Typeset in 11pt Georgia by Troubador Publishing Ltd, Leicester, UK
Printed and bound in the UK by TJ International, Padstow, Cornwall

Matador is an imprint of Troubador Publishing Ltd

For Julie

By way of a preamble

London is warm and sunny as I saunter to a casting studio in a cul de sac behind Soho Square. Pressing the buzzer in a manner calculated to smash all opposition, I leap a pile of junk mail and, taking two steps at a time, ascend the dingy, creaking staircase. A few grunted greetings from the disparate huddle of other hopefuls and I take my seat under a white-board upon which is scrawled 'Keep Camden Clean'. A laudable initiative and one in which I feel I might excel.

"Henry Robson?"

Three male executives on the sofa, one sparsely bearded with clipboard, denim jacket, dirty jeans and grubby Che Guevara T-shirt; another fiddling with a mini video camera and a third looking serenely effeminate with plucked eyebrows and orange tea-cosy hat.

"OK, look," drawls Beardy, "what Camden is looking for is a bloke coming out of his house one morning, kissing his wife goodbye –"

"He's all dolled up for the City," interrupts Tea-cosy camply. "Suit, briefcase and umbrella. Put this bowler on."

I do as he says although the hat is a cheap pantomime imitation and far too small.

"Yeah," resumes the first. "He comes down the steps onto the pavement and does the business right there."

"The business?"

"Yeah, right there on the pavement," he reiterates. "Then he waves to the vicar who's walking by –"

"And off he goes to work," says Tea-cosy, now peering into a monitor.

"So," I persist, still at a loss, "you want me to come down the steps and do what?" They're looking at me as if I'm from another world – which I am.

"Look," snaps the cameraman, speaking for the first time, "you come down the steps, drop your trousers, take a shit on the pavement like a dog – all perfectly normal – pull up your trousers and bugger off to work. We at Camden Council are having an anti-dog shit campaign. Did no-one tell you?"

Agent P's message might conceivably have been more specific, I suppose:

Henry, commercial casting
12.20 Thurs. Health & Safety.

"Got it," I murmur.

"It's not acceptable for you or me to shit in the street, is it?" he wanks on. "So why do we let our dogs?"

As a professional actor I must strive to appear unruffled.

"D'you want me to do the whole trouser thing now?"

"Yeah, that'd be good. Off you go. And ... Action!"

Obediently, I waft down my imaginary front steps, straighten my bowler, lower my hosiery and squat, leaving my boxer shorts in situ for the sake of what little dignity still remains. As I wave cordially to the passing vicar, Beardy perks up again.

"Ok now, Henry, strain a bit for me." Inwardly, I raise a

disdainful eyebrow, but outwardly I do as he says, grimacing in what I hope appears on screen to be pure defecatory Stanislavski. "Push a bit harder." I feel my face going red, the veins in the side of my neck becoming engorged. (I may be on the cusp of over-acting.) "Alright, look up and wave to the vicar again."

At which point, inspiration bursts over me, a *coup de foudre* to guarantee me this most prestigious of jobs, a masterstroke with which to dazzle a sofa. Camden's Anti-Canine Faecal Campaign will blossom to cult status with me as its star! This is why I trained to be an actor.

Thus, I do the unthinkable: improvising wildly with a Starbucks paper napkin I happen to have in my pocket, I create a moment of comedy gold.

I wipe my bum.

(Having once featured in a tri-lingual moist toilet paper commercial in Switzerland, I am an expert in this narrow but crucial field of human endeavour.)

A sudden silence descends; I steal a glance towards the sofa. They are motionless, dazzled in the face of this firestorm of raw talent.

"Ok, erm, Henry, let's try that once again from the top," says Tea-cosy, sounding rather miffed. "Don't worry about the arse-wiping this time. Thanks."

In the past I have been buoyed up by castings, but this time, as I trudge southwards through Leicester Square, a potent sludge seems to pour over me like the bowl of mouldy chicken stock I've forgotten at the back of the fridge and which I inadvertently upset when trying to find the pesto. Had this all been just a cynical exercise in degradation? I can imagine the execs heading back to Beardy's trendy basement dive in Islington and inviting a few chums round for a private screening. Twenty middle-aged men debagging themselves and straining for Camden? I can almost hear their laughter.

PART ONE

1

Estivation in the Environs

 "I say, look at that one!" says Cecil, pointing across me with his walking stick. "I've not seen her before. What do you think, Henry? Nine out of ten?"

Four days have dragged by and I have heard nothing from the Camden casting couch. I am therefore sitting on a bench halfway up the Village Green being initiated by Cecil into the art of (as he puts it) 'ogling the young mothers' who gossip on the grass after school has begun. "If I was fifty years younger," he goes on, "I'd have no hesitation in introducing myself to her."

"I bet you wouldn't," I say, staring pointedly in the opposite direction. "But, you know what, I *am* fifty years younger and I'm asking you very nicely to stop bellowing like that or whoever it is will hear you." He snorts defiantly and continues to leer past me.

"On closer inspection," he adds in a loud stage whisper, "I'll go for a ten. Go on, young man, take a look."

With a sigh of mock-resignation, I turn my head, the better

to 'ogle' the bouncing auburn hair and energetic gait of a slim and spry personage striding towards us.

Cecil's watery blue eyes have not deceived him; the object of his admiration is a good-looking girl in her late thirties, a little pale perhaps, but oddly grim-faced on such a sparkling spring morning. Indeed, as she hurries past us up the slope towards the church, I am struck by a distinct absence of *joie de vivre*. "In my experience, Henry," declares Cecil, his guttural old voice quavering with an enthusiasm entirely disgraceful for a man of his age, "that beautiful young woman is in urgent need of cheering up." He nudges me with a leather-patched elbow and I feel the weight of eight decades of consummate seduction being brought to bear. "And you, sir, are just the man for the job."

A pilot light of excitement flickers then fades as I gaze after the girl. "Are you trying to match-make?" I ask, giving him a look. "She's probably married."

"No gentleman can see a damsel so evidently in distress without riding to her aid," says my old-fashioned friend, grinning like a naughty schoolboy. "Have you never read Dornford Yates?"

"Dornford who?"

"Ah me, such ignorance!" he sighs. "I have his complete *oeuvre*. I'll drop you one in later. Dornford will improve your technique no end."

"Can't wait," I smile, rising and rubbing the back of my trousers, the bench being slightly damp. "But now it's time to nail some auditions."

"One more thing before you go, Henry."

"Yes?"

"I saw you. Admiring her bum."

Am I really that transparent? "Cecil," I say, feeling myself beginning to blush, "I'm in the presence of a Master; and as the younger red-blooded male round here I'm always keen to pick up tips."

*

4

As I sit down at my desk, I receive a text.

Casting. Tomorrow 14.50.
Tall acting. Fromage frais.

Which reminds me to speak to Agent P about the potential side-effects of his adherence to the school of minimalist syntax.

2

Profile of an Actor

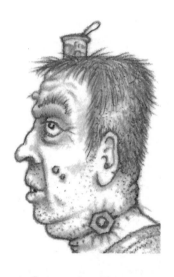

"Henry Robson?"

I close Cecil's first volume of Dornford Yates (to whose 1930s shenanigans I am already addicted) and stuff it into my rucksack.

I am pleased that Agent P is being so industrious in his provision of castings for me, but I would have preferred an 'audition'. A casting does not aspire to the theatrical gravitas of an audition. You know you are at an audition when the door is opened by a nice old gentleman wearing a scraggy beige suit, a collarless shirt and a pink cravat. He is carrying a crumpled script and welcomes you in to a shabby rehearsal room with a quasi-masonic double grip of your outstretched hand, covering it first with his left and then rolling it over to the side. This unexpected and intimate manipulation, coupled with soul-searching eye contact over half-moons, results in the certain knowledge that you can trust this avuncular chap as unquestioningly as when last you suckled at your mother's bosom. By these simple yet generous gestures he has already gained intimate access to your very being; he has established a profound level of understanding of your need to please and to be employed and cherished by *him* and him alone. Like a mother, he makes you feel special, important, relevant and, above all, loved.

At a casting, on the other hand, love is absent. Nobody comes out to meet you, except the actor before you with whom it is customary to exchange a whispered 'good luck, darling.'

As I pass through the hallowed portals, I realise with alarm that I am angry. I am angry because I am still bubbling with resentment over the Camden débâcle. This is bad news because no self-respecting advertising executive will want his brand of fromage frais to be associated with an angry tall person.

Who has addressed me? I can make out virtually nothing until my eyes adjust to the contrast of bright lights and gloom, but a plump silhouette shakes my hand in a peremptory way, and announces "Henry Robson, Nick. Come through darling. This is Carol, Ashley, Brian. This is Henry, guys" and pulls me forward into the glare of the lighted area. Blinded, I stand in front of where I imagine the camera to be. Nick repeats "Henry Robson?" accusingly and, when I have nodded my smiling assent, taps my name into his computer. Carol, Ashley and Brian will be scrunched up in the darkness on one of the two sofas. The second contains shadows of anonymous and non-participatory execs who will remain cocooned in a mystique of silent importance, cloaked by warm and fusty darkness.

I have caught a glimpse of my hostess now; the clipboard gives her away as a female casting director, disdainful in her frumpiness and in appearance not unlike a visiting aunt down for the weekend who has been coerced into attending a primary school jumble sale. Like me, she is prone to terminal disappointment, someone for whom life is the stuff of abject misery, a self-styled Olympian deity with her golden talons firmly gripping my thespian scrotum; someone to be nurtured, written to and fawned upon. She riffles through bits of paper while Nick rattles buttons and focuses his lens on me; I hear myself saying "Good afternoon one and all" a little too cheerily, firing off my most obsequious yet characterful smile in the general direction of the execs who are quite thrown by this irreverent attempt at human contact. I receive embarrassed nods and grunts in exchange. I can make them out now, peering up at me, glancing back at their laptops, checking whether this new offering matches the image they had in mind, the one sketched on the story-board. Actors as commodities; as brand definition. There is little difference, I think glumly, between me and a sample pot of marigold matt emulsion on the shelf at B&Q. Will they choose me? Will they pop me into their trolley and try me on the wall at home? Or will another sample suit them better? Will I be put back on the shelf?

"Just stand on the white cross, Henry. Thanks, darling. If you could say your name and agent into camera." *And if I couldn't?*

Guidance for Castings: Flirt openly with the camera. Desire it. Squirm in front of it. Yearn to snuggle up and caress its smooth black lens which you long to insert into unspeakable places. Let it be seduced and smitten by the tantalising and irresistible charms of your unique and incomparable talents. Ignore any prior commitments you may have to self-respect; abase and prostitute yourself at the feet of its very tripod. Become, in short, the love of its life. Anything for a couple of grand, a glamorous day or two in a foreign studio, free bowel-improving fromage frais, a plush hotel and who knows what romantic possibilities thrown in.

"Could we see your profile, Henry?"

I turn to the left and realise that what little adrenalin I have mustered is already reverting to disappointment and irritation. This is premature and unforgivable, because Nick is still filming me and I know the execs are watching my every emotional nuance on their monitor. I force myself to appear cheerful and positive but inside the bile is beginning to rise. How much time and money have I wasted coming all the way up to London? There doesn't even appear to be a script; the tossers are just *looking* at me, for Christ's sake. I didn't train for *this*! I'm not a model! Are they not even going to make me improvise? Am I to go home and never hear from them again? – feel like shit for a couple of days as the rejection seeps through me? Don't mind me, you dicks, I've been here before and you know what? – I'd rather be a pot of paint.

"And the other, please."

I turn and give them my left. I raise the downstage eyebrow and flutter my puckered lips at the fuckers. And then, from the depths of one of the sofas I hear the honeyed words I long for in my wildest dreams: a sound redolent of the post-coital groan of an obese female smoker wallowing naked in a bottomless vat of custard powder:

"Oh, wonderful!"

She likes my profile. I'm made! I'm happy.

However, this is no time to bask in the glory that shall soon be mine, for the casting director is advancing towards me brandishing a biro. My talent, that fearsome stallion, full of confidence and ambition now, rears up and whinnies. I am about to be unleashed and put through my paces. This is what I love about my chosen career.

The woman opens her mouth to describe the tone of the commercial when the door opens. Enter a minion bearing coffees from the *Prêt-à-Manger* round the corner. The casting director's comely posterior (only partially contained, I note, by some generously cut blue jeans that I think may be a sartorial misjudgement) undulates away from me towards the execs and I am left on my white cross offering the camera a medley from my extraordinary range of *Come hither, employ me* faces until I realise that Nick is also at the trough.

Only seconds ago, I knew that my profile had secured me the job. Now, being ignored by all those I so wish to impress, my thoughts yo-yo back to the maudlin. What a triumph my life in

Acting has been so far. Here am I, clinging by one buttock to the remains of what might have been a very splendid career, standing like an oaf in front of a mob of indifferent dickheads taking a coffee break. Did I spend many thousands of pounds training at a drama school that no-one's heard of for this? Listen, I have learnt all sorts of things: I can use my organs of articulation, for example (the lips, the teeth, the tip of the tongue) to speak in Received Pronunciation. Like Bertie Wooster's demonic Aunt Agatha I can now 'bellow like a mastodon across primeval marshes' without getting a sore throat and, by dint of shuffling bad-temperedly at the back of bi-weekly tap-dancing classes, I am now able, according to my pretty Swedish dance instructor, to walk across a stage and talk at the same time. In short, I am a serious actOR. After all this expensive burnishing of my immense talent, can it be that I might fail to be cast in a fromage frais commercial as a result of not impressing a sofa-full of geeks even with a left profile like mine? (If this text is being studied for an examination in English Literature, the word *Irony* should now be scribbled in the margin.)

"Do sit down, Henry. Sorry to keep you. Short conference. Thanks."

I sit on a green plastic chair next to a piano in the corner. A memory stirs.

A black-painted studio theatre in a drama college one evening in December. Twenty-three Postgraduate students sitting in silence, hungry for praise, desperate for a kind word to tell them that they have, above all other trainee actors ever, a glittering future.

A skinny, hunched and crow-like figure rises uncertainly to her feet. She wears a long black dress and a red scarf, her cropped hair dyed slightly too black to disguise the fact that she is nearly eighty. Leaning on a far younger woman (with whom, they say, she is 'in a relationship'), she totters down the auditorium steps. We gaze at her in awe, for she has attended our performance in order to gauge our progress. Confident in our own new-found actor's voices, we hope to have satisfied her that success 'in the business' is only a step or two away.

The lady whose good opinion we crave is none other than Myrtle, the Principal, the Founder of the College and generally *le grand fromage*. I imagine that we have offered her a prime cut of a Hungarian play ungrammatically entitled *Have*. This is a piece whose sublime worthiness has baffled us to the point of complete mystification, but nonetheless we have performed a scene from it on a set entirely made up of green plastic chairs not unlike the one upon which I am now perched. Myrtle pauses near the exit. Her eyes, o'erhung with ill-applied mascara, peer slowly around, aware perhaps of our need for praise, of how insecure we are, of how much we yearn to be loved by a paying public. And then she speaks, apparently addressing her companion, her voice a tiny, creaking whisper only just audible in the awed silence:

"I'm so lucky to have such lovely students, don't you agree, Miriam?" Miriam nods and squeezes Myrtle's arm. "But, darlings," she resumes, turning her gimlet gaze upon our eager faces, "you must, *must* work on your voices. And never forget, darlings, that acting is *reacting*." She pauses and waves a crinkled hand at us. "Thank you for all your hard work so far," she quavers, smiling beatifically. "Goodbye, darlings, and remember to love each other."

"Henry! Hi, sorry to have kept you waiting." The casting director rematerialises once more and I rise from the green plastic of reminiscence.

"Could you just show your hands to the camera, Henry? Both sides. Thanks. Any commercials running at the moment?"

"No." *As if.*

"Any past commercials likely to clash with fromage frais?" A brief image of gladiators duelling to the death in pink, creamy slop flashes through my head.

"No."

She explains the commercial: I am Herman Munster bedecked in cobwebs and sitting up in his coffin. My head is flat, my brows beetling and I am holding a pot of fromage frais in my enormous, warty hand. Quite why they have insisted on tall actors today is a mystery since we are doing sitting-down-in-sarcophagus acting, but mine is not to reason why: the sofa must know what it's doing. They want tall: tall they shall have. I measure six foot-five in my socks, and frankly I'm used to looking down on people, but out there in the waiting room, I was the little guy, the runt of the litter. Some of those other buggers were coming in at seven foot six.

Twice I sit up holding a yoghurt pot for them, first with comic Munster-like glee, the second time – as directed – faster and with menace. I am not required to speak, but with a profile like mine, I don't need to.

And then it's all over. "That's it, Henry. Thanks for coming in". Power smiles, overt sincerity, convivial handshakes. I glance towards the sofa as I head for the door. Do I prostrate myself at their feet, hug assorted legs to my bosom and salivate over expensive footwear before bowing myself out? No, I do not. Agent P would take a dim view.

As I hasten through the giants' waiting room (*Good luck, darlings*) and into the reality of Greek Street, I recognise again the onset of post-casting syndrome, the after-effects of excess adrenalin and optimism. On the one hand, I know that my chances of nailing this job are about one-in-twenty; on the other, they had liked my profile. They had smiled when I arrived. They had distinctly nodded at each other when I left. We had bonded, friends for all eternity. It's a dead cert.

After so long with no job, it occurs to me as I board the train back to the provinces, that it might be a plan to leave my ego at home next time. No use bringing it out to be flattered, burnished and buffed up only to have it stamped underfoot at some unspecified later date. Actors are assured that it's nothing personal, it's just that 'we know what we want, darling,' and if your face, voice or teeth don't happen to fit, you won't get the phone call. The problem is though that the more I try and quell my desire for glory, money and excitement, the more I crave it. Acting is an affliction, like a mosquito bite you scratch until it bleeds.

Also, meeting my smiling girlfriend for afternoon tea at Fortnum's might partially have compensated for this emotional roller-coaster, but regrettably I no longer have one.

3

Return to Waterloo

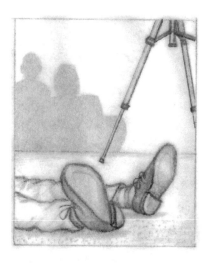

When not forlornly eyeing my telephone, willing it to be the bearer of good yoghurt news, I spend the following days justifying my existence on the planet by doing battle with my computer, urging those casting directors to bite and invite, offer me work; but the more I try, the less they rise to my entreaties.

I am sustained to a certain degree by the view out of my window. Sitting at my desk, I am treated to the constantly changing vista of Village life; we're not exactly talking Covent Garden piazza, but with all this buzzing community available to me just over the road – the squadrons of pretty young mums jostling for gossip twice a day – it occurs to me that if I am not to be the Face of Fromage Frais, I might as well go and sit out on Cecil's bench and cheer myself up with some discreet ogling; who knows, I might even bump into the mysterious and alluring auburn haired girl again.

Pausing only to grab my latest Dornford Yates, I am soon ensconced on the bench where I am duly rewarded for my daring proactivity with a nod and an actual 'hi' from the girl as she hurries by. The next morning, the silence from Agent P continuing unabated, I repeat the process and this time she actually stops in front of me, so close that I can smell her perfume and count the freckles over her beautiful nose. There are seven. My stomach lurches as I fall into her green eyes.

"Excuse me," she says, slightly out of breath, "I'm guessing you live round here."

"Right there, actually." I gesture towards my cottage.

"Oh, okay. Apparently there's a path leading down through the woods to Molescombe Farm. Do you know it?" I do. "The man in the shop said it starts somewhere behind the church." (Or, translated from the original Wessex: *Who are you, you sad and parochial waster, frittering away your life leching after other men's wives, some of whom, like me, are tasked with bringing a neighbour's child to school every day?)* "We've just moved into the old farmhouse and I'm bored of the lane."

Despite her wearisome use of the first person plural, I close my Dornford and chivalrously escort my lady to the spot that eludes her, a stile hidden from view behind a screen of elder bushes at the far end of the graveyard. "I'm Valerie, by the way," she says as I turn to retrace my steps. "Thanks so much."

"Henry. Henry Robson. A pleasure." We shake hands rather formally, considering the location. Her skin is soft, cool and delicate and her touch sends a tingle of excitement through me. "Perhaps I'll see you another day."

"Perhaps," she replies, clambering over the stile and giving me a little wave as she strides off down the path. I watch her surreptitiously through a gap in the foliage, revelling in the wash of delicious emotions conjured up by the energised swing of that tantalising behind.

*

As I walk slowly back to my house, my phone buzzes.

> Can u manage last-minute
> casting at 2.20?
> Sounds like fun for
> the Scandinavians

I rush for my car keys.

"Do come through."

After the early evening light of the waiting room, the clinical glare of the studio is dazzling, but I remember to smile ingratiatingly towards the sofa; four jaded faces swivel towards me, look me up and down, appraising, bored. Biros skitter over pads of paper.

"Thanks for coming in, darling," says a tubby young man behind the camera; he wears a black T-shirt disconcertingly declaring 'bacon strips &' five times in white lower case. He does not look up, stubby fingers busily adjusting dials and buttons. "You've seen the storyboard, I take it?"

"Yes indeed."

"Right, off you go, then."

"How long do I have?"

"As long as you want, darling."

A low black chair and a stainless steel barstool have been placed in readiness.

"Are these for me?"

"Absolutely, darling."

A blonde girl on the sofa smirks through heart-shaped red spectacles.

I pause. "D'you mind if I lie on the floor?"

Surprise flickers over five faces. "Well, I suppose so, darling. It's just that we've not actually had anyone lie down today."

As elegantly as I can for a man of my age and height,

16

I prostrate myself upon the blue office carpet. "Am I in shot?" I enquire, once recumbent.

"Absolutely, darling," he repeats. "Got you covered."

Here goes: in for a penny. This is why I have come all the way into Town again; this is what I do, what I crave.

With the merest hint of a sigh, I begin to writhe and undulate, my body curving and arching, gently at first, then faster and more rhythmically, my hands roaming expertly over the familiarity of my own torso and thighs, stroking and exploring hungrily. (Is that a squashed Ribena carton or a condom packet under the table?) I open the throttle a little, gauging with cynical professionalism whether my excitement is augmenting with appropriate verisimilitude. My lips part, allowing my sighs to crescendo into groans; and when I judge the time to be ripe, I throw back my head in blissful torment.

Through half-closed eyes, I shoot a glance at the sofa; the faces are spellbound, biros still. Another ten seconds should do it.

As I bring myself to timely fruition, I sigh her name – I considered messing with my head and using Valerie's, but then plumped for the casting director's instead – then open my mouth to cry out once, twice "Oh god, yes!" (too much?) and then, in a culminating shout of ecstasy, stiffen into stillness, only the sound of my own heavy breathing breaking the silence.

As the camera's little red light goes out, the group bursts into laughter and applause. I scramble to my feet and straighten my jumper.

"Well, that's a first," I wheeze. "In a long time. For me, at any rate – in public, I mean. Is that it?"

"That's it, darling. Thanks very much."

"Thank *you*."

"We'll be in touch."

Outside in the street, I consult my watch; if I hurry I should be able to catch the 16.40 back to Tisbury.

*

17

I stride breathlessly over Hungerford Bridge, considering not for the first time how much I resent the almost two hour train journey back into darkest Wessex. Only a few months ago I could do the whole thing, door to door, in less than half an hour. Currently though, I am required to write off an entire day for the privilege of spending a few glamorous moments in Soho.

Twenty minutes later, we pull out of Waterloo; I am shoe-horned into a corner of the last carriage next to a tall, fragrant blonde, so close that I can feel the warmth of her body. In my idiotic British way, I lower my gaze to avoid inadvertent eye contact, concentrating instead on her long, brown and artistic fingers loosely clasped over her handbag. Ignoring the inevitable presence of an engagement ring and wedding band, I find myself wondering how it would be to pass my lips across those delicate digits.

The object of my fantasy wisely wanders off down the train to look for a seat when the crush eases up after Woking. Absurdly, her absence only increases in me the inclination to fester and moulder about my sad, useless, frustrating and lonely existence. The fact is that I miss London and, more to the point, I miss intimate female company.

I too find myself a seat after Basingstoke but am further mortified by the fact that, as I am not even competent enough to have any cash about my person, I am not going to be able to purchase one of those cloying yet sustaining hot chocolates (with a shortbread biscuit) from the man with a patch over one eye and a refreshments trolley. Low blood sugar in the descendant, self-pity engulfs me and I fall to considering whether the changes I have recently made to my life are beginning to take their toll.

Ten short months ago I was bedded down in an uneven relationship with a dumpy but reasonably sexy girl called Lucy in a trendy Thames-side apartment on a site previously occupied by Deptford power station. I think we had loved each other initially, but my feelings for her were undermined when she refused my hand in marriage, insisting instead on being called my 'common-law wife' at parties. Maybe her seemingly hysterical horror of children was genuine at the time, or maybe she was unable to trust herself to beget offspring with a man whose career prospects were as unreliable as mine. Whichever the case, I soon realised that I was on a hiding to nothing when it came to the nesting season. Lucy's monstrously successful career in international PR took indefinite precedence over my vernal collection of twigs and pieces of fluff, and although for many years she kept me on as her 'common-law house-husband' in a style which I can no longer even recall without breaking into a cold sweat, she was constantly on her guard against any 'mistakes' we might make in the thorny area of contraception. The topic of children was *verboten*, and we might have gone blithely on into staid old age had she not been swept off her feet during a brief stint in the Americas; firstly by Jesus and subsequently by a swarthy Texan named Bill with whom she now plans, according to a saccharin Round Robin Christmas email, to set up home and procreate.

Considering the parlous emptiness of my current love-life, it is ironic indeed that I have expended so much energy today desperately faking an orgasm for the benefit of people who don't even know me.

On the platform at Andover Station, a child sits slumped in a pushchair and stuffs its globular face with Danish pastry. If I time it right, I muse, I should be able to leap off the train, grab the sweetmeat and be back in the carriage just before the doors close. Failing this, I could sit and await an epiphany; I can feel one coming on.

Sure enough, before the guard has even finished listing the rest of this evening's planned 'stations stops', I reach the perennial conclusion that I am a failed or at least failing actor. I have never been in a soap nor an expensive costume drama, never been invited to bray about my stellar achievements on

BBC Radio 4 and never worked with anyone famous. I have been unemployed for far too long. Pretty much all I aspire to in public places these days is plot dastardly ways of snaffling food from innocent children.

To give Lucy her due, she had recognised and understood the delicate balance of the actorish ego I nurture. Uncles, aunts and old friends of my parents too have the decency to be politely mystified by my lack of current employment and enquire naïvely whether I am 'resting'. Strangers however invariably open with: "An actor? Really? Should I have seen you in anything?" To date I have been impeccably behaved with such people and have managed to retain a façade of inscrutability, deflecting their queries with a nonchalant "it's a bit quiet at the moment"; but how many times at a drinks party has some boring acquaintance sidled up to me and made the dread enquiry "Still 'resting', Henry?"

"You'll have to speak up, Debbie!" I roar. "The music's very loud."

"I was thinking the other day," she squeals, "why doesn't Henry do radio plays? Why *don't* you, Henry?" She gives me the earnest, concerned look. "Have you never thought of being in television drama? You'd be everso good. I can see you in a wig." *I can see you in a coffin, Debbie, with an axe through your skull.* Seemingly unaware that what is left of my hair is rising, she continues: "Do you have an agent?"

"Of course, Debbie. Agent P. I've been with him for years."

"Are you going to sack him?"

"No."

"I can see you doing those John Cleese parts," she says, unaware that she is messing with a closet psycho. "I bet you can do that Ministry of Funny Walks thing." *Yes, I can, Debbie, in spiked climbing boots, all over your ovine face.* "Why don't you do something like Mr Bean?" she persists. "You're so like Rowan Atkinson." At which point she stops, unable to speak, for the gleaming blade of the antique scimitar I always carry about my person has slid between her ribs, perforating all vital organs in its path and pinioning her firmly against the dado rail. The glass of bubbly she is holding tips, falls and smashes onto the parquet and gollops of blood erupt from the side of her mouth. Her head lolls forward. I notice that her feet are off the ground.

"Is it something I said?" Debbie manages a terminal gurgle.

"No, darling, it's just that being an actor, *I'm a little sensitive*. In your gross naivety – " (thoroughly ex-closet by now, I jerk the sword handle upwards to concentrate her mind) "– you seem somehow to be criticising my efforts to find work. All I want is to be loved, remember?" I swiftly withdraw the blade and Debbie's cadaver slithers to the floor. I glance about: nobody has noticed, the roar of polite conversation continues unabated even over the defiantly loud music. God, I hate parties. And although I know it to be too late, I grab my erstwhile companion's face with both hands (*have I slept with her? I can't remember*) and force her to listen to me, to make her understand, to give her some insight into the anguished soul of the out-of-work luvvie.

"Debbie, I don't get John Cleese or Rowan Atkinson parts because John Cleese or Rowan Atkinson get them! I try my best, Debbie, but the only opportunity actually to *act* these days is at castings. And before you ask – no, I am not bitter! It's just that producers have randomly ganged up against me and hate my guts. As consummate media professionals, they are aware that I talk too bloody posh. They know that the average punter doesn't want to hear from toffs like me, they want irritating and trendy regional accents – especially Geordie and Scottish. One day, they may even sink to West Country. Do you follow me?" I am spitting on her lifeless face. "Just don't get me started!"

I doze off and sleep through Salisbury, waking up only as the train gathers speed down the long hill towards my destination. No-one, I ruminate drowsily, thinks of acting as a proper job;

when tipsy, even Lucy enjoyed a good bout of public mockery at my expense in the wake of one of Agent P's rare calls. "Listen, everyone," she would call, standing on a chair and tinging her wine glass, "Henry's got an audition! Someone actually wants to see him! What a relief for us both." And then she would reach down and squeeze my cheek and I'd want one of us to die.

I had abandoned metropolitan life because, I told myself, I wanted peace, quiet and a reduced cost of living. I love the silence of the countryside and after a casting, relish the moment when I stand in the dark at the end of the platform and watch the red tail-light of the train curve away out of sight towards Exeter St Davids. Were I a smoker, I would light up now.

I watch my fellow travellers queueing to pass through the narrow side gate towards their private lives. I even think I discern my tall blonde lady scurrying amongst the dozen or so figures across the car park, but this I dismiss as wishful thinking, especially when my attention is caught by someone altogether less ephemeral. Waiting in her car near the exit is my new friend Valerie.

A sudden surge of excitement takes me by surprise as, in the lamplight, I see the tell-tale sadness in her beautiful face. A man, presumably her husband, opens the passenger door and climbs in. They do not kiss. Perhaps she too is in need of a friend.

4

The slippery slope

I spend what seems like most of the night obsessing about this Valerie, hatching and rejecting plans and plots; and peering between the curtains the following morning, I am just in time to catch a glimpse of the girl's exquisite form as she hurries past.

In a late morning bath, my favourite time and place to ponder the imponderable, I reach a decision. I resolve to honour the Casuists of yore by following Cecil's suggestion and becoming proactive as a Knight in Shining Armour. The Casuists, as I recall from reading my Pascal, were fiendishly adept at making up plausible justifications for doing something Bad. Duelling, for example, may have been illegal, but two chaps *happening* to meet in a field at dawn with a pair of pistols and a reliable friend each was not. Thus, although adultery is Bad, Valerie is married and miserable. This too is Bad, but if I decide to offer myself as the friend and confidant I am certain she needs, I will not be an adulterer – merely a charitable out-of-work actor in search of mutual consolation. Which is Good.

Determinedly hoping for the best, and ignoring the anti-casuist voice of moral rectitude in my ear, I station myself unobtrusively at my front window behind a fold of curtain. I am poised and ready, my brown brogues laced and polished. Seeing Valerie cross the road, I leap into action and out of my door, walking just slowly enough not to draw attention to myself from neighbourly busy-bodies; I catch up with her near the church.

"So, good morning, good morning, good morning," I hyperbolise. "Spotted you walking past and wondered whether I – ?" Words fail me for a moment; she is looking at me with a mixture of suspicion and amusement, sending another jolt of excitement through my abdomen; "– only if you don't mind the company, of course."

"Sure. Why not? Walk some of the way with me." It is the first time I have seen her smile properly.

"I wouldn't want to intrude, but I have nothing on this morning." *If only.*

Irritatingly, it rains hard for the next three school days, but as soon as the weather clears up again, and despite what she now knows about me, Valerie actually knocks on my door and invites me to join *her*, if I'm free.

Unaccountably, I am.

To say that I look forward to our conversational rambles would be a gross understatement because I think about her virtually all the time, especially in bed; and so when I pluck up courage to ring her and she (not her husband) answers, I am ready with a suggestion:

"What about a walk a little further afield?" I suggest. "I know where there are some good bluebells in the forest. It's only ten minutes in the car."

"That sounds lovely," she replies, arousing me by both the

tenor of her reply and by her voice itself. "I'll bring a mid-morning snack."

Within two weeks of almost daily meetings, and with the drag-lift of Destiny scooping us by our buttocks inexorably up the slippery slope, Valerie is declaring that I am the only person who has ever listened to her, ever been kind to her, ever really understood what it means to be her, especially considering what a complete and utter bastard and cold, unfeeling shit her husband is. The banishment of their ten year-old daughter Millie to an expensive boarding school near Blandford is a constant bone of contention between them, as is his propensity to spend two or three random nights a week at his best friend's penthouse flat in Limehouse.

Conversations which started on the hoof then begin to occupy more thought-provoking facilities such as stiles and logs before graduating to sunny meadows, orchards, woodlands, and (if wet) a secluded hay-barn. As she begins to trust me and I become more adept at listening and sympathising, Valerie invites me to her house and we sit and sip tea at her kitchen table where, already suffering tell-tale twitchings above my left temple, I feel encouraged to reach across and take her hand, maybe stroke her hair, let my knee rest against hers under the table.

In short, my inner Casuist is beginning to show signs of strain.

"Come on," she says one day, finishing her glass of water and slapping me matily on the shoulder, "come and see *my* bluebells."

We skirt two fields down to the wooded dell at the back of her house, climb a fence and leap across the dribble of brackish water that passes for a stream. The last of 'her' bluebells are shimmering in the pale morning sun. We pause at a point where the path forks, undecided about which way to go.

"You make me so happy, Henry," she murmurs.

"I love being with you too," I say, taking her pale, soft hand and looking down at her. She slips an arm under my jacket and pulls me towards her for a first, breathless embrace. I am trembling and dizzy with excitement, with fear and desire, intoxicated by the smell of her hair and the feel of her warm body pressed against mine.

"You're quivering," she whispers.

"That's because – " I pause and glance around for peeping Toms, "– because I want to kiss you so much."

She looks up at me and I see tears in her eyes. I kiss them away but more keep falling, darkening her freckles momentarily.

"Oh, Henry," she sighs, "come here." I push back her hair, take her face in both hands and kiss her lips.

We kiss for a long minute, as if for the last time. I try to concentrate on living to the full the sheer wickedness and excitement of this moment, but I am struggling with a new and unexpected terror, that of being seen by a neighbour or a friend of a friend, of being caught out. Despite the warmth of our embrace, I can already see the vengeful face of a husband, public flogging and exile from the village.

Unconsciously, we have taken the left-hand path and walk on slowly, her arms still clasped about me, her head leaning on my chest. At the end of the wood, we find a stile where I sit her on my knee, take my glasses off and balance them on the barbed wire. Like awkward teenagers, we kiss and canoodle in the sunshine, our hands exploring under each other's shirts, our lips and tongues searching hungrily for that which is not ours. And who knows what might not have happened in the woods that morning had not Valerie been obliged to resume her child-minding duties at midday.

The following morning, after sleepless nights, we take to our bicycles; at the far end of a sloping apple orchard, far away from prying eyes and with a view over nearly the whole of rural Wessex, we take off all our clothes and at last make love in the sunshine. Her body, sculptural and firm, gleams alabaster white, her skin pale and slightly damp after the ride. Naked as jay birds, we lie down on clothing I have spread out in the long grass, and I am filled with a desire for her so strong that for the moment all thoughts of the unseen husband are banished. I am mesmerised and enraptured by this girl. My hands flow over her breasts, down to her hips and feet, fingers tingling as they move up her thighs to follow the smooth contours between her legs. I am utterly lost to her, the summer sun on my back and gentle zephyrs wafting balmily amongst the regions of my anatomy generally unused to such delicious exposure. I am at one with her and with Nature, whose ample supply of symbolic brambles and nettles we hardly notice, such is the excitement and release of this encounter.

Afterwards, I lie beside her in the sunlight, kissing the cool skin of her shoulder and making her sigh and shiver by trailing my middle finger between her breasts, down towards her tummy button and beyond. Is it some delicate perfume she wears, or is it her natural fragrance which completely overpowers me? Listening to the birds and the sound of a distant tractor, I remember something I once read about the power of pheromones on the human libido; perhaps I am no more than a male moth lured inexorably to a mate by the irresistible smell of the female. Does that make it all right? Am I going to blame hormones for opening the floodgates to adulterous bliss? And are we going to be happy? Not a bit of it. Having indulged our mutual longings in this pastoral act, we catch our breath and realise that we have signed up to a future of something that, in an excess of selfish passion and sympathy, we have chosen to ignore: a life of Guilt and Deception. We were aware of the small print but, in our haste, chose not to read it.

My bicycle has the unerring knack of twisting its handlebars towards my mistress's house. With my heart in my mouth, I pedal through familiar and peaceful country lanes, up the track and through the Molescombe farmyard that guards her home like the bailey of a Norman castle, hoping against hope that no peasant crone will spot me as I rattle through. I peer round the corner of her drive to make sure that the husband hasn't unexpectedly come home from work. Hiding my bike round the back of the shed, I creep up to the front door, my heart pounding, longing for her smell, her kiss. She unlocks a hundred security devices and opens up, offers me a glass of water, and we sit primly at her table while she unloads her latest batch of marital woes upon my willing shoulders. Sometimes she makes me wait for my reward by putting on some rock music (I think it's called 'Rock', although the cognoscente might describe it as 'Heavy Metal') so that I can watch her dance.

I never dance. I decline to dance at any time, let alone at ten-thirty on a Wednesday morning, and so I sit spellbound, patiently watching as my new lover gyrates and undulates, flinging her glorious hair about, dancing like an eighteen-year old without a care in the world. (When *I* was eighteen, incidentally, I was more likely to be found in the seclusion of my bedroom fantasising furiously about girls or conducting an opera from my vast classical record collection.) For a gentleman-caller on heat, the spectacle of a beautiful, sad and enticing girl dancing for him is traditionally and biblically one of the most erotic experiences he can be expected to withstand.

At the end of the CD, Valerie stops bounding about, ruffles my hair and sits on my knee. And now, after all this raucous pre-foreplay, she allows me to kiss her and snuzzle in her neck. She then slides off my knee to an adjacent chair and rests her legs on mine: "Rub my feet, Henry," she croons, gazing at me with her big green eyes. Achingly, I obey, undoing her laces and pulling off her shoes and socks, an electric current shooting through me as I touch her bare feet. After ten minutes of having them caressed, squeezed and licked, she smiles and giggles and

I know that I am nearly through the labyrinth, that (if I may mix my mythological metaphor) I have almost completed my Labours.

"Come on then," she says, and lowers herself seductively to the floor. I kneel over her, gently lifting her top and kissing the tiny pale hairs leading to her tummy-button. I fumble to undo her belt and the brass button at the top of her Levi's before crouching back and lifting her bottom, allowing her to slide her jeans down to reveal the warm glow of those longed-for smooth white thighs. She lifts her arms for me to remove her T-shirt, and there she is, lying curvaceous and exotic in black lingerie upon her own kitchen floor. I have never dreamt of seeing anyone so lovely, so tantalising and so previously unattainable. She smiles, inviting me to go further. Am I dreaming? Will some Swedish porn movie director suddenly materialise from behind a camera and shout "Cut!" and if not, what does Valerie's husband think he's doing? How can he be so despised? What is there not to love and worship about this girl?

The terracotta tiles are cold, but we care nothing for this minor inconvenience as I clumsily undress and scrabble to put my glasses out of harm's way by the toaster. Sometimes I can undo her bra with ease, and sometimes I have to fiddle with it whilst kissing her. And then her knickers are off and kicked aside and we roll together, naked and warm, the smoothness of our skin and the velvety softness of her belly pressed against mine.

"Wait a minute, gorgeous man," she gasps, and almost before I can detach my mouth from a nipple, she has pushed me off, is on her feet and scampering for the door, her bottom a hazy perfection to one as myopic as me. I lie on that cold floor, propped up like a Roman on one elbow until she's back next to me. At subsequent trysts, we will be permitted the warmth of the sitting room carpet, and months later, if He is definitely in London, we actually climb into bed; but for now, she makes much of unwrapping and applying the condom she has fetched and we make love desperately like lemmings until the kitchen floor has, one way or another, moved for us both and we can lie back, our chests heaving, to contemplate the underside of the table and chairs above us.

"I love you," I whisper into her hair. I feel I must say it.

"Do you, Henry?" she smiles. "Or is it just about the sex?"

I pass her the Waitrose kitchen roll. What do I say to that? I want us to hurry through this initial stage so that I can begin to love her truly, to reassure her and allow her to believe that she is the girl of my dreams; that I will save her from her marriage. But of course right now it really is a very great deal about the sex because her physical presence is absolutely irresistible and I am powerless against her. I do not dwell upon how it would be to grow old together because we are only at the very beginning of an affair and I am addicted to her, to making love with her, to listening to her voice, to being a sympathetic ear. I fulfil that role and have my reward.

5

A Clash of Titans

Civil Enforcement Officer 15550 watches as the ostentatious bulk of a vast BMW X5 sweeps into the station forecourt and comes to a halt directly in front of him, its front wheels precisely straddling the white lettered instruction "SET DOWN ONLY". The habitual mastications of the corpulent official's fleshy jaw cease abruptly, allowing a sneer of outrage to seep across his florid physiognomy, a potent combination of boggle-eyed disbelief mixed with the insidious cruelty of a seasoned bureaucrat poised to strike. "Can't park there," he squeaks to himself, resuming his chewing and shambling forward. "It's 'set down' only. Can't he read?"

The lone occupant of the car is a Headmaster. Taking no notice of the approaching public servant in his ill-fitting green uniform and peaked hat, he turns off the engine, opens the door and steps blithely down from the vehicle. The piggy grey eyes of the Warden are fixed upon him.

"What are you staring at, man?" enquires the Headmaster

as he opens the back door and grasps his coat and briefcase.

"Can't leave this vehicle here, sir."

"No?"

"No, sir. Drop-off only. If you don't remove it, I shall be obliged to issue you with a penalty notice."

"A ticket, you mean?"

Warden 15550 puffs himself up to his full five foot five. "Yes, sir. A Parking Enforcement Notice."

"Really?" The Headmaster squeezes his key fob to secure and immobilise the car.

"Yes, sir," the little man repeats. "The vehicle is parked in breach of the terms and conditions advertised."

"Mm, I know," says the Headmaster, reaching with his handkerchief across the warm bonnet of his pride and joy and wiping the smeared remains of some injudicious insect from one of the golden peacocks of the School crest.

"Have it your own way, sir." With an indignant snort, 15550 shuffles round to the front of the car to key its registration number into his machine.

"I invariably do," smiles the Headmaster, smoothing his hair. "Tell me, how much will this contravention cost me, you officious little tosser?"

15550 is about to bridle at this provocation, but his training prevails. "I would caution you, sir, against verbal or physical abuse of an officer of Bridlington Council Traffic Department." He presses a red button on his machine. "A Parking Enforcement Notice Charge of ninety pounds is now due." The man seems to relish quoting the ticket as it spews out. "However, if payment is made within twenty-one days the charge will be reduced to forty-five pounds."

The Headmaster glances at his watch. "Is that the best you people can do?" he sighs, looking this servant of Satan up and down. "Do you imagine that someone who can afford a car like mine is going to be bothered by a paltry sum like that?" He takes a step towards the warden. "One of my drivers will be along shortly to collect the motor. In the meantime, I must ask you to step aside or I shall miss my train. Good morning to you."

As he strides away, the Headmaster hears a suppressed expletive and the satisfying slap of ticket against windscreen.

A day later, the same vehicle draws slowly into the car park of a country church. The Headmaster reaches into the ashtray for the crumpled parking ticket still in its adhesive yellow plastic pocket. With a grunt of disdain, he rips it open to peruse the contents. For many moons he had dreamt of encountering the legendary Warden 15550, a jobsworth with a reputation for consummate officiousness in Bridlington, a man who during a funeral the previous month had surpassed himself by booking both the hearse and two black funeral limousines outside the church of St Bartholomew. That the man was a congenital idiot with neither family nor social life was self-evident, and the Headmaster had long been waiting for an opportunity to knock him down a peg or two. The brush outside the station had been one of his better performances but because he'd had no-one to regale with the story, the euphoria had lasted only a few minutes.

He glances up the path towards the church where the usual cluster of staff and prefects obsequiously await His arrival, expecting something from him, wanting to witter on at him about some detail of School life: broken toilets in a boarding house, leaking roofs, low assessment grades, smoking, snogging in public, bullying or merely mistakes in last month's salary cheque. With a resigned sigh, he slams the car door and runs through his weekly check-list: hair unruffled, gown regal, Assembly notes in breast pocket.

It starts even before he reaches the church. There are noises emanating from behind a vast yew bush near the lych-gate: skiving pupil voices. He blenches at the slurred and lazy diction, the burr of the local accent and the guttural mangling of the

Mother Tongue. Unable to translate what they are saying ("You feelin' behah, Georgia?" "Yeah, a bi', but when the gavvers come up, I told 'em to 'ide their doobs or they'd knick the stash,"), the Headmaster steps smartly off the path and confronts the stragglers.

"We speak English at Gussage Court, you peasants!" he barks. They hardly flinch, but two surly faces register his presence. "Mr Dyson," he glares down at the sulky little boy with a blotchy crumpled face and a scar through his right eyebrow, "no-one seems to have taught you that there are two Ts in the word 'better'; and another one, Miss Pankhurst, at the end of the word 'bit'. Be good enough to speak the Queen's English as it was intended or go back to the chav school up the road where you came from." The Headmaster notices a fleck of his own articulation-fuelled saliva soaking into the material of his pin-striped sleeve. Miss Pankhurst scowls and flicks a strand of lank hair behind her ear.

"And those earrings are not allowed in School," he snarls. "Remove them!"

"Wha', naaoo?"

"Of course *now*, Miss Pankhurst." His eyes narrow. "Are you wearing make-up as well?"

"Yeah."

"Yes, what?"

"Yes, sir," she sighs, unscrewing her left earring and rolling her eyes to the sky.

"Don't do that!" he shouts. "You're not at home now, Miss Pankhurst. I'm not your father, thank god. And you'll take that slap off as soon as we get back to School. Do you understand, you impudent little girl?"

Despite the freshening autumnal easterly, an acrid smell of stale tobacco and Polo mints permeates the atmosphere around the two teenagers. The Headmaster makes a note to have a prefect discreetly sniff and punish them afterwards. He also observes the absence of Dyson's top shirt button and how his blazer is smeared with what he hopes might be only yesterday's Bolognese sauce. The pair are a disgrace to his School but he is aware that they have both been expelled from all comprehensives south of Hadrian's Wall and that Gussage Court is their parents' last hope. He decides to save these latest sartorial observations for a post-assembly, last warning and pre-expulsion chat in the warmth of his own office, remembering to pop into Accounts first to see whether the Dyson and Pankhurst fees have been paid up to date before making any decisions he might regret. He must also hand over the parking ticket for payment. In fact, it occurs to him, Dyson and Pankhurst can bloody well pay the fine between them – they'll never notice twenty-two pounds fifty on their bill for 'miscellaneous charges'.

As the urchins shuffle away, the Headmaster calls to his second-in-command who is waiting by the porch, arms folded, his large head thrust forward like a bulldog's. "Dr Thorpe, are we ready at last?"

"Good afternoon, Piers," his deputy smiles knowingly. "I think we're ready for the off. Has there been unpleasantness in the graveyard? Miss Spankhurst been living down to expectations?"

His employer scowls. "Bloody chavs, lowering the tone. I think I'd better draft an ad for an elocution instructor." Gingerly, he smoothes his hair. "In line, prefects," he barks. "Let's get on with it."

6

Actor in Residence

Here are a few of the most important lifestyle ingredients for an adulterous relationship: a constant sense of guilt, a morbid fear of discovery, a propensity for pre-tryst stumbles through dank and prickly undergrowth, snatched and edgy meetings and infrequent bouts of fabulous sex. Adultery isn't all it's cracked up to be.

On good days, I am Mr Smug, whose manly ego revels in the erotic excitement and danger of an illicit liaison: I have won the trust and intimacy of a lovely and lonely woman; I have prevailed and conquered. On bad days, Reality raises its ugly head and the full weight of adulterous skulduggery and deceit squashes the joy out of even my fantasy world. I had never realised how stressful it would be to spend every waking hour planning new and improved ways of seeing my lover without being suspected (or worse, actually spotted) by either a fierce and humourless spouse or – more locally – by eagle-eyed curtain-twitchers. And on really bad days, usually after Millie has been home for the weekend, Valerie refuses to see me at all, the thought of destroying the family unit plunging her into a mire of abject misery. My own craving for carnal adventure is no match for my lover's maternal instincts and so, at these times of lonely self-pity, and in preparation for receipt of my marching orders, I mope around the place wondering what she can possibly see in me. Presumably it gives her some satisfaction that her considerable physical attributes make her irresistible to me, but apart from that, what have I to offer? No vast salary, no condominium in Miami, no potential step-children to become best friends with Millie, no title deeds to a rambling family pile in Shropshire and no entry in Who's Who. Is she perhaps drawn to my height or the remains of my once *Cruel Sea* hair (now sadly topped off at an altitude of six foot four with a gleaming patch of bare scalp)? Is she lured by the glamorous possibilities of my chosen vocation, or has her generous and motherly nature spotted my need for companionship and love? Or is she simply relieved to have found someone more available than her wealthy commuter husband? I am a friendly face and a good listener; I live alone in a rented cottage in what some have disparagingly called 'The Village of the Damned', but am I really a catch for the long-term?

I love my cottage. It is a chocolate box residence in the heart of rural Wessex, as warm and snug as a mother's womb. I feel secure here – especially in the bath – consoled by the view of the church at the top of the Green and by hearing bell-ringing practice on Thursday evenings and the clunk of cricket balls on Sunday afternoons in summer. Two years ago, at the conclusion of that frenetic decade in South East London, I headed south-west down the M3 until I found what I was after, a cosy lair where I would be swaddled and cushioned from the world. When I was first shown through the low front door, I knew I was home, the slight smell of damp notwithstanding.

As the agent's blurb had promised, 'the accommodation boasts' a grubby sitting-room with miniature inglenook fireplace and a Lilliputian kitchen accessible through a low doorway under the stairs; 'the first floor amenities benefit from' a relatively capacious front bedroom ideal for any self-respecting dwarf and, jammed at the rear, a box-room and a dank bathroom 'featuring' mildewed grouting, a rotting window and a plastic suite in tasteful 1980s avocado. Every beam has been carefully exposed to alarm generations of estate agents, each one being riddled with insect holes which dribble a fine sawdust onto the carpet. Centuries of diligent and conscientious mastication have taken their toll on the infrastructure of the cottage, and the industrious inhabitants of those beams spend several weeks every May and June repeatedly tapping seven times to each other in an attempt to find the mate of their dreams lonely and chewing in a lump of ancient oak adjacent to their own. I am soothed by the presence of the death-watch beetles, particularly since they are the responsibility of my landlord, Reginald Richbastard of Singapore to whom I pay an exorbitant monthly rent by direct debit. I find these domestic infestations a novelty because my former abode was altogether too sterile and unimaginative an environment to be of interest to any self-respecting beetle, mouse, rat or rot, whether of the dry- or wet-variety. With a bit of luck I will be long gone by the time the work of *Xestobium rufovillosum* is done and the cottage finally crumbles into its shallow seventeenth century foundations.

7

Small Ads

I am sitting disconsolate in the quaintness that is my kitchen drinking a cup of tepid decaff because I have heard nothing from Agent P for weeks. Valerie is away with her husband and I have slithered into my habitual slough of despond, bemoaning the Actor's Life of constant rejection. I am also rodent watching.

This is an activity not unakin (one of the Skywalker brothers, I imagine) to bird-watching but with the added bonus for the observer of being filled with a deep self-loathing and disgust: outside in the courtyard garden an enormous brown rat is gnawing at the crusts of bread I put out for the birds. It is an ugly and humongous creature auditioning for the rôle of Harbinger of Things To Come. "Henry," I say aloud to myself, "you're sitting alone surrounded by rats and death-watch beetle. What does this say about you?"

Now would be a good time to mention the fact that I count amongst my oldest friends an intellectual gent from the Emerald Isle called Donal. A man of monstrous intellect, Donal is one of those rare coves who relishes the challenge of being blindfolded and coerced into playing six games of chess simultaneously. We shall be hearing more of him. He tends to pop up in times of stress like a *deus ex machina*. Or a cold sore.

To take my mind off the rat, I dial his number. One hour and twelve minutes later, my old chum has agreed with me that – leaving aside any moral issues appertaining to my love-life – it may be time to cast about for a more reliable source of income. "Henry, if your thespian career in its entirety consists merely of attending occasional castings" (he castigates verbosely) "which have themselves degenerated into an exercise in systematic financial haemorrhage, then might I take this opportunity to advise the hebdomadal perusal of the classified advertisements to establish some more responsible way of replenishing the Robson treasury?" I reach for the *Wessex Week* Magazine and turn to *Situations Vacant*.

"Talent Spotter"
Term-time only – Part-time
We state and maintain that – "Every child has a talent"

We now need a person to spot talent, encourage and ensure that each talent is nurtured. This will cross all boundaries of sport, music, arts, and academia and you will need to access all facilities to enable the students to accomplish great things. Must be enthusiastic and able to impart this feeling into students who may be shy to try something new.

I have absolutely no idea what this means. It seems to be written in an English of sorts, but not one with which I am at all familiar. The grammar seems to be built upon shifting sands and I sense something deep-seatedly bizarre in the make-up of the copy-writer: dyslexia, paranoia, Google translate? I decide to leave well alone and scan further down the page.

WANTED!
Reliable Cake
Making Cook!
May suit retired person who
we could leave to run our new
small "Coffee Shop" on
campus. Working term-time only.
Make cakes, serve and wash
up. Must be good with money.
If you come for interview –
bring a sample of your Cake!

I do make cakes, but not on an industrial scale. I turn the page and find Gussage Court's final contribution to this week's publication. I read it twice in disbelief.

Elocution and Pronunciation Instructor
required to knock teenage glottal-stopping miscreants into shape.

Apply in writing to Dr T Thorpe,
Headteacher, Gussage Court School

I can't resist. Within minutes my letter and cv are in the post. Within thirty-three hours, a fierce secretary called Carola has invited me to interview for all three jobs if I want; at the forty-sixth hour I have looked out my least moth-eaten suit and am in the car heading south. I don't inform Valerie about this; she'll only scoff.

A professional actor knows how to be punctual at auditions and so I set off with plenty of time to spare. On the way, I consider the full implication of the wording of the advertisement. Is there not something slightly old-fashioned in its tone? A Dickensian headmaster such as Mr Wackford Squeers might have felt his 'miscreant' pupils achieved their best results after being 'knocked into shape' by the deft application of a knobbly walking stick to the side of the head, but I am a little surprised to find such vocabulary in the early twenty-first century. Also, I notice that Dr Thorpe requires an 'instructor' of elocution, not a 'teacher'; what can the difference be, I wonder?

An image takes shape unbidden in my mind: a square-jawed sergeant-major type, barrel-chested with a G.I. crew-cut and grey uniform, the instructor carries a giant's club in his left hand and barks rounded vowels and tight consonants at serried ranks of Gussage Court inmates. They cower timorously behind old-fashioned wooden desks, the ones with a lid and an inkwell. Dutifully, they chant "Maa – May – Mee – May – Maa – Maw – Moo – Maw – Maa" back at him, but he knows they will revert to their normal speech patterns after the lesson and this is why he hates them so much.

Being a conscientious applicant I begin to improvise a lesson plan to impress Dr Thorpe. He is bound to ask how I intend to instruct elocution.

1. Pick on one of the potentially *glottal-stopping teenagers* mentioned.
2. Make him stand up and stop fidgeting.
3. Ask him the following question: "Boy, what do you normally put on bread?"
   If he responds with an impertinent answer such as "Jam, sir" or "Cheese, sir", then he has proved himself to be
   a) a clever-clogs and
   b) a true *miscreant*.
   But as yet, I have no information as to whether he is
   c) *glottal-stopping* or not.
   If, on the other hand, he responds with the word "Butter" but pronounced *sans* the two central Ts then he has proved himself to be both a *miscreant* and, more importantly, a *glottal-stopper*. At which point you may

4. *Knock* him *into shape* using any or all of the implements left in a desk-drawer: vis the club, the empty fire-extinguisher, the knobbly walking stick.
5. At the end of the beating, make the boy sit down again and stop whimpering.
6. Try another one with the following question: "Boy, how do you pronounce the first letter of the word Hogwarts?"

"Haitch, sir."

"No, boy, you pronounce the first letter of the word Hogwarts with an AITCH; not with a hHAITCH. So, to recap, how do you pronounce the first letter of the word Hogwarts, boy?"

"Haitch, sir."

"No, you bloody miscreant chav. Are you listening to me?
7. Repeat 4 (above).

Thorpe won't be able to argue with that. I've got this instructor thing down to a fine art already. I'd be *wasted* as a teacher.

Leaving the thatched village of Gussage St Giles a mile behind me, I negotiate a right angle bend in the lane and chance upon the entrance to the school. A faded signboard swings from a rusting scaffold: 'Gussage Court' it declares, and underneath, in determinedly unpunctuated lower case: 'competitive like the world'. Without my having to press any buttons or speak to any disembodied voice, the six-foot oaken gates swing very slowly open, each one emblazoned with an oval plastic coat of arms depicting a golden peacock preening itself on a blue backdrop. Curled underneath is the inevitable scrolled ribbon motif bearing the motto '*Qui Vincit Rex*' which my schoolboy Latin translates as 'He who wins is King'. As soon as the patronising gates are open enough to let me pass, I mutter a heartfelt '*Speramus Optimum*' under my breath and move forward.

I drive half a mile along a rutted track through deciduous woods before eventually emerging into playing fields. Beyond these, skulking behind the storm-rent remains of a cedar tree is Gussage Court, a dreary Victorian pile in grey stone with what an English Heritage handbook might describe as a Doric porch and delicate fanlight windows. Some of the first floor ones are hung inside with grubby towels and foreign flags; a pair of trainers has been exiled onto a window ledge. Parked ostentatiously below, next to a smug silver BMW, is a dusty blue vintage Rolls Royce, both sporting the ubiquitous coat of arms, the blue four-foot version on the BMW's bonnet contrasting nicely with the silver filigree one embossed on the Roller's front doors. There is even a miniature version on the sign by the doorbell that announces 'If windy, please use South entrance'. It isn't and so I climb the steps, seize the brass knob and push open the black-painted front door.

Inside, there's a smell of churches and apple logs. High on the wall opposite, a deer's head fixes its supercilious gaze upon me, daring me to touch any of the paraphernalia gathering dust on every available ledge: a collection of African sculptures littering an ancient upright piano; myriad Russian dolls standing to attention on the mantlepiece. An oblong glass case at the foot of the stairwell houses a vast samurai sword; I lean closer to decipher the inscription on a tiny copper plaque:

In the battles of old, leaders were given swords representing the passing of a war.

I wonder whether the presence of such a weapon in an unlocked case means that the School is maintained on a constant war footing. There are certainly signs of a competitive spirit; hundreds upon hundreds of silver cups adorn every step of the grand staircase and, as I look up admiringly, my gaze is met by a small olive-skinned boy with enormous brown eyes. He is leaning over the balustrade and dropping pieces of popcorn into the leaves of an aspidistra twelve feet below.

"Excuse me," I say, my voice resonating pleasingly, "is there a receptionist here?"

"You go right, sir," comes the reply, a piping treble, heavily accented.

"Can I help you at all?" A reassuringly local voice steers me through a narrow doorway and into a cosy sitting room where a log fire burns. Tight peroxide blonde curls. Heavy crimson lipstick. Carola.

"I've an appointment with Dr Thorpe. My name's Henry Robson."

"Mmmm. The new elocution teacher. Oh yes." Why is she looking at me like that? "Have a seat a moment, Mr Robson. I'll just call him."

There is a sudden shout of "Pick all that crap out of that plant, you moron," and a short, wiry man with a goatee beard and half-moon spectacles sweeps in wearing, to my consternation, a grubby beige suit, a red waistcoat and a lop-sided orange bow-tie. He brushes past me and begins a conspiratorial conversation with Carola. A seasoned eavesdropper, I lean forward to inspect an old school photograph and am about to become party to state secrets when a skinny, odd-looking creature, a cross between Quasimodo and a bottle brush, fires up his yellow hoover in the doorway. The gentleman at reception raises his voice in some irritation.

"Barry, you idiot, not here, not now! Can't you see I'm busy?" The hoover stops and Barry begins to wind up the flex again. The little man turns back to the female minion. "If the mother calls to see me, just tell her I'm not in. Matron can deal with her, the bloody lesbian." *Who is? The mother or the Matron?* I steal a glance at the man to ascertain whether he's joking, but his profile is set in such a glare that I resume my study of the wall hangings without further ado. I have time only to glean that there's something very odd about his hair. Anyone can see it's dyed because it has that give-away matt-black sheen with insubordinate white bristles in the sideburns; but my main concern is about how it lies horizontally across the back of his head. Can it be a wig?

"Is that the post?" he snaps, reaching over the counter and snatching up a bundle. I pluck up courage and ask politely if he is Dr Thorpe.

"No, I'm Mr Halliday, the Head*master*." (Ah, it's a classic comb-over.) "Barry, I don't pay you to stand about looking vacant."

"That's Piers," whispers Carola, pulling a frog-face, as 'Piers' stamps laboriously up the stairs. "Don't mind him, he's having one of his off-days. Dr Thorpe is the Head*teacher*. He'll be with you in a second."

Side-stepping Barry, busy once more with his domestic equipment, I wander back into the entrance hall. A Headmaster *and* a Headteacher? Sensing the gaze of many glass eyes upon me, I glance up at two fox heads, the deer and a badger riddled with woodworm. Is Piers' Museum of Roadkill trying to warn me off?

"Mr Robson?" I turn at some Birmingham inflections. An authority figure with big hair and sunken cheeks. "Tom Thorpe. Welcome to Gussage Court. Sorry to keep you." We shake hands. "Carola, can you sort out some coffee, please?"

Twenty minutes later, the job is mine, but I had wasted my time preparing the Lesson Plan; Dr Thorpe is more interested in an early career triumph of mine, an appearance on the *Sooty Show* as a mad professor.

"A mad professor, eh? You'll fit in fine here. By the way," Dr Thorpe adds, tossing a floppy paperback over his desk at me, "you're also teaching GCSE drama, alright?"

"Well ..."

"You can teach drama, Mr Robson. You're an actor. Try acting being a drama teacher."

"But ..."

46

"Good. That's settled then. See you a week next Tuesday. Nine o'clock start."

A bell rings three times and I make my way back to my car, noticing this time a netted enclosure behind the cedar tree containing three chickens and a potbellied pig. I wonder whether my grateful acceptance of this job has been in any way an error of judgement. A malevolent squawk from above stops me in my tracks. A peacock eyes me curiously, its head on one side. My car windscreen bears witness to its vindictive presence.

8

In Extremis

For a snapshot of Happy Times, the high point of my relationship with Valerie, crack open *Google Earth*, tap in 'Odeon, Shaftesbury Avenue, London WC2' and take a look into the foyer. There I am coming up the stairs, not attending an audition (because there isn't one) but celebrating one of my few remaining free weekdays before I start my part-time job at Gussage Court. I am alone because Valerie is still in the gloom of the basement doing whatever it is that girls do for fifteen minutes in the Ladies.

I switch on my mobile, hoping as ever that there is a positive message from Agent P. There isn't, but I dial his number anyway, leaning against a pillar and looking out at the traffic crawling past in the drizzle. A full sleeping bag shifts slightly in a doorway opposite, and a polystyrene burger box blows across the pavement into the road and is flattened under the wheels of a white mini-van.

"Is that you, Agent P?" I enquire, hearing his dulcet tones.

(Actors know it is not done to ring agents to ask if there's any news.) "Is there any news?"

"I think you'd be the second to know if there were, Henry," he replies with a tinge of disappointment and irritation. "I hope you're not harassing your agent." My heart sinks. Why had I called? A police car storms past, sirens wailing. "Where are you, anyway?" he demands, his tone softening a little.

"In a cinema."

"Where?"

"Shaftesbury Avenue." I try to sound lackadaisical, confident.

"What the hell are you doing in a London cinema at two-twenty on a Tuesday afternoon?" It's a fair question. "Are you alone, Henry? What are you doing in Town without telling me? What's going on? Spill."

Destiny's dainty fingertips brush the back of my neck, making my hairs tingle. Is this perhaps the moment to break the log jam and reveal the secret life I have been leading? Agent P would understand; he's a man of the world; wouldn't be judgmental. I snap on my subtext filter.

"No, I'm with a friend."

"Male or female?" *Bugger, filter malfunction.*

"Female, actually."

"Married or single?"

"Well ..." I pause, queasy, feel myself falling. I glance at the stairwell but there is still no sign of Valerie. I brace myself.

"Henry?"

"Mm?"

"Are you having an affair with a married woman?"

I pause again, just too long.

"Yes, as it happens," I say, a little too loudly.

"Henry, you beast! Congratulations! I'm proud of you! Who is she?"

The top of Valerie's head heaves into view in the stairwell. I know it's bad form to cut off one's agent mid-confession, but there's nothing for it. "Can't explain right now, mate – got to go. Call you later about that casting. Thanks! Byeee."

When Valerie has buttoned her coat and arranged a copious black scarf to her satisfaction, I take her hand and escort her out into the fume-laden grey of Soho. Something has changed: now that I have fessed up to Agent P, I feel that Valerie and I, in contravening the age-old code of Western morality, are somehow an item, official in the eyes of the world. Which is odd, since the world (apart from Agent P) knows nothing, as yet.

We choose the Odeon because it is not one of the capital's most populated cultural oases on a Tuesday morning and as such, permits us to canoodle like teenagers in the back row. Today Valerie had taken advantage of the gloom to remove her shoes and socks, drape herself across two of the plush velvety seats and present me with her feet to massage. Always ready to oblige and curry favour with my lover, I willingly acquiesced to her whispered entreaties, my subsequent state of arousal completely obliterating any appreciation of the film. After such a prolonged period of sensory bliss with Valerie's toes and the cathartic admission to Agent P, I feel myself floating, gently buffeted by warm zephyrs, euphorically turning and rolling in the cumulonimbus duvet of Cloud Nine. I am, in short, buzzing with sexual excitement.

Is this joy? Is my heart's desire now within my grasp? Might a life with Valerie now be possible? Will she contemplate divorce?

We cross through the traffic and turn left down Earlham Street past the striped awnings of the market barrows. Jeans, T-shirts and Indian shawls brush my shoulder as we push through crowds of damp tourists. As a market, Earlham Street is tame, missing that raucous dishonesty and rotten vegetable quality of, say, Deptford or Borough where you go armed with a sack and they fill it for you with "a pahnd a mush an' free pahnds a 'taters, mate"; but here, with the pre-packaged delights of a new Tesco Metro just around the corner, they're touting Union Jack bowler hats and iconic posters of Bob Marley, Marilyn and The Beatles instead.

Valerie and I squeeze into a doorway to let a fully-laden double buggy through. The girl pushing it is smoking and spotty, her pink tracksuit stained on one shoulder. I feel oddly superior: not for Valerie and me a life of drudgery. We are above all that. We are smug middle class lovers who carefully and responsibly take preventative measures.

I do not share these thoughts with Valerie for fear of the look she will give me as she reminds me of her working class roots.

The final stall is groaning under a fragrant display of absurdly large and exotic flowers imported from distant continents. I am aware of the ecological nightmare involved in harvesting these blooms and can imagine the misery of the chain-gang of insecticide-impregnated workers picking them; had I a calculator I could probably determine the amount of aircraft fuel consumed to fly them here, *but, Henry*, I say to myself, *this is no place for mealy-mouthed political correctness. This is the time for Romance! Be a hypocrite and buy your lover some flowers!*

But how would Valerie explain them away when her spouse returned that night? "Oh, yeah, I just felt like buying myself thirty-five quid's worth of blooms. A spur of the moment thing. After all, you never buy me flowers, do you?" Or she might say: "Yeah, my lover bought them for me."

In fact, the strength of her lover's feelings today calls for more than a mere floral tribute; nothing less than the immediate and unpremeditated purchase of something tangible and permanent will suffice; something small and expensive which Valerie can squirrel away from prying eyes and secretly take out and admire, assured in the knowledge that her lover has, in true chivalrous manner, offered unto her this gift as proof of his eternal love and devotion.

Valerie may yet be someone else's wife, but today I have decided to live life to the full and show her how it feels to be worshipped and adored. I stamp underfoot certain anxieties I have about the cultural chasm between us, and indeed about some arguably weird aspects of our sex life: to whit, a tendency she is developing to rebuff my sexual advances just at the point when, after a lengthy foreplay of foot and calf massage, I am ready to burst. Even this morning, after ninety-six minutes of filmic fondling, she is refusing to hold my hand. Marching independently at my side, she had detached herself from my gentle grasp as soon as we had crossed Shaftesbury Avenue; she had than proceeded to realign her body to the vertical with a satisfied sigh. It's a yoga thing, I imagine. If I try for manual contact she will complain that her shoulders aren't straight and that I'm in her space; if I wish to hold her hand, then I must walk in the road, actually in the gutter, vaulting over cars, litter bins and parking meters while she strides beside me on the pavement. Wouldn't it be creepy if deep down, she's one of those women who think that hand-holding and physical intercourse are symptoms of male dominance?

I banish such dark thoughts because today is a Happy Day: Valerie and I are alone together in London and, as she says, we are made for each other.

Dodging taxis and vans hurtling around Seven Dials, we turn right down St Martin's Lane and pause outside a shiny black-painted shop with gold letters over the window. Improbably slim-fitting dresses, silver boots, tasselled shawls and mysterious pieces of silk adorn the display, but on the left is a golden velvet box draped with black necklaces of the utmost delicacy.

"How lovely," she says quietly. "Look at those."

A plan begins to form. "Why don't you try one on?" I say, pushing open the door for her.

The shop is a class establishment: small, intimate, warm and welcoming with the strains of Fauré's *Pavane* emanating from speakers concealed behind racks of frilly confections whose uses are not immediately apparent to the male of the species. Out of my depth, I stand aside and let Valerie pucker up and do her thing with the lady I assume to be the proprietress; a diminutive woman, immaculately dressed and made-up, who shimmers forward to greet us like the long-lost friends she would like us one day to be. I have no need to assume Richard Gere's character in *Pretty Woman* because full-on sucking-up is second nature to this razor-sharp little harpy. Of course, she simpers, it would be no trouble at all to lay out as many necklaces as Madam wants to see. But would she not like to take off her jeans and winter jersey and put on a little *je ne sais quoi* in order to show off each item to its fullest potential? Would not this eight hundred pound floral summer number with the plunging neckline suit? What about these shoes? Please, do pop into the changing room, whilst I organise half a dozen Filippino slaves to anoint Madam's delicious breasts with ostrich liver oil, bergamot and thyme? What about a gentle bath in warmed cinnamon-flavoured whale milk or – she presses the velvet button on an intercom disguised as a conch – Bjorn, would you mind stepping in here to look after the lady while we lay out some necklaces? And, Charlie, take the gentleman outside and give him a bucket of water and some hay to chew on while he's waiting to pay.

While she changes, I do in fact hover near the door, twiddling my Fedora and feeling lumpish and superfluous. We have been found out. The proprietress is probably whispering to Bjorn even now that the tall bloke with the hat is far too doe-eyed to be the woman's husband. I mean, just look at him salivating, and at his age too.

I am at the mercy of women in this boutique and I know that lavish expenditure is only minutes away. Will Valerie go for the whole outfit, shoes, dress and all, or will I merely get away with one of the necklaces she is even now trying on at the back of the shop? In the full-length mirror, she is the very image of beauty and perfection, but a little moue is playing about her lips, as if she is as bewitched by her appearance as I am. Even at this moment, at the very apogee of our liaison so far, I quiver as a frisson of terror runs through me.

The necklace itself saves the day. It is a series of miniature chains and tiny black stones forming an intricate spider's web, and as I gaze upon it spread across her white décolletage, I am subsumed by both joyful pride and longing which dispel for the moment any lingering doubts.

At last, Valerie drags herself away from her own loveliness and looks up to notice me smiling behind her in the reflection.

"What do you think?" she asks, giving a little half smile of anticipation. "This or the other?"

I force my leg muscles to function and move up behind her, tentatively placing my hands on her warm bare shoulders. I am overcome by her scent, helpless with infatuation.

"I prefer this one," I murmur, with no knowledge of which is the most expensive. My voice sounds thick and unfamiliar.

"So do I."

"Would you like it?" I ask. She turns and looks up at me with what I hope is an adoring, not merely grateful gaze. "I'll buy it for you – an early birthday present," I say. "Try them both on one more time." I risk a kiss on the top of her head; my hands are trembling slightly as I fumble to hold the two necklaces against her one after the other. I am so cack-handed with the ridiculously tiny clasps that She-wolf feels obliged to take over. I want to explain to her that it's just that I am battling with urges to kiss the back of my lover's neck and that my fingers have ceased functioning. Do you not find it a singularly enticing and irresistible neck, Madam? What about you, Bjorn? Oh, no – of course not you. I wonder, would they mind if we popped into the dressing room for ten minutes?

And afterwards, would her professional mask slip when, flushed with spent passion, we beat a hasty retreat, having handed back the remnants of the floral summer dress, now sadly crumpled and torn?

Against all the odds, and without having to lash out on a hotel room, Valerie and I do find an opportunity to make love later that day. Actually, the word 'love' is a misnomer: I balk at the memory of that explosively frantic and sordid session astride the lavatory of the 15.40. It is all over in a trice and our clothes are back on before the train rattles over the points into Clapham Junction. The smell of a train toilet will sicken me until the end of my days.

After a lonely supper of cream cheese and peanut butter sandwiches, I am cogitating glumly in the bath. My mobile bleeps:

> Thank u for my lovely
> necklace. U have won my
> heart. X

Given that I immediately burst into tears, I suppose that something is going to have to give, or I shall go mad.

9

The Martyrdom of Wolfhart

It has been a breathless exercise in bluff, shouting and improvisation, but I have survived three days as Elocution Instructor at Gussage Court and am now about to be initiated into my first School Assembly.

A tiny Norman church stands at the end of a narrow lane with the wind blowing across lichen-furred gravestones and rustling the leaves of an ancient oak. I clamber out of my car and straighten the school-teacherly tie, an anodyne autumnal number which blends nicely with my once-expensive grey suit, now moth-holed below the right shoulder.

Although the Sports Hall on campus would be perfectly serviceable as an Assembly venue, the school is obliged twice a week to march across three fields to the church in order to benefit from the feeling of family fellowship it affords. Previously shiny black shoes are muddied and sullied after the walk, and a regiment of prefects (who have been driven down in a minibus) gleefully issue detention slips to those who haven't restored their footwear to a state of acceptability with the aid of an old towel kept for the purpose in the lychgate.

I wait until the latest form-group has shambled into the church before tentatively following them in and sitting down in the choir stalls. A Japanese teenager is at the organ hammering out double-speed Oriental versions of *Jerusalem* and *Praise my Soul, the King of Heaven*. A small fat parishioner peering through thick National Health lenses tolls a single mournful bell, the indistinct funereal sonority jarring with the strains of the organ. Undeterred by the dissonance, Mr Evans, the moustachioed and gleamingly bald Head of Music, wrests control of the organ from his pupil and we begin a romping and equally inaccurate medley from which I recognise the theme from *633 Squadron, The Dambusters March, The Arrival of the Queen of Sheba* and a couple of bleeding chunks improvised from that Bach *Toccata in D minor*.

Another quarter of an hour passes whilst the church fills. The School sits silently, a sea of green blazers and yellow waistcoats, kept in order by a phalanx of lime green-gowned prefects, some wielding carved rods of office. Everything clashes in this place: colours, sounds, mood.

I am approached by one of the prefects who hands me a loosely folded black cloth.

"Good mornink, sir. Zees for you." Eastern European, I surmise. "You must vare." What the hell is it? Not a schoolmaster's gown, surely? They wouldn't put me through *that*, would they? – I'm only part-time.

The Headmaster, in full academic regalia, is watching me from the porch. Let's hope he doesn't send in a mortar board as well. The Bulgarian lad (I have plumped for a nationality) watches as I hold the grubby old rag up; it looks far too small and I am aware of the eyes of the School fixed on me as I try to wrestle my way into the bloody thing. Not wishing to draw attention to myself, I remain seated with the result that a cufflink pings off and I have to rummage under the pew for it;

then my jacket sleeve becomes entangled with an extraneous black loop which in turn tugs the sleeve up and reveals a hairy forearm. Then, in the ensuing attempt at releasing this tangle, my left elbow somehow becomes wedged under the ledge behind me, dislodging three prayer books and an old Parish magazine which crash to the floor. I am trussed up like a turkey and only the ripping of a seam puts an end to my plight.

"Now, sir, vee march in. You must come." The Bulgar has been watching my sartorial struggles.

"What do you mean? We march in? I'm already in!" This is becoming surreal.

"You must come, sir. Mr Halliday, he says."

Sweating with embarrassment, I follow him out of the church again, feeling the eyes of the congregation fixed upon the tear in my gown. Assembly begins with the Head Boy rapping the flagstones with a ceremonial staff, a gift no doubt from some African potentate. He then bellows the single word "Schoo-ool", an invitation for the inmates to rise.

The current Head Boy is a charming young man who has previously introduced himself to me as Yuri Kozhevnikov. Piers presumably selected him for high office for his youthful, photogenic and therefore highly marketable good looks. His exalted status at the School, however, is not matched by physical development; barely five foot tall, his voice has not quite broken, and today his reedy exhortation does not have the desired effect. The stick smacks onto the stone but the vital exclamation itself cracks down the middle, rent asunder by a gob of spittle wedged across a pubescent vocal cord. The result: an unmanly squeak and the sight of the Head Boy choking and being thumped on the back by the Head of Games.

A communal giggle is quashed as twenty pairs of authoritarian eyes swivel and glare at the congregation. Isabel, one of the prefects standing in line, is already suffering from the absurdity of the situation and doing her utmost not to guffaw and bring disgrace upon her gown of Office. Her eyes are beginning to water as she bites the inside of her cheek; she knows from experience that her tight-lipped grimace could explode at any moment into a Teutonic bellow of mirth. Despite her best endeavours, she emits the most insignificant of snorts, the tiniest nasal eruption, but one nevertheless with seismic potential. How fortunate for her, then, that she heeds Dr Thorpe's warning hand on her shoulder. However, it is too late for her compatriot, the tall and effeminate Wolfhart, whose self-control is notoriously limited in a public place. He is now overcome with a desire to throw himself to the floor and scream with laughter. To Isabel's horror, he emits a sound so splendid in the silence of the church that people will speak of it with wonder for weeks to come. It is a noise akin to gorilla flatulence after feeding time at Whipsnade Zoo and it resonates majestically around the building. Wolfhart's joy, however, and that of the School as a whole, is short-lived, for Piers' hand shoots out, grabs him by the collar and tugs him backwards through the doorway and into the porch. Staff and prefects jump out of the way.

"Be quiet, you idiot!" hisses the Headmaster. "How dare you make that disgusting noise?"

"But, sir ... "

"Silence, boy!" Piers heaves once more at Wolfhart's collar so that he topples backwards, banging his head. We stand and gawp, nobody daring to intervene as Piers bends down suddenly and drags the boy bodily out of the porch.

"Get up! Get up now, Wolfhart!"

"But, sir, I'm sorry ..."

"You will be more than sorry for this!" Piers grabs the prefect by the lapels and forces him to his feet, pushing him against the flint of the church wall. "How dare you mock my ceremony? You're supposed to be setting an example! How DARE you?!"

"Sir, *ich habe Ihnen doch schon gesagt, das es nicht meine*

Absicht war…" Tears are pouring down the prefect's cheeks but Piers does not heed them.

"Speak English! And stay out here! I don't wish to see you again today." He turns on his heel. "Dr Thorpe, what are we waiting for?"

Eyes cast down, the other prefects and members of staff say nothing. My own cheeks hot with shame, I shuffle into line. I am ready to march in, but Fate has one more ordeal for me up its sleeve. As a final endurance test, our nerves are pulverised by a noise so vile, that for an instant I think the end of the world is come. It is a din that would under normal circumstances send strong men scuttling for cover, diving behind gravestones, hands pressed tightly over their ears, their screams echoing around the ruins of all they had come to love and cherish.

Bagpipers.

A quavering, low whine rises to a shrill shriek, a truly appalling, screeching cacophony, discordant and excruciating. I spin round to see four student bagpipers (an Aryan beanpole, a bespectacled African and two plump Anglo-Saxons) emerge from behind a buttress to lead the march into the church. Spattered with diabolical squeaks, what was probably meant to be 'Amazing Grace' begins to emerge, decimated and defiled, setting my teeth on edge. I suck my molars trying to deaden the pain.

The pomp and ceremony over, we are installed. The Headmaster remains at his lectern, his gown gleaming gold in the gloaming, his comb-over still lacquered to perfection. Having regained his composure, Piers is relishing the power he wields.

"Good morning, everyone. Sit down." His glare passes across the silent multitude. "Stephen John!" he barks suddenly. "Make that boy at the end of your row stand up!" We freeze again. There is a shuffling and a second's pause. "*Don't* do that, you STUPID LITTLE BOY!" The School is so quiet that I can hear the rasping squeak of the weathercock at the top of the church spire. "Do you regard a public display of mono-digital nasal inspection as being an activity worthy of a member of Gussage Court School? Do you, boy?" There is a scarcely audible whimper. "No! Sit DOWN! See me in my office at break. With a clean handkerchief." Piers changes gear: "Today's Assembly is being given by Mr Harvey." A putter of applause as a young teacher ascends to the pulpit.

"Good morning, everyone," he reads, unaware of the immediate soporific effect of his dreary, Estuary drone. "I want to speak to you today of the power of language." Oh god, I slept through dozens of inept addresses like this thirty years ago. "Boys and girls, how many times have we used our tongue like a knife to hurt other people? How often have we said to someone: 'You're stupid! You're thick!' or 'I hate you'?"

Irony hovers like a purple gauze around the pulpit and then drifts across the chancel to drape itself over the Headmaster, his face as expressionless as a cobra's. Oblivious, Mr Harvey chastises and castigates, careless of where he is treading. Reports have already reached my ears of staff being invited to collect their P45s after an assembly where offence has been taken. "But I ask you today," he is winding it up at last, "to think of how a surgeon uses a knife, not to harm and wound, but to heal and mend. In short, to do good. If you are one of those who are liable to use your tongue as a knife, then why not, like a surgeon, try to use it to heal and be kind rather than to cut and destroy? Thank you."

Mr Harvey resumes his seat, looking round eagerly for approval, but we avert our eyes. Piers rises and turns to face the pupils, who are now wide awake again.

"Thank you, Mr Harvey," he sneers, dashing the purple gauze aside. "Most insightful."

"I have a story for you, ladies and gentlemen," he begins, arranging his papers on the brass eagle of the pulpit. "There was once a man who lived in a village, a tight-knit community like ours. He was much loved and respected until one day he got drunk and stole a sheep from his neighbour." Somnolence begins to overtake me as Piers hectors on about the villagers branding the thief's forehead with S.T. (for Sheep Thief) and exiling him. Years later, the man returned and made himself so useful that people assumed the S.T. stood for 'Saint'. "Of course we know better –" he pauses, "don't we, Felix?" I am suddenly awake again. "Stand up, Felix," he spits. Felix stands up. "Ladies and gentlemen, take a good look. Felix is a thief." The boy lowers his eyes as the multitude turns and gazes at him. "Must we brand his forehead to remind him JUST WHAT HE IS? – a thief. Felix, in this close-knit community we have no room for thieves. See me in my office after lunch. I'll have your father on the line from Berlin. Sit down."

Riding high on the third fearful silence he has generated in thirty minutes, Piers majestically sweeps once more across the narrow nave. "And now we will bow our heads for the School Prayer."

After which, Mr Evans lets fly with something reminiscent of Widor's *Toccata* and Assembly is over. I never do find out what Felix stole. Perhaps Wolfhart knows, but he has remained outside weeping silently. The east wind gusts round the corner of the church and his prefect's gown billows and flaps against a tombstone.

10

An Ill Wind

A day off at last and I am alone in my cottage on a blustery, grey morning. The phone rings.

"This is the Robson residence," I intone, Jeeves-like. "How may I help you?"

"Hi. It's me. Can you hear me?" My heart leaps. It is Valerie calling from Antarctica. "We need to talk."

"Hullo, gorgeous. Where are you? The South Pole?"

"I said we need to talk. Meet me at the usual place. Now. I'm nearly out of battery."

The car park is empty except for Valerie's blue Toyota. I pull up alongside and clamber out, zipping up my anorak against the wind and drizzle. The pine trees creak and wave menacingly overhead. I open her door. Her face is blotchy and tear-stained and she does not kiss me.

"What's the matter?" I try to pull her towards me but she resists, turning instead to lock the car. My practised eye seeks the compensation of a glimpse of kissable pale skin; between the collar of her puffer jacket and her scarf, I see that she is wearing the necklace I gave her.

"Why the jewellery? Are we invited somewhere? I can easily buzz home and change into my D.J."

"I've put it on for safe-keeping," she says, ignoring my attempts at frivolity, her voice sounding husky and raw. "It's over, Henry. He knows." An icy claw grips my diaphragm and I feel suddenly nauseous. "We need to talk. Come on, walk with me."

"What do you mean, he knows? I thought he was in Kuwait for a month." (Valerie's husband is 'in oil'). "Did you tell him?"

"Of course I didn't. He found out. He read your last letter."

"He read my – ? You *kept* it? I thought we agreed that –"

"I know, I know," she snaps, before softening and briefly squeezing my hand. "But you wrote such lovely things after Earlham Street that I couldn't throw it away. I had to keep it."

I recall that even by my standards I had waxed rather more than lyrical in that last communication, penning innermost thoughts about her, the details of which make me want to retch as I remember them, details I had not been planning to share with the cuckolded husband. I try taking her hand again, but she's having none of it. We stride on further into the woods. I am becoming breathless; only twenty minutes ago I was in the bath.

"So what happened?" I venture, tugging the rim of my Fedora down to stop it lifting off. I hazard a glimpse at her face. Her expression is as cold, hard and white as alabaster. I have not seen a woman like this before, and a gnawing suspicion takes root inside me that I am in the midst of an attack of Real Life for which I am about to be held responsible.

"He was packing for the trip last night," she goes on, not looking at me. "One of his shoe-laces broke, so he went to my cupboard and took one of mine. He found your letter stuffed into the toe of the shoe. It had to be *that* shoe, didn't it?" Again, the hand of Destiny. "He's cancelled the trip, by the way, so that he and I can *talk*."

64

We have come out into the open now. The track is crossing a tundra of sawn pine trees, piles of discarded branches strewn across deep trenches made by the Forestry Commission's machinery of mass destruction. Stumps have been uprooted and tossed into heaps; the bare earth has been churned and blasted. I am reminded of those grainy black and white photographs taken after the Battle of Cambrai.

"Where is he now?" I ask. We are tiptoeing gingerly around the edge of a brown quagmire.

"He's waiting for me at home. He told me to come and find you. 'Run to the arms of your lanky out-of-work lover, see if he can promise to give you what I have given you. Come back by twelve and let me know what you both decide to do.' He's so *fucking* triumphant. Said he's known for months, just had no proof. Now he's cock-a-hoop because we've saved him thousands in private detectives' fees. "

"Right."

"Millie's coming home next week and he's threatening to tell her what a bad mother and shit wife I am."

"Right."

"Is that all you can contribute, Henry? 'Right'?" she snarls. "What are we going to *do*?"

I pause slightly too long. "Well, he can divorce you and in the meantime you can move in with me. Millie can have the little bedroom during the holidays."

"What planet precisely are you from, you fucking *arsehole*?" she yells, jumping to firmer ground and storming away again. There are spatters of mud up the back of her jeans. This is the first time Valerie and I have been in the open countryside without trying to find somewhere cosy to nest and make love.

"Stop a minute, will you? I can hardly keep up."

She comes to a halt without turning and, standing behind her, I put my arms around her middle and press myself into her back. She is breathing heavily and I can smell the tantalising scent of her hair.

"Think about it, Valerie." I have to shout over a blast of wind. "It's not too bad an idea. It'd be fine until things settle down." My Chekhov training affords me the privilege of listening to my own subtext rather than to my actual words. There's the smell of beseeching desperation festering under the languid tones of male impracticality; I can't bear the thought of losing her. What does she want to hear from me? *Could* we live together? Would we actually get on? I try to turn her to face me but she won't move, so I squeeze her more tightly and murmur "I do love you, though" in her ear.

She shakes herself free and stalks off down a side-track through young pines. I follow, my heart beginning to crack. The pitiless gale is causing tears to course down my cheeks. Round a bend and out of the wind at last, she turns and looks me straight in the eyes for the first time today.

"I've decided to leave him, Henry, but I'm not moving in with you. Nor is Millie. You'll never sleep in the same house as my child. I don't want her seeing me in bed with *you*, Henry. You're not her Daddy, are you?" She flicks a strand of hair away from her eyes. "I'll be renting somewhere, but before you ask, we're not going to be close neighbours. *You* might be able to face down those villagers, but I can't."

She walks away again. Once more my gaze is drawn to her bottom and legs; I am completely obsessed with her. She has a power over me to which I am addicted and for which, suddenly, I despise myself.

I run after her, my feet sounding heavy and clumsy on the soggy pine-needles. I grab her arm, lean back against a tree trunk and pull her forcibly towards me.

"Valerie, I said I love you."

Her eyes fill with tears and at last she buries her head in my chest. I hold her tight and listen to her sobs and the wind howling in the tops of the trees. It is beginning to rain in earnest now.

"I can't deal with this now, Henry. I can't think about us.

Don't you see? You've destroyed my marriage and my family and I've lost everything because of you."

"Because of *us*, Valerie."

"Piss off, Henry. That's such a *man* thing to say."

I let her go and she takes a step backwards and stands with her arms akimbo, looking me up and down with some distaste. "I'll let you know when or *if* I move out. In the meantime, just keep away from me." She glances at her watch. "I must go."

She hurries off in the direction of the car park. I lean my head back against the tree and feel the rain on my cheeks and neck. A sob rises from within me as I realise that I haven't even kissed her goodbye.

The Village of the Damned is going to love this.

I miss her call that evening because I am driving in a pathetically fallacious thunderstorm. I am tired, dirty and frowsy after a consolation trip to Ikea where I've been rooting through that grubby zone by the tills where you can pick up an only slightly broken 'Billy' bookcase for five quid. I have lugged it upstairs and filled it with my collection of unread and unperformed plays (in alphabetical order of playwright). My heart misses a beat or two as my phone demands my attention.

Moving out Saturday. Alone
Can u help? Miss u. V x

PART TWO

11

A Bad Night for Don Giovanni

"Well, imagine you," says Valerie, "my naughty schoolboy, holding down a real job after all those years as a resting actor." A jab of irritation in my guts. "Rub my feet, Henry," she simpers.

For once, I don't obey her immediately. Instead, I uncross my legs and lean back against the lavatory cistern, surreptitiously rearranging myself within the reduced confines of my boxer shorts. Valerie lies just out of my reach in the bath, languidly lifting and lowering a yellow flannel, letting it drip onto her nipples for a moment before draping it tantalisingly over her breasts. With an aqueous squeak she sinks a little lower into the tub, the steaming water swilling over her pale abdomen and eddying between her legs. Near me, ten painted nails, like shiny holly berries gleaming against a Christmas snowdrift, gleam through the clouds of foam as she splays and stretches the toes I worship. It's another weird yoga thing. Pleased with all she surveys, she closes her eyes and smiles.

"Henry, I said rub my feet, plee-ease".

A tantalising leg emerging from the foam slides seductively backwards and forwards along the rim of the bath. The thought of touching her again now is too much to bear. I simply dare not run the risk of disappointment and so pretend not to hear. How many hours and in how many improbable places – cinemas, trains, kitchens, cars, barns – have I spent with her glorious feet in my hands, my heart hammering with longing, putting myself through divine torture in the hope of being allowed further – only to be turned away? Fear of rejection has now become a fact of life. I wipe my forefinger along the damp windowsill, pointlessly inspecting the smear of old grey talcum powder ridged along it. I am atrophied, petrified with desire, able only to gaze at my powdered digit and listen to the supersonic hiss of my tinnitus. My whole being is humming with the desperate uncertainty of anticipation.

Weeks have passed since that miserable tryst in the forest and I am struggling to ignore how those winds of change managed so acutely to realign our relationship. On the face of it, Valerie and I are enjoying an evening together in her new rental house four miles from my own cottage, and until five minutes ago I had been propped up, uncomfortable and semi-recumbent against the bath, stroking her firm warm legs and breasts until she had complained that I was in her space (which was exactly where I wanted to be). Drying my arm on an enormous white woolly towel, I had retreated to the porcelain pedestal, rolled down my shirt sleeve and buttoned it at the cuff.

Things have changed between us since her marital meltdown: gone is the dangerous season of exquisite guilt and desire, heady days of nervous exhaustion and illicit passion, pastoral moments seized at a time when cleverness and deceit were becoming second nature to us. But so much storm water has been forced under the old stone bridge that the venerable structure has now collapsed leaving only jagged ruins visible in the mud at low tide; felines are ex-bag and stable doors lie splintered on manure-strewn cobbles.

Net curtains notwithstanding, we have decided on a bold policy of facing down our erstwhile friends and neighbours by being seen openly leaving each other's houses after an intimate, normal and grown-up breakfast together; but we are still pained by being treating differently. I have been pretending to myself that Valerie and I will prevail, given time, and that one day we will attain the *Shangri-La* or *Mon Repos* of a Happy-Ever-After. Recently, though, I have acknowledged that I am doing battle not only with other people's changed attitudes towards me, but also my lover's.

"You *are* just a naughty schoolboy, aren't you?" she resumes, slicing through my torment and bringing me back to the steamy reality of the monochrome bathroom.

"I suppose so," I croak, my voice having ceased to function properly. I am sinking further into the mire, remembering the time when I had first been termed 'a naughty schoolboy'. I had liked it in those days, proud of appearing so young and reckless to my mistress, but recently the appellation has taken on a more disapproving and accusatory note, as if by now I am supposed to have grown up and become satisfied with a more comfortable love-life of country walks, conversation, omelettes by the fire and visits to the theatre, leaving the youthful attractions of a wild and lustful passion far behind. And, as if to underline this new distance between us, I am still forbidden from meeting her daughter Millie who, when not at school, seems to me to spend hardly any time at all with her father. However unwittingly, she does furnish her mother's newly liberated virtue with a splendidly effective Victorian chaperone, and when Millie is in residence I do not exist, any contact with my lover being restricted to the occasional clandestine phone call, usually late at night.

All I can see now of her intoxicating body is a shiny, white knee and a explosion of glossy hair bursting through the foam and over the white enamel rim of the antique bathtub, one of those expensive, reconditioned affairs resting on ball-and-claw feet. Balls gripped by eagle claws. That's the second time I've mentioned my reproductive organs in the grip of a bird of prey, isn't it?

"Pass the towel, please, Henry." She is pouting sulkily. *And to think I spent an hour rubbing her feet in a field this afternoon.* She climbs dripping out of the bath, steam rising from her slim, sculptured figure. She has me in her power and she knows it. I am under her spell, under control, her lap-dog. Transfixed, I feast my eyes on her naked form, my throat tight and sticky with longing, choking back a scream of joy, a roar of excruciating desire welling up in my soul; something which, if released, will erupt and consume us both. I force my eyes to look elsewhere, fearing above all another accusation. Of course I am a naughty schoolboy *now*, but I was never naughty at school – at least, not with girls. Surely Valerie wants to be my boon companion, to be worshipped and adored, desired and loved? And would I not, after all we have been through together, expect to be loved and enfolded in return?

Surreptitiously I watch as she dries herself, dropping the towel to the carpet and reaching for the talc. I brace myself. This is the breathless moment I dread and for which I ache, especially if I suddenly imagine it when I'm in Tesco's. She lifts the upended talc bottle above her shoulder and, with deft and seemingly deliberate pornographic movements, writhes and twists, shaking an avalanche of powder over her arms, caressing it under her breasts, down her legs. Lovingly, she smoothes it into her tummy, massaging and defining her yoga-trim torso and hips, armpits and shoulders, her hands moving knowingly across her body and finally (I have to say it) between her legs.

I long to be permitted somehow to participate in this ritual, to be included in what is an almost sadistically exclusive ceremony dedicated to Narcissus. I might feel a little better if she saw fit to vouchsafe me a single affectionate glance, averting her eyes for one second from the mirror. But I have attended these steamy rites before and know better than to try to interfere by caressing or – worse still – actually embracing her whilst she is preparing herself at the temple of her own beauty. Preparing herself for what? Surely she's just getting out of the bath? Does she feel she is about to sacrifice herself on the altar of love? Does it have to be this complicated? I'm not some Inca high priest about to slit her throat with a diamond-encrusted dagger; I just want to make love with my girlfriend.

However, I'll have to be patient for a little longer for she is not quite finished. Even without the wailing and chanting of ten thousand native devotees prostrated naked at her feet, without her being robed in gold by fourteen virginal handmaidens, I know what is coming. The crisis is upon her and, as the talc cloud begins to dissipate and settle, she leans forward towards the mirror above the basin and wipes the steam away with a flannel placed nearby for the purpose. I stare at her bottom because if I look up I will see a little moue playing across her mouth as she gazes with rapt admiration into the glass. She speaks the holy words:

"Mmm. Not bad for forty-two."

I smile inanely at her as she looks to me for agreement before loosening her hair, turning and leaving the bathroom. The cooler air from the corridor enfolds her as she takes up Position 2 in front of the full length mirror at the top of the stairs. I stand behind her, daring myself to place my hands around her waist, clasped over the perfection of her smooth and powdered tummy. Gently but firmly she removes these blots on an otherwise unblemished portrait and together we gaze upon and worship her naked form, ignoring the tall and pathetic bystander gibbering inwardly behind her. *Please turn around, let me hold you in my protecting arms, treasure you and love you. Show me a little vulnerability now and again, reveal a tiny chink in your armour-plating where I, the man, your man, might be permitted to care for and worship you.*

Cecil has by now given me his entire collection of Dornford Yates novels. "At ninety-three, I have no further use for them, Henry." Have I been adversely and anachronistically affected by them? They boast intriguingly irresistible titles such as *Gale Warning, Blind Corner, Perishable Goods, Shoal Water, Fire Below* or *She Painted Her Face*. They are rollicking tales of rich young men and their servants rushing 'without the law' around France and Austria in 1930s Rolls Royces like the one at Gussage Court; they are hunting down impossibly bad villains and rescuing implausibly beautiful and aristocratic women who faint away at the slightest gust of wind. Valerie's outlook on life is more pragmatic, more feminist, and she despises this genre of literary snobbery. I have tried to enthuse her with classic Dornford, tales of diamonds secreted behind waterfalls in the vaults of miniature fairy-tale castles; soul-searching trysts in flowery meadows high in the Pyrenees; headlong plummets into mediaeval wells at the dead of night; manly strength and womanly fragility in beech woods as rosy-fingered dawn creeps up behind beetling crags. But to no avail. Valerie is a determinedly modern woman, intent on belatedly studying GCSE Psychology and Sociology, a girl who spurns whitewashed villages with red roofs, utterly rejecting car chases through hushed forests, and dismissing as farcical life and death adventures with white slave traders working from a deserted wharf downstream from Rouen. All of which is a shame because an understanding of Dornford Yates' psychology is in my view a must for any satisfactory relationship. Were these most gentlemanly of gentlemen so very wrong to put their ladies on pedestals?

"I'm a beautiful woman, Henry," she declares, moving away from the mirror and into her bedroom, the erotic sway of her bottom pulping what little is left of my self-control. I follow and gingerly undress myself, leaving my clothes neatly folded on a chair by the window. She is already in bed under a crisp white duvet. Trying to appear calm despite the thumping of my heart, I remove my spectacles. The frames of this particular pair are so expensive and thin that they disappear from view as soon as they are off my nose, and I must remember their precise whereabouts if I am ever to find them again. I place them next to the glowing digital display of Valerie's unforgiving clock radio and then realise that I have omitted one vital thing: to check the expression on her face. Is she benign? In James Bond films and during every Dornford Yates honeymoon she would be, but I know better now than to count any chickens.

"I love you," I murmur, my voice tremulous with many emotions.

"Love you too".

I would have preferred her to add the personal pronoun to that reassuring cliché, but I ignore her trendy American speech patterns. Any comment from me would provoke irritation and justifiable accusations of pedantry and snobbishness. *And I'm like – woah, dude – like you've never like seen 'Friends', man? And I'm like todally, euhh, no-oo! I reelly like – like that episode when Monica and Chandler were like – yeah, and I was like – dude, that was like reelly awesome.* Like it or not, I'm a linguistic dinosaur. At school I have started to bleat on about my verbally constipated pupils gagging and stammering over every phrase they try to utter; a colleague recently reminded me that it may be an elocution instructor's nightmare, a pedant's purgatory, but it's just the way they talk, Henry – language developing. Ignore the Like-Fest. Get over yourself.

Valerie is facing uninvitingly away from me as I lift the duvet and climb into bed behind her. The moment, as always, is one of utter ecstasy. Since Meltdown there have been many more opportunities for making love indoors, in an actual bed, rather than enduring the less comfortable facilities provided by Mother Nature. And now, having been privileged to witness the evening's bathing, drying and powdering ceremony, I lie beside her with a sense that all must surely be as well with the world as ever it could be; I am happy and supremely alive. Any recent pain will soon to be swept away because Valerie's naughty schoolboy has doffed uniform and grubby cap to reveal an ardent Byronic lover, poised to adore his lady, ineffably lovely as she is, clean and scented, silky smooth under the influence of half a hundredweight of talcum powder. After we have made love, I will stroke her to sleep and lie awake myself, gratefully basking in a starburst of release and the miracle of my feelings for her.

I don't move for a minute or so, waiting for a sign as a bird-watcher waits, ready to make a move only when the observed creature has lowered its guard. Valerie gives a little shake of her body, the green light for my hand to move slowly over her hips, down her left thigh, caressing and exploring, relishing her warmth. I kiss her hair, nuzzle into her, tasting the talc below her ear and under her jaw amongst the delicious chaos of her hair. I lean up onto my elbow and brush her cheek with my lips, kiss her closed eyelids, linger near her mouth, breathing in the glorious scent. It's going to be all right. I move slightly, check the presence of the prescribed single condom under my pillow, reach gently over her to take her in my arms. More than anything in the world I want her to roll over towards me and hold me tight. I long to feel her breasts cushioned against my chest, to kiss her deeply, to be inside her, to be naturally united – ignoring of course the desensitising desecration of the spermicidally lubricated gossamer-thin barrier between us. Latex is our reality: we both refuse the snip, and the pill, being in Valerie's view an unnatural and dangerous hormonal interference, is out of the question.

In this pre-orgasmic state of torment, your average naughty schoolboy would only want to explode inside his lover, but the

Byronic male needs more: he needs to know that she loves him, that she too is content, that he alone can make her happy. He wants to hear her say she that she adores him and will live with him forever, that she needs him as much as he needs her, a united front against Village, jettisoned husband and the rest of the world. And in a more practical and egocentric sense, he is pretty keen for her to realise what a talented, patient and giving lover he is. He wants to hear her moan or better still, cry out with uncontrolled passion, sexual fulfilment and mutual love. He is, in short, poised upon the threshold of complete happiness.

Valerie whimpers seductively. I smile, quivering from head to toe, pressing myself against her side.

"God, I love you," I wheeze.

I bend to kiss her lips again but unaccountably my mouth encounters only hair. Her face is gone. She has rolled away from me, pulled up her knees and, true obsessive yoga fanatic, has deftly inserted a spare pillow between her legs. A glacial claw grips my heart.

"I don't want nookey now," she giggles, snuggling up with the pillow and pulling the duvet tight around her.

Every limb in my body goes limp, and from my thighs to my chest I am filled with dark, purple chemicals. My heart races, white spots dance in front of my eyes. What is this witch who performs for me the Dance of the Seven Veils, who tantalises, teases, taunts and tortures my very being, lures me Circe-like into her bed, only to reject me in favour of a pillow between her legs? I would rather be turned into a pig.

And 'nookey'? Is 'nookey' all my passion means to her? A shag? A *fuck*? She has led me through the velvet curtain behind the altar at the very centre of her temple and instead of reaching for the stars with me she has whipped out a dagger and with five deft words has castrated and emasculated me, reducing me with consummate ease to a state of selfish misery, self-loathing and frustration: humiliation in its purest form.

Sick, angry and deflated I lie very still, waiting for the poisons in me to subside, fearing what I might say or do if we begin to quarrel.

"I'm sorry, alright?" she murmurs. "I just don't feel like it. Let's just get some sleep. It's late."

"For Christ's sake," I hiss.

"Don't start. I've just left my husband because of you." She adjusts the fortunate leg pillow. "Henry, I'll make love to you when *I* want to, not when *you* want to."

Struck dumb with horror at these words, my mind in turmoil and my body screaming, I lie on my back next to her and squint at the clock. Almost ten o'clock.

She gives another little wriggle. *What this time?*

"Rub my back, plee-ease." The same simpering tone she had used in the bath. Automatically, my hand begins to stroke her, and by three minutes past ten she is asleep.

Whatever this is – love, desperation or obsession, it can't go on. I don't relish the prospect of being sexually decimated for the rest of my life, of suffering mental and physical anguish akin to cutting off my own testicles with a pair of garden secateurs, or slicing into the tip of my penis with a rusty razor blade. Why would I put myself through it? A Dornford Yates hero wouldn't put up with it; he'd sell the bitch into white slavery as soon as look at you. Even now, a little voice is asking me what kind of a deeply weird relationship have I fallen into? What are you doing, Henry? Get up and get out! Are you her eunuch?

My clothes are only a few feet away. Should I try doing a bunk? I could end it all right now and escape her control. I'd be free. Now is the moment for action, Henry. Do it!

I sit up carefully, trying not to wobble the mattress and wake her. Leaning forward, I slowly put the weight on my feet, hoping the floorboards won't creak. But I sit back again, nauseous and shivering as remorse, cowardice and cold fear sluice through my body: I love her, and if I lose her then I shall be alone. Is solitude the price of freedom? Can I do without the sex? Ha! What sex? And then I am on my feet, fumbling for my glasses and my clothes. I creep unnoticed to the bedroom door, reach the top of the stairs with only the hoot of an owl in the Scots pine outside disturbing the competing roar of my tinnitus and thudding heart.

There is no movement from the frigid warmth of the duvet. I shudder, wishing this torture were over. Here I am, a lanky middle-aged bloke standing distraught and stark naked at the top of a staircase, my clothes and shoes clutched absurdly to my bosom. How on earth have I arrived at this low point? Where is Byron now? Where is Dornford? I have sunk to the level of some grainy black and white anti-hero in a recently unearthed copy of a surreal B-movie, a failed Don Giovanni, the tears of his shattered ego coursing down his cheeks and into his fake cavalier moustache. The hackneyed orchestra screams and soars in sympathetic F sharp minor but in the morning, my 'lover' will wake up alone, smile to herself, say "I am a strong woman" and get on with her life without me.

Now shivering uncontrollably, I creep downstairs; having dressed in the bleak silence of the kitchen still redolent of omelette, I sit down and write what she will probably regard as a rather plaintive and pathetic letter suggesting we give each other a break until she feels more settled in her new life.

The tradition followed by Don Giovanni or Zorro or D'Artagnan or whoever it is we're talking about – your generic Lothario in a tricorn hat and black cape – is that a wild leap from the balcony will land him on his black steed, and to a reprise of a triumphant love theme, this time in blazing C major, he will gallop away into the grey light of dawn.

There are two observations I would like to make here: firstly, that the fleeing gentleman will have had his oats, and secondly, that in favouring the balcony route he has neatly avoided the necessity of using the front door. So, there being neither balcony nor horse available to me, my next problem is how to make good my escape without leaving the house unlocked. It would have been easy with a Yale, but that option is not available, Valerie's rented accommodation being fitted with a stout old-fashioned lock from the late 'forties. I scribble "The key's on the loo window sill" on the back of my resignation letter which I leave folded on the stairs. I open the sash window in the downstairs lavatory and then creep through the house to let myself out.

The night is crisp and silent, and I lock the front door behind me with its enormous iron key. I turn to my right past an old coal shed and make my way past a laurel bush on the corner. Cobwebs cling to my face as I stumble through the dank undergrowth behind the house. Reaching up, I place the key inside the lavatory window, half expecting to see her white face framed in it: "What the hell are you doing, Henry? Come back to bed!" But, apart from my heart thumping, all is still.

Tugging the window sash carefully down and making my way back round the house, I realise that I am no Don Giovanni, only a naughty schoolboy, a failed actor and lover, reduced to making good his escape from a stranger's house in the wee small hours of the morning.

As I turn the ignition key I am astonished to see that it is still only twenty to eleven

12

'Discovery' as Art Form

A Thursday

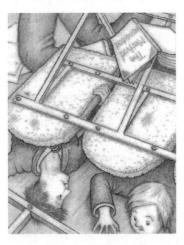

Piers manages to inspire fear despite the absurdity of his chosen hair-style; as a new boy at his School, I am more terrified of him than I was of any of my own authority figures in days of yore. My stomach lurches whenever I see him and I instinctively assume that I am to be blamed for whatever is burdening his soul that day. In repose, his face naturally falls into an expectant glare; only rarely does he allow his malign façade to crack into a smile, and then usually for the benefit of visiting parents he runs into by mistake.

He catches me off-guard today because my head is still spinning from the after-effects of having presided over (as distinct from 'taught') a chaotic Elocution lesson for twenty-one recalcitrant fourteen year-olds in the corner of the art room. I reel out into the sunshine and spot the Presence making a bee-line for me across the courtyard. Something between a smirk and a sneer plays about his features.

"Mr, erm, Robson, walk with me," he commands. "You've been here a few months and frankly I've noticed no marked improvement in the spoken language of our more Chav clientele. What am I paying you for, Mr Robson?"

That's it, he's going to sack me. I'm screwed.

"Well, I – Headmaster –" I stammer, all pretence of being a grown-up abandoned, "it's not ideal trying to teach pronunciation to twenty teenagers at a time. I really think that if –" I peter out because Piers has swung to the left and is berating a tall African girl for wearing her skirt too high. Like a little dog hoping not to be beaten by his master, I follow, reminded of another flawed and dysfunctional lapcanine relationship in my life. I catch up as he bends down to pick up a discarded chocolate wrapper. "Bloody children, Mr Robson. Here, Miss Pankhurst," he collars the passing unfortunate, "put this in the bin. And Miss Pankhurst, why are you still wearing those earrings? See Dr Thorpe at lunchtime." The girl sidles off and, unremarked by Piers, stuffs the chocolate wrapper deep into a clump of the Headmaster's prized 'Here Be Swingers' pampas grass. "I've had a word with Management," he continues, building me up for dismissal, "and I've told them we're going to drop Elocution *per se* and concentrate on Drama."

"Oh, that's ... great," I babble. "Thank you." Relief surges through me as I unexpectedly side-step both mockery from Valerie (*Couldn't manage to hold down a real job, Henry?*) and financial discomfiture. "So I'm making you a state-of-the-art drama room with proper seating and a stage. I want you to put on shows, get the buggers doing something. I've also found you a drama assistant. He's very keen, so use him, all right? Keep him busy. He wants to put on *Grease*". (This is Piers' favourite show, I'm told, with *We Will Rock You* and *Mamma Mia* vying for second place.) "The room's as far away as I could put you," he continues unsmilingly, "so you can make as much noise as you want. Room 3, down past English. It's got the best view in the school and will be ready next week, alright?" A little man in culinary garb trots past brandishing a tray of used coffee paraphernalia. "Chef, I want a word."

And with that, Piers is gone.

Monday

The view from Room 3 does indeed please the eye. Far away from the sound of bells and academic pursuit, there nestles a remnant of Olde England which would have spoken to Dornford Yates' heart and brought a tear to his eye. *The prospect was fair as ever,* he has written, *meadows and hanging forests, standing against the blue: a neighbouring brook was making its pretty music, and the scent of mown grass was still lading the windless air.* However, as I survey the scene more closely, I notice a few discrepancies between D.Y.'s honeyed words and reality: beyond the trees, behind a distant hill, the mono-digital gesture of a lone power-station chimney smokes Man's supreme indifference to the skies. To the left, the motionless blades of a dozen ironic wind turbines further besmirch the environment. At the foot of the slope before me is a brown pond, protruding from which is a spookily green plastic chair; in the foreground, a collection of dilapidated fencing panels have been roughly nailed together to form a squalid den for smokers. Dornford, where are you now?

Unusually narrow for a theatre, my new facility is a sixty-foot portakabin jacked up on breeze blocks. It lowers malignly over the defiled vista and, despite Piers' attempts at disguising it with blue weatherboarding, is frankly an eyesore. As I approach for my next lesson, I hear laughter and crashing, sounds of little children being thrown against a wall by an eight-foot green teddy bear.

Warily, I open the door. Bodies and furniture are in constant flux, heaving and cavorting, bobbing up and down like targets at a fairground shooting gallery. At the heart of the chaos are a dozen sets of high-backed cinema seats welded together in threes and upholstered in dirty pink; seating arrangements which, because Piers has declined to bolt them to the floor, are a challenge too far for miscreant teenagers. The resultant cascade of plummeting pupillage is a health and safety disaster area to which, fearful of a court case, I determine to bring some order.

"Good morning, little ones," I bellow. "Just listen a sec. It's perfectly simple. I need three of you to sit down *together*. You three – yes, you – try it first. Lower the seat, sit down together and keep your feet on the floor." They try it, giggling and snorting uncontrollably. All appears well. "Excellent. Now you three try." As the next batch manoeuvre themselves into position in front of their seats there is a scream and a crash as one of the first trio deliberately raises his feet and all three fall forwards onto the floor. The place is once more a mayhem of upturned seats, pupils, school bags and flying feet. One small boy is catapulted so efficiently to the north that in his efforts to save himself, he falls onto a radiator and wrenches it from the wall. I don't suppose it matters much because in this ramshackle hut the water pipes connecting the radiators are made of white plastic and bend quite easily. Besides, in Drama, we're not connected to any heating system. However, I'm not sure how well the adjacent double thirteen amp socket would fare when squirted with rusty water; most of its front cover has been smashed away and bare wires are visible behind the silver gaffer tape holding it to the wall.

Should I be grateful to Piers for this shambles?

It takes some concentration, cooperation and threats of detention to adjust the whole class to the vertical, but in the end I prevail. "Today," I begin, suddenly inspired by the endless possibilities vouchsafed us by the eccentricities of the seats, "we are going to imagine what it would be like to be in a plane crash."

Unfortunately we are destined never to explore these possibilities because at that moment a red-headed prankster called Daniel leans forward and tugs at the seats in front. The entire row collapses backwards and, when the rest of the class turns to enjoy the spectacle, they too are tipped onto the floor. The final scene from *Alice in Wonderland* plays out until, in desperation, I pretend to have heard the bell and they all scamper away ten minutes early. I make a note to source some traditional chairs with a minimum of four working legs. I already know where to find at least one, but I wonder whether anyone can be persuaded to drag the pond for more.

Tuesday

My drama assistant, Piers' other whimsical gift to me, turns out to be a self-declared Creole and Hollywood-based resting actor enigmatically called RJ. He had been discovered, it is rumoured, wandering disconsolately about a small African airport telling anyone who would listen that his wife had thrown him out of their condo in L.A. before disappearing downtown in the company of their small son and her muscular policeman lover. Piers took pity on him and RJ is now employed as general dogsbody, housemaster and, most alarmingly because I wasn't even consulted, my assistant. I am discovering that Piers invariably follows his whims and never consults anyone about anything. It is part of his fascination.

By contrast, RJ has no fascination at all for me. He is a mere irritant with ginger Afro hair and a perfect dento-smile as wide as the Golden Gate Bridge. His speech is ponderous, complacent and Californian and he has a thick brown neck and a squat bulging torso supported on short sinewy legs. Is it too cruel of me to suggest that he is a teensy-weensy bit pleased with himself? He turns up uninvited to nearly all my classes where, having worked out the safest corner in which to roost, he leans back and pokes fun at less talented pupils.

I had been hoping he wouldn't show up today, but he sidles in twelve minutes late, just as I finish the operation to brace the children in their seats against the wall. It's a new idea I've had and it works tolerably well, there being now only one direction in which they can topple.

"Good morning, RJ, how lovely to see you," I say, safe in the knowledge that as an American he will fail to notice any sarcasm or irony in anything I say. "How are you?" *And don't say "I'm good," you tosser.*

"I'm good," he says. *Tosser.* "Hey, guys!" he continues, doing that irritating and sporty arms-out little flick of the hips that cool Americans do, "gimme *five!*" Three boys do, making a total of fifteen. It's only a matter of time before I kill him. "Hey, Robson, how're you *doin'?*" *Don't flirt with me, you toad-faced wanker. I'm programmed never to be your bosom pal, pal.*

"I'm *well*, thank you, RJ," I reply, pointlessly emphasising the moribund adverb. (As I am still seething from my nocturnal escapade with Valerie, I think I am permitted to suggest that she would love RJ. Perhaps I should get them together sometime for a Lack of Sense of Humour-athon to the death.)

"What you guys doin' today?"

"Oh, role play in a disaster situation. Plane crash. Making the audience believe you really are experiencing fear. That's the general gist."

"General gist? Ri-ight." He flashes me the dazzling dento-grin and I smell trouble. Facing the class, he does that patronising crowd-pleaser 'Durr, what the *hell*?' thing: another peculiarly American pose with thighs bent and palms upwards in disbelief. "Hey," he sneers, "'General Gist'? Who the hell is *that,* soldier? I'm like WOW!" He explodes with laughter. "Your Mister Robson talks like todally weird."

"By 'gist' I mean 'idea', RJ; 'General idea'."

"Sure."

"Is that OK with you?"

"Sure."

I turn to my pupils but he interrupts at once. I am losing both them and the will to live.

"Hey, Robson, are you aware of Meisner?"

"Meisner?"

"Uhuh. The Meisner Technique," he drawls. "When I was in Hollywood I was like really into Meisner. Ben and I used Meisner like a *lot*." The pupils are beginning to rock and plummet. Let them. "D'you know Ben?" he continues.

"Ben?"

"Ben Affleck. Really great guy. Maybe you saw him in like *Good Will Hunting*?"

"Um, yup." I haven't seen it, of course, but I am a weak and intimidated drama teacher. What I can't say to RJ is that nobody in the room believes that he is chums with Ben Affleck. Nobody really believes he has ever been to Hollywood.

Afterwards I look up Meisner in Wikipedia:

Meisner students work on a series of progressively complex exercises to develop an ability to access an emotional life, and finally to bring the spontaneity of improvisation and the richness of personal response to text by emphasising the blah blah blah blah …

Oh Christ. I realise where all this is leading; RJ needs to impress with his method acting skills and where better to find a captive audience than right here in a blue portakabin? He is looking for an opportunity to star in his very own Hollywood *manqué* psychodrama action thriller.

"Hey, Robson, you know what?"

"No."

"Will Smith and I are always going up for the same parts. I know him like reelly well."

"Will Smith is a friend of yours too?"

"Sure".

"That's great. I did enjoy his performance in *Independence Day*." This is one of my all-time favourite films because I am a cynic. I actually live in the hope that one day the planet *will* be destroyed by aliens, unimpeded by either Mr Smith or the U.S. Airforce; the human population will all be eaten or enslaved as a timely reminder to focus a few minds on the stupidity, greed and corruption of our race. Valerie does not hold with this view, of course, but then she isn't bitter and twisted like me.

"I guess I coulda done better than Will in *Independence Day*," says RJ.

"I guess you could," I reply. I am ignoring my class, but they seem to be enjoying this name-dropping repartee.

"So, Robson, I forgot. What precisely are you guys doin' today, man?"

I tell him again.

"Cool. Let's do it," he drawls, settling back into his corner.

As they begin, I sneak a look at him; the expression on his face is not entirely legible, but I detect behind the patronising smirk a darker, more sinister gleam. Is his ego about to get the better of him? Will he be able to resist the lure of performance? Only time will tell.

Piers has decreed that the inmates eat orientally on Tuesdays in order to make them culturally aware. 'Orientally' implies chopsticks, and chopsticks imply problems. If the food were served in a bowl, there would be less of a difficulty, but the fact that the deep fried pap in industrial orange sauce is invariably served up with rice on a flat dinner plate makes for trials and tribulations especially amongst the younger pupils. With the weekly trial by chopstick hanging over them, I make allowances for the lacklustre performances offered by my pubescent charges. They are not finding it easy recreating the moment when, after the crash, one of the air-hostesses finds the pilot (her boyfriend, apparently) dead in the cockpit, his innards perforated by a piece of fuselage. Amy has gone as far as to kneel beside him, but there the verisimilitude ends. Amy is no actress and turns to look balefully at me.

"I don't know what to say, sir."

"Well, Amy, you are an air hostess. What would you be thinking when you find your beloved boyfriend pierced by a piece of the aeroplane he's just managed to crash? You have survived. He is dead. How are you feeling?"

"Don't know, sir."

I take a deep breath. "Try it again, Amy; you're doing really well."

After a pitiful second attempt, I release her.

"Who else would like to try? Zoe?"

"Do I have to, sir?"

"'Fraid so, Zoe."

"But, sir..."

There is a movement from the corner behind me. "You know, guys," simpers my assistant, "where I come from, when the teacher like tells you to do something, you do it." The atmosphere freezes over. "Hey, Robson, d'you like want me to do 'Discovery'?"

What is he talking about? "Yes, please, RJ," I squeak. "Why not?"

"OK, Zoe, you be my dead girlfriend and I'll discover you on the bathroom floor."

Zoe looks beseechingly at me but I remain for the moment loyal to RJ. "You'll be fine, Zoe. Just play dead," I whisper.

"Trust me, Zoe, OK?" RJ intones; I can tell by small movements in his feet and shoulders that he's getting into character. *Please no.*

The class gathers round as Zoe curls herself up on the floor at RJ's feet. Her fate is sealed unless the school secretary comes to fetch her away for a last-minute cancellation at the orthodontist's.

RJ is beginning to breathe, sucking in the air through wide dilated nostrils and exhaling slowly through his smile, teasing open his throttle to blow us away with a Meisner Effect Force Ten. He takes two steps back and then suddenly lunges towards the corpse. Falling to his knees, he lets out a heart-rending cry. He gasps, his voice a croak of purest horror. "No," he whispers, "No! Zoe? Zoe, darling? Zoe, it's me, Phil! Oh, Christ!" His eyes are welling up with spontaneous tears. His mouth is open, his breathing coming faster as he scrabbles at the fourteen year-old's commendably inert body (is this legal?), turns her face towards his, kissing her forehead and shaking her. Method in his madness. I hope to god Marketing doesn't choose this moment to turn up with a prospective parent. "Zoe? ZOE?" he yells, "Oh god, nooooo-oooo!"

The boys at the back are now snorting with mirth and many of the girls are looking beseechingly at me, begging me with bulging eyes to make it stop. I give them the benefit of one of my fiercest stares, but they know whose side I'm on. I have bitten my lip so hard I can taste the blood. When will it end?

"Please god, don't take her away from me!" RJ is about to orgasm on this one. "Zoe!" he explodes, "Aaaagh!" He collapses forwards, shuddering and snuffling onto poor Zoe. I make a mental note to give her a house point.

And then suddenly, it is over. The storm is past. RJ sits back on his beefy haunches, his face no longer contorted, the dento-smile back in position. "There you go, guys, that's 'Discovery'." He beams around him, basking in the ripple of tepid applause which dutifully breaks over him. But what he perceives to be our love is in fact pure relief tinged with mockery. "Hey, Robson, you got a tissue?"

"'Fraid not, mate." I manage not to say 'dear boy'.

"Have you ever bubbled up like that? The kids reelly love it. One minute I'm like in, the next I'm out."

In the distance, I definitely hear the bell ring. What

wouldn't I give right now for a pair of sharpened chopsticks? I'll put it to Piers that if he's going to lumber me with idiots like this then perhaps he could see fit to supplying me with the tools appropriate for the spontaneous puncturing of outrageous ego.

13

The Don rides again

I've made it through to the end of another part-time week at Gussage Court. It's Friday: my day off. I am jolted awake by the telephone ringing beside my bed.

"Hi, it's me."

The sound of Valerie's voice promptly banishes any beneficial effects a few lonely hours of fitful slumber might have wrought. So, after a nearly fortnight she now rings me up to wreak further torments upon me. Did she not read my late-night missive and if so, why is she ringing me now? Can't she leave me alone?

I lean forward and tug open a curtain, squinting myopically at the idyllic view. In the blur that is the top of the village green, the church tower gleams against a perfect blue sky. The cricket square, sparkling in the dew, its turf rolled and mown to perfection, is even now undergoing its daily inspection by Mr Brackenbury, the elderly Chairman of the Parish Council. He is a tall gentleman, bald and slightly stooped, his beige corduroy trousers riding so high that his red socks are clearly visible even to me. In a couple of decades, I shall be a Mr Brackenbury.

"Henry, are you there?"

"What do you want?" Dare I put the phone down on her?

"How are you?"

"How do you think I am?"

Wedging the receiver against my ear, I scrabble for my glasses and put them on. Life with all its domestic miseries comes into sharp focus. It really is a very beautiful morning.

"We need to talk," she says, her voice tense.

"What about?"

The neighbouring shop doorbell tinkles as one of the old ladies potters in for her weekly order of bruised fruit and veg, a pot of primulas, a roll of Happy Shopper loo paper, a packet of custard creams, a tin of Bachelor's chicken soup and a brown paper bag of bird seed. The landlord of The Bell opposite drops a broken barstool into a skip. Two lank-haired young mums in pink jogging bottoms and fake fur jackets pause with their buggies under my window and light a cigarette.

"I did read your letter," Valerie is saying. "I understand you, Henry, and I'm sorry, alright?"

My heart is racing again: a familiar physical response to a damsel in distress. *Careful, Henry.*

"I'm constantly crying," she persists. "I can't bear it. I've been crying since seven this morning. You're usually here on a Thursday night. We have tea and toast together." *She knows just which buttons to push to create fault lines in my resolve.*

"I've been completely miserable too." My voice is almost a whimper.

"Let's have a walk," she sniffs. *Ah, it always begins with a walk.* "This afternoon after my yoga? We can talk then."

I stare out of the window. Our two-week radio silence had convinced me that I'd rather end up a dribbling old flirt in a retirement home for ageing Lotharios than subject myself to a life of torture and manipulation with Valerie. I may be drearily male in my need for physical intimacy but her ideas and mine about expressing love are poles apart. "Some women," she had once explained, "prefer to show their adoration by cooking their man a lovely quiche rather than showing him how they feel for him in bed: sex isn't everything, Henry." It's a point of view, I'd thought, ideal for the life of a fridge magnet, but not one to which I can necessarily subscribe on a long-term basis.

I turn and glance across my bachelor bedroom at my print of J.W. Waterhouse's *A Mermaid (1900)*. Historically, I've always been jealous of Waterhouse, partly because he was able to paint so exquisitely but mostly because he spent his days gazing upon sublimely beautiful girls in order to paint them as Mermaids, Mirandas, Penelopes or Ladies of Shalott. And anyone who tries to tell me that J.W.W. didn't sleep with his models is a pompous and naïve old art historian.

The Mermaid sits on a stony beach coyly combing her hair, her smooth silvery tail curled erotically beneath her. It strikes me that my love-life would probably be less stressful were I to hire snorkel and flippers, track down and seduce that mermaid. I am undaunted by the imponderables of copulating with a half-fish amongst sharp rocks, broken shells and semi-desiccated seaweed somewhere on the Dorset coastline; these problems pale into insignificance when compared with the atrocities of my present predicament. Deep down I know why I am drawn to this picture; I love it because Waterhouse speaks volumes to me across the bedroom, and I ignore his warnings. He knows that we delicate Romantics are lured by the dangers and frustrations inherent in becoming obsessed with an ethereal and mystical temptress who is incapable of making love with us in the normal way. And is it time to admit that there is something about this Mermaid that reminds me of Valerie? Although admittedly not endowed with a fish tail, my 'lover' is a true Waterhouse heroine. She is the embodiment of these cursed mythical creatures: my Nymph, my Circe, my Siren, my very own Belle Dame Sans Merci, my Mermaid. And she will finish me off in the end.

As I look at my print, the Mermaid seems to smile a little as another wave crashes onto the shingle. Dimly I hear a voice saying "Alright, Valerie, three o'clock it is" and realise with a sinking heart that the voice is mine.

*

I knock on the blue-painted door and wait in the sunshine for her to unlock it and let me in. Why does Valerie incarcerate herself in broad daylight in the middle of a village surrounded by benign neighbours? Her face is pale and as tight as the kiss she gives me. I take slight encouragement from the latter: things have improved since the time only three weeks ago when she had actually greeted me with a kiss on the cheek. We had rowed about it at the time, but she denied any deliberate intention to snub.

"Come in. Sit down. Do you want a glass of water?"

"No, I'm fine, thanks." My tummy is quivering.

I take a seat in the kitchen, breathing deeply through my nose so as not to betray any emotion. This is a mistake because I smell her scent immediately and it makes my heart miss a couple of beats. Silently, I watch as she laces her walking boots, sturdy footwear she bought last year in preparation for a holiday to Iceland with her sister.

Five minutes later we are strolling across a beautiful meadow on the edge of her village, dodging cow-pats and the silver stalks of last year's thistles, past oak trees and fir plantations. *Below the hanging forests, the writ of Husbandry ran,* writes Dornford Yates. *But Nature had not been ousted: the merry waters sang in their ancient beds; the sweet, rich grass arrayed outlines beyond the reach of art; grove and orchard and paddock were rendering unto their Mother the things that were hers.*

Unintentionally defiling the heritage of this most inspirational prose, Valerie and I had oft made love in these bowers and, walking with her on this glorious, crisp afternoon I realise that I am on the point of forgiving her. My Mermaid is weaving spells to win me back and soon I am to be reborn, in love again, the horrors of recent times receding into a misty unreality whose truthfulness and reliability I am beginning to doubt. Invigorated by the intensity of the light and the fresh afternoon breeze, I reach for her hand, the softness of her skin to my touch sending tingles of pure longing through my whole body. All is well. Valerie and I are as one.

"Henry, you know I can't hold your hand," she says, wriggling free. "My shoulders aren't straight."

Her words deliver a smack of such violence to my solar plexus that for a second I have white spots in front of my eyes. With my heart pounding with the misery of this sudden yet familiar put-down, I drop the hand and step away from her. Even in my dazed and nauseous state, I have the presence of mind to imagine Freud suggesting that now might be a good moment to tell her to sling her bloody hook.

"Can you stay the night?" she smiles, ignoring my silence, secure within an irony-free bubble of her own impregnable construction. Despite everything, her well-aimed question has ignited a tiny spark of sexual anticipation, but any burgeoning optimism is now tinged with a dark foreboding. As I climb over a stile leading into the gloom of a fir plantation, I wonder whether I dare take her hand and offer to help my lady over. "I could make you some supper and then maybe we could, well –" she tails off, glancing coyly at me. My heart leaps again and I feel myself plummeting into a familiar hole, a flickering pulse palpitating at my left temple, a kind of nervous twitch, nowadays usually the harbinger of tears. I stand on my side of the stile and put out my hand to pull her up. She accepts it readily enough and cautiously I help her over, take her in my arms and tentatively kiss her lips, being careful to hold her away from my body to avoid any disparaging comments about signs of arousal to which this physical contact gives rise. "Come on, you," she murmurs, disentangling herself and striding away into the plantation, "this is supposed to be a walk."

A pheasant, surprised at our presence, sputters out of the undergrowth and flies off across the field.

Valerie declines my help preparing supper, desiring me instead to talk to her back or look at the paper. Sitting at the kitchen table watching her fuss with courgettes and herbs, I recall what she once wrote to me:

> *You make me SO happy. Life is very short and you arouse a wild and carefree spirit in me. Also, you give me such fab sex.*

Where had it all gone wrong? These days, if *my* spirit shows signs of being wild and carefree she'll say "I never know when you're acting, Henry. Are you acting now? Do you *really* love me?"

We sit together in the cavernous dining room eating a minute steak (and when I say minute, I mean tiny) with new potatoes and fried courgettes, a lacklustre fire I've lit crackling and spitting in an undersized grate. She breaks a long silence with: "I'm looking forward to our bed." I risk a glance at her, trying not to betray myself; yes, the look in her eyes could be construed as loving, and Valerie is no actor. Cautiously, I allow myself to relax.

"Henry," she says in a tone that in any other girl would be described as seductive, "why don't you have a bath before bed?" Like the fluffiest of white lapdogs I gaze up at my Mermaid in stupid adoration. I put my head on one side and with enormous round eyes and a little whine, beg her to let me get a closer sniff at the tantalising scrap of tender sirloin she is dangling just out of reach. I stop short of actually panting, but I know that my nose is shiny black and my quivering pink tongue is hanging out, aching to lick her all over with gratitude. I stop short of leaping up onto my hind legs and barking for joy.

"My naughty schoolboy," she giggles, brushing my sleeve with a slim forefinger.

"I love you," I reply huskily, leaning across the corner of the table and kissing her hair. "Thank you for supper. Shall I wash up?"

"No, leave it. I'll do it in the morning. Go and get in the bath."

The water is very hot and in the bathroom the scent of talcum powder still hangs in the air, but the atmosphere is quite different now, and the memories of my last sojourn here fade into the realms of improbable pre-history. Valerie perches at the far end of the bath and occasionally strokes my right knee, a physical contact so rare that sends frissons of excitement through me. I cross my legs in the hope of concealing any giveaway subaqueous signs of tumescence. When she leaves, I lie back, wash my hair twice with her expensive shampoo and allow myself to slip inexorably towards contentment, my body once more buzzing with unexploded desire.

What follows has already been described in some detail on Page 79.

The finger of Malign Destiny presses the rewind button and, to my unutterable horror, I experience a precise action replay of my previous nocturnal visit; that is to say until the poignant moment when, instead of compliantly rubbing her to sleep after she has uttered the fatal Nookey Refusenik words and stuffed the pillow between her legs, I fling myself out of bed and scream obscenities at her.

"Just stop it, Henry," she responds in a level voice that enrages me even further. "I don't know what gets into you sometimes. I don't like you being like this."

"Like *what?*" I roar, pulling on my shirt and trousers and shoving my socks into my pocket. "How can you be so heartless? Do you understand nothing about men?" I am already halfway down the stairs. "I want you out of my life, you sadist – you, you – frigid, torturing weirdo!" I grab my coat and car keys and stumble half in and half out of my shoes towards the front door. It is locked and the keyhole empty.

"Where's the key?" I yell.

Pulling on her white towelling dressing gown she catches up with me, the enormous iron key in her hand.

"You know what, Henry?"

"What?"

"Being adopted really screwed you up, didn't it?"

I am dumbfounded. She brings this up now? I stare at her in devastated disbelief.

"You *bitch*." I say, very quietly. "How dare you?"

"I'm not a bitch, Henry."

"Oh, but you are. A cruel, heartless, *fucking* bitch."

She looks at me defiantly, fiddling with the key.

"Open the bloody door!" I scream suddenly, my voice wracked with tears. I try to wrench the key out of her hand but she grips it all the more tightly. "How can you do this to me?"

"Henry, you're frightening me. Stop!"

"I'm sorry if I frighten you! But you're *killing* me! I only want to make love with you for Christ's sake! I just want a normal relationship!" She looks blankly at me. "Give me the key or open the door!"

"No, Henry, I want you to stay. Stop being silly. Come back to bed."

"Open the door, Valerie, and let me out!"

Still she gazes at me. I struggle with an urge to grab her by the neck, throttle her, shake the life out of her. I am powerless and want her dead. *Hast come to this?*

I grab her wrist and rip the key from her beautiful fingers. I rattle it into the lock and throw open the door which bangs against the wall.

"You've hurt me, Henry," she whimpers. "You've made my finger bleed."

I am of course filled with remorse but for once, I persevere. "Why the fuck should I care about your finger when you are breaking my heart?!"

And then I am back in the car again, hurtling home along deserted country lanes.

Two entirely predictable events occur the next morning: the first is that she turns up on my doorstep at 8.30am and the second is that I let her in so that she can assure me that she understands how I'm feeling. We sit at the bottom of the stairs while she cradles my head as I snivel into her lap. I kiss her finger better and she says sorry for mentioning the adventure of my birth. This makes me cry even more. She herself does not cry, and when my storm has passed and I have stopped sobbing, she takes me by the hand, leads me upstairs to my bedroom and there consents to make love with me to make it all better. She has thoughtfully brought a condom with her in the back pocket of her jeans.

Later that afternoon, with Valerie safely at home writing an essay, I ring Donal to titillate his appreciation of the Surreal with an expurgated update on my love-life. I knew he would appreciate Valerie's views on my adoption.

"My, my, Henry," he chortles when I finish, "might now not be a felicitous moment to contact Somerset House in order to lay to rest some of the mysteries vis the origins of the Robson species?" Taunting me like this has long been one of Donal's favourite pastimes, but until Valerie's ground-to-groin missile last night, I had managed to ignore him. But now I capitulate, and before retiring to bed with headphones and a vocal score of *Martha,* an unerringly tuneful and optimistic opera by Flotow, I draft a letter to the relevant authorities and begin my quest.

14

Retail Therapy

I take a bath for various reasons, sometimes because I am dirty, and occasionally, as this afternoon in the wake of Valerie's attack upon my origins, when my spirit needs time to heal.

Whilst I am immersed in the *Gemütlichkeit* (I think that's the right word) of the tub's amniotic warmth, I allow myself to muse upon my own Chapter One. The combined effects of hot water, a generous dollop of Co-op's 'own' herbal bubble-bath and my intense short-sightedness ferment the most fecund of fond cogitations about my own genesis. Where better to analyse my cravings for love and attention and to mull over why I failed to emerge like other babies from the distended womb of the woman who brought me up?

I am the oldest and tallest of four children bearing no discernible family resemblance. I was the first to be told, slightly before I was old enough to understand, that we were 'adopted'. Other people's mothers (my oldest friend Michael's, for example) provided their first-borns with baby brothers or sisters by ballooning temporarily to enormous size; whereas my siblings and I were evidently sourced via an alternative, less cumbersome arrangement as described in a slim hardback entitled *Mr Fairweather and his Family*. In this tale, read to me repeatedly by Mama at bed-time, adoption is the norm and any alternative theory of baby provenance is either glossed over or deliberately hushed up.

The scenario is painted thus: Mr and Mrs Fairweather require a baby. Male is the gender of choice and so, according to the book's ample illustrations, our eponymous heroes enter a darkly-inked and watercoloured office. No mention is made of why this perfect Caucasian couple are unable or unwilling to procreate for themselves using the Becoming Fat Method (perhaps the truth is too heart-breaking to divulge to the early learner), but they sit down opposite a rotund provincial magistrate who opens the interview without further ado:

"And what do you have for this little boy, Mr and Mrs Fairweather?" queries he in his gentle north Dorset burr. Perhaps he is concerned that this latest pair of prospectives may live up to the Fairweather name and abandon the child when things get rough. After all, even in 1958, a child is not just for Christmas; and let's face it, all the children at the adoption shop have been abandoned at least once already.

"We have a fine blue bedroom," says Mr Fairweather perkily, tightly gripping his wife's elegant and well-manicured hand. "And a pretty garden with a tree and a swing."

"Anything else?" sniffs our jobsworth, raising an eyebrow.

"We have a lovely cat and dog," hazards Mrs F, becoming flustered.

"Anything *else*, Mr and Mrs Fairweather?" persists the magistrate, leaning back in his leather-buttoned chair, his free hand poised claw-like over a bell which will end the interview.

"Oh, *I* know!" ejaculates Mrs Fairweather, happily unaware that they live in an era decades before that word raises a titter and before training becomes available to prepare you for this sort of occasion. "How silly of us not to say so at the outset." The clock ticks five times, opportunity enough for our happy couple to gaze deeply into each other's eyes.

"Well?" chides the magistrate impatiently. His next clients are due in one minute thirty-seven seconds.

"*Love,*" murmurs Mrs F, smiling at her husband with a tinge of unspoken sadness. "We also have love." (Undulating Romantic music accompanies the gossamer sound of angels' wings beating overhead.)

"Excellent," says the bureaucrat, beaming at them. "Sign here and you can go through and choose a baby. This week's special offers are on the second shelf near the exit. Do make use of a Moses basket. Have a nice day." His hand comes down hard on his bell. "Next!"

Actually, I made up the supermarket analogy – we didn't have supermarkets in our part of Dorset in 1958 – but nonetheless, it is a matter of some pride that my parents chose me, their first child, from the top shelf and at Full Price. My first sister, arriving two years later, was selected, I'm happy to say, from the same shelf. Said sister and I however have our suspicions that our brother may have been somehow shop-soiled and reduced in price, and all three of us know for certain that our youngest sister, bought in 1966, was definitely marked down for a quick sale. We like to imagine her nestling plumply on the shelf in her anachronistic green polystyrene tray, her dear little face peering hopefully, pleadingly, enticingly through the cling-film at passing shoppers. We won't go as far as to say that she was past her sell-by date: no, that would be mean, and anyway they too would be anachronistic; after all, we're still five years before decimalisation. But retail gimmicks were not unheard of even in those dark days:

FOR SALE
Baby Girl – one careless owner!
~~Was £29 10/6~~
~~Now £19~~
~~FINAL REDUCTION! 10 guineas~~

and then, slapped unceremoniously over her chubby little thigh, a bright orange sticker:

Now only £5!
With TRIPLE Green Shield stamps!

How could my parents have resisted such a bargain?

And so it came to pass that our Mother, having undergone treatment for tuberculosis in 1952, was unable to conceive children herself. Yet she survived, and with our Father, adopted and brought up as her own, four unwanted little mites from four disparate sets of parents and circumstances.

One of my spies told me of an incident which took place when I was six weeks old in April 1958, the afternoon before my history officially begins. She related to me how she stood at the hall window and watched her daughter and son-in-law walk out to the car each holding a handle of an empty red carry-cot.

"It was pathetic," she whimpered, rooting in her handbag for a lipsticky tissue.

"It's alright, Grandma," I assured her, giving her bony shoulders a gentle squeeze, "just imagine: a quick round trip to Weymouth and that carry-cot would be returned. Full. Of me."

I wake up suddenly, submerged in cool and coagulating bathwater, and wonder how I arrived at this tremulous point in my life. Had I not been adopted, had I not been in possession of two mothers, would I still have been drawn to the Acting Lark in a desperate bid to find love, approval and validation? Would I so unreflectingly have prostrated myself at Valerie's feet and yearned to be mothered by her and never again rejected? Had I been born and brought up like my friend Michael, would I have become quite as proficient at gazing so gloomily up my own fundament?

Having sunk to this nadir of anality and self-pity, I hook a crinkly toe around the plug chain and hoist myself out of the foetid tub.

15

Far from the Madness

Let the trumpet sound for I have landed a job at last!

Perhaps it makes a difference to have taken my first tentative step towards illuminating my origins; perhaps purely serendipitous forces are beavering away to improve my frame of mind, but whatever the truth, my career prospects appear to be looking up.

It had been my first appointment since the orgasm acting débâcle; Granada Television have cast me in *Far from the Madding Crowd* and I will be seen potentially by the entire planet giving it large in a west-country accent. Piers, acknowledging my new status as Actor in Residence, releases me for two days and even Valerie seems pleased for me, her pleasure tempered perhaps by certain conditions attached in the small print. These imply that whilst I am away in far-flung reaches of the Empire I would do well not to Disappoint her, not to give in to my disgusting, primal and masculine urges and seek solace and comfort in the arms of beautiful make-up girls, grips and runners. I promise to text her hourly.

Agent P called me almost before I left the casting suite.

"You're my star, Henry; they loved you. You're off to Manchester next week to play 'Farmer One'. A thousand quid plus expenses for one scene. A day's filming on location. Oh, and don't shave, alright?" *I'd not shave for a quarter of that.* And as I'm in Soho, I celebrate by making a bee-line for Maison Berthaud and devouring two of their legendary almond croissants with a cappuccino.

Five days later, I am installed in Manchester's Victoria and Albert Hotel (fabulous pressure in the bath taps and a pretty good selection of mini soaps and shampoos) and at six thirty the following morning, a minibus arrives to transport us to what Granada TV have selected as quintessential Thomas Hardy country, the Derbyshire Peak District. We travel for over two hours across difficult terrain and arrive somewhere very wild and hilly at the Granada Outside Broadcast encampment. As far as the eye can see, the steep landscape is littered with generators, caravans, make-up trucks, catering lorries, a pink double-decker bus, camera and lighting equipment, costume trailers, scenery dock, props department, cables, stables, carts, sheep-pens, dog kennels, a mobile editing studio and executive suites.

"Henry Robson?" A skinny young man with a clipboard and tightly coiffed hair. His tanned and shaved navel is just visible under the flamboyant knot he has tied in his checked shirt.

"Yes, hullo."

"Hi, Henry, love, I'm Andy and I'll be looking after you today." Andy is immensely pretty and knows it. (Lucky for Valerie, I have hardly any homosexualist tendencies. Many years ago I was put off the whole thing after in-depth and vivid discussions with two colleagues in a dressing room on Worthing pier.) "If you'd like to come with me I'll show you to your Winnebago and then you're off to make-up. Can I get you a coffee or some cake?"

"Yes, please," I stammer. "Coffee and cake would be lovely."

He minces away and is soon back with the comestibles before showing me to my quarters, a family-sized caravan with all facilities. It is my first (and probably last) experience of a real Winnebago with my own name in the window. I'm only 'Farmer One': imagine how they must treat the lead actors. I throw my bag onto the settee and, remembering to demonstrate profuse gratitude and immense good humour to Andy because he'll be a director one day, I trot over to Make-up.

Three girls with wigs, brushes and powders await me in a pantechnicon stuffed with all manner of disguises and I note with pleasurable anticipation the pair of shower cubicles at the far end; another nine hours and I shall be rinsing away the sweat of a day's honest labour. The girls gather round me to design and then execute a rustic windswept facial skin-texture with full beard, involving shaving off the laughable and itchy stubble I have propagated as per Agent P's instructions. They decide on no moustache, which means I'll be able to have Andy's cake *and* eat it.

"More coffee or tea, Henry?" Andy is back to escort me to the Wardrobe lorry next door where, above the buzz of a wall fan, we discuss my rustic attire: boots, scraggy trousers, old shirt, jacket and wide-brimmed hat. Once fully togged up, I try my one line out in the mirror, imagining myself driving a picturesque horse and cart along a lane and addressing the wench walking in the mud beside me: "You're a pretty one," I leer, "I'll give you a lift wherever you want to go". I wonder who this wench will be; I have yet to meet any fellow thesps. Will she indeed be pretty? Will she be as pretty as Andy? Will she be lonely and, against all the odds, available? Best not tell her about Valerie even if affairs on tour aren't supposed to count.

Promising Andy not to eat anything sloppy in my cozzie, I am led back to my Winnebago where I continue to practise my line (on which I'm sure the entire plot will hinge) until I can't remember it any more and begin to panic. On a positive note, there is no mobile phone signal up here amongst the Peaks and so Valerie will have to wait for news of my misdoings various, should any occur. Being so far from her clutches, I am wallowing in a wonderful sense of liberty and lightness of spirit. When I return home, I promise myself to attempt to draw another line under this miserable liaison. Even at a distance of two hundred miles, her disapproving face is spoiling my view.

After coffee and cake I potter up the track to where they're filming a pony and trap approaching the front half of a toll-booth someone has built in the corner of a field. The camera is up the hill behind me waiting for the hoards of burly men and women to finish converting this pleasant spring day in Derbyshire into a Dorset winter wonderland. One man in full protective garb is assiduously strimming down the profusion of young nettles, thistles and ragwort; another is employing a machine to spray snow everywhere in shot – over the roof of the half toll-booth, the north side of the dry stone wall (another curiously non-Dorset feature) and over the lush green grass underfoot. A sound engineer waves an enormous furry microphone at the cloudless heavens and curses the all-pervasive tweeting of a skylark: "We'll never edit that bastard out," he mutters.

"About forty minutes, Henry, ok?" Andy is beginning to look flustered and his shirt knot has come undone, which is a shame.

I sit and sweat in the sunshine. My costume is beginning to itch, as are the glued areas under my beard. For take after take, the pony and trap trundle backwards and forwards in front of the half toll-booth and shouts from the bank of cameras behind me imply that the director is getting impatient to move on to the next shot. Perhaps the pony is having trouble with its subtext or, like me, wondering why its wintry breath isn't steaming. Another hour later, Andy scurries back up to me to say that we are summoned to luncheon, an excellent repast on the top floor of the pink double-decker bus. The stars too are at the trough but they think I'm an extra and so don't talk to me. Instead, I practise my line in my head.

"About forty-five minutes, Henry", calls Andy as he beetles back up the track to see how they're getting on with the sheep-dog scene. I hear distant barking, cries and whistles and wonder whether I should go and have another look, but decide to make the most of my private accommodation and read my Laurence Olivier biography in peace. I'll bet old Larry enjoyed a few decent Winnebagoes in his time.

"About half an hour, Henry," says Andy, popping his head through my door an hour later. "Perhaps you'd like to shimmy over to make-up for a touch-up?" An offer I'm loathe to refuse. "Any tea or coffee for you?" Andy's hair has gone limp.

I am thoroughly touched up by the girls for twenty minutes and, while they poke and prod at my beard with fresh gobbets of glue, I continue to rehearse my line to within an inch of its life. I give it every variation in stress that I can think of, but still don't manage quite to transform it, to bring it to life so that people will sit up and take notice. "Yeah, I saw that *Far from the Madding Crowd*. It was ok, I suppose, but that First Farmer gets my BAFTA nomination." Sleepily, I wonder whether I'll actually be driving the cart. That would be a first. And will the horse behave or will I be last seen galloping out of shot – and control – across the Dales with a gaggle of Granada ostlers in hot pursuit? As my eyes begin to close, I wonder why I can't sit here for ever having my hair tweaked and my nose powdered by a pretty girl chatting to her mate in a sexy Mancunian accent and completely ignoring me.

Suddenly the door bursts open. It is a burly female assistant director bedecked with clipboards and spare scripts and hung about with walkie-talkies, torches and a hammer. She is flushed and out of breath after her sprint from the half toll-booth:

"All right, guys, it's a wrap," she puffs, glaring bleakly at the cosy gathering. "If you'd like to get out of that make-up and go along to wardrobe; we won't get to the cart scene today. We're having trouble with the fucking sheepdogs."

My heart leaps. Another luxury night full of romantic potential in Manchester! Back again in the morning? Another thousand pounds? Yes, please, don't mind if I do.

There is in fact to be no 'double bubble'. Agent P calls me that evening to tell me that the director has been sacked, my pivotal cart scene cut and my presence no longer required.

Sometimes, I muse, as my taxi delivers me back to the station, all this glamour is just too much to bear.

16

Outside Interference

Monday

Piers' exaggerated perception of my illustrious television career has resulted in Drama at Gussage Court being upgraded again. The portakabin has been abandoned and I am now housed in a creaking square prefab towards the bottom end of the campus. This time I have a view over the tennis courts where girls practise netball under the tutelage of a lady recently sacked from Marketing. Having never deliberately watched a netball match before, I have a suspicion that a net is likely to be one of the prerequisites of the game; the fact that two of the taller girls are employed solely to hold their arms up high to impersonate hoops gives rise to doubts as to the authenticity of the arrangement.

Emerging from my nice new room, there is a choice of destinations on offer: up the slope straight ahead is the back door to the main house containing on the ground floor the dining-room, Sales, many of the boys' dormitories, the mini-baronial hall and, in the old library, the Headmaster's Office. The first floor is devoted to more dormitories and, above them is Piers' private flat, a domain forbidden to all but the chosen few. Down some stone steps is a Stygian passage leading to the stinky laundry room, Nursey-Worsey's den for sick and skiving pupils and of course the kitchens, smelling of E numbers and cooking oil. Directly to my right are more classrooms, some wooden boarding houses, the staffroom and loos, the girls' changing-room, a car park and riding stables further down the slope.

Imagine my dismay then when I arrive to find my usual route to the staffroom and sustaining coffee barred by a vast mole hill, a six foot pile of topsoil dumped on the path to the right of my door. Piers has been flexing his muscles again, exerting his power. He has woken up in the middle of the night and, in a blinding flash of inspiration, has thought of a splendidly vindictive way of inconveniencing employees and pupils alike. By blocking the path with this miniature Mount Olympus, he forces me to make a forty-five second detour up and down and round and about before I can resume my journey towards coffee and temporary respite. It's a petty and manipulating little landscaping project that winds me up something rotten, and not necessarily only in the state of Denmark, if I may be allowed an irrelevant allusion. Am I being churlish? A mere pile of topsoil might not be expected unduly to upset someone with a love-life like mine, but there is another contributory factor to my tetchiness: over and above normal day-to-day teaching duties, I am also gearing up for the arrival of an Eminent Dignitary at the end of the week. Poised in the wings is a Visiting Examiner whose role it is to moderate and mark the practical drama offerings of my most flamboyant pupils.

Repressing topsoil-induced bile, I enter the building and

open my classroom door: something is amiss. At the end of last week and at some physical cost to myself, I had laid out some hefty staging blocks to accommodate my pupils' various exam offerings. Now, however, I perceive that they have been stacked vertically in the corner. Also, my twenty chairs have vanished.

I stand for a moment gawping and dumb-struck, trying to focus my vision through a swirling reddish mist and acutely aware of a sudden surge in my tinnitus.

"For Christ's sake!" I screech at no-one in particular, for I am alone. "*Shit!*" I smack the wall with the flat of my hand and it hurts.

"Pleece, sir," a reedy foreign voice behind me causes me to spin round, my heart banging with fury and embarrassment. A possibly Uzbek boy has opened an adjacent door and is standing aghast, looking at me fearfully and shifting uncertainly from one foot to another. "I sink zees are your chess." He indicates a stack behind him.

"Ah. Right," I mutter, massaging the palm of my damaged hand. Will he tell his parents there is a balding psycho loose at his school? "Thank you, um, *(I have no idea of his name)* young man. Sorry about the shouting. Bad morning."

"No problem, sir."

Unpleasantness in the offing, I storm up the slope and through the School, ignoring every "Good morning, Sir" on the way. People stare as I sweep past. At the end of Matron's foetid corridor I emerge into Reception and address Carola's skinny *derrière* as she busies herself at her log fire.

"Is Piers in?" I snap.

"Good morning, Mr Robson." *Punctilious cow*.

I cross the hall and, without knocking, storm into Piers' office. He is alone at his desk faffing at his computer.

"Yes?" he says, without looking up.

"Just to say, Headmaster, that I hereby give notice of my intention to leave at the end of term." My voice doesn't sound like me, but its wrathful quality makes him look up and get to his feet.

"What's brought all this on?" he enquires, moving evasively round his desk and pushing past me. I set off after him.

"I came in this morning," I persevere in low tones, "to find not only a mountain of earth outside my door but my room *completely* buggered up, all the furniture gone and the staging piled in the corner. What the *fuck* have you been doing? Why didn't you bloody well *ask*?"

"I don't know what you're talking about. I merely got some of the boarders to tidy it up a bit."

"Tidy it up? Why?"

"It was your turn." *Have I fallen into a Dali painting?*

"Headmaster, all I ask is that you just stop bloody interfering in *everything*! Your *constant* meddling pisses everybody off." I'm beginning to project; my voice is nicely reverberating off the silver Speech Day cups. Carola is assiduously applying the bellows to a sluggish blaze. "I'm trying to rehearse twenty bloody duologues this week and you take it upon yourself to tidy my room up! Well, thanks a million – now I've got to set the whole bloody thing up again!"

"Whatever, Mr Robson," he snarls, and like Odysseus grabbing onto the underside of a sheep to escape the Cyclops, Piers collars his tame architect and bustles him out of the front door.

Piers' considered response duly arrives via email:

> I was most shocked by your outburst this morning. I am more than happy to have a conversation with you in my office but not in the hallway in front of others.
>
> Piers Halliday, Headmaster

Tuesday

I arrive this morning and pick my way gingerly across the muddy car park towards the staffroom. Piers and Dr Thorpe are surveying their domain from the first floor balcony of the new Admin building (a larger than life cuckoo-clock affair), a vantage point favoured by the Headmaster for intimidating his minions. I have seen him up there before wearing a Russian fur hat like Khrushchev reviewing an armaments parade in Red Square. My stomach lurches as I approach; I am obliged to pass under the balcony to reach my room and I wouldn't put it past Piers to empty his coffee over me. Perhaps I should have apologised last night.

"Good morning, Mr Robson," he sneers, nudging his Deputy. "I hope you've taken your pill this morning after yesterday's outburst."

"Certainly, Headmaster," I reply, "a big fuck-off one, don't you worry."

"I'm glad to hear it, Mr Robson."

Outside my door, Sisyphus (the long-suffering school gardener doomed almost to finish a job just as Piers changes his mind and forces him to abandon or undo it) is already beginning to spread Mount Olympus over my pathway prior to grass-seeding. Aware of Piers' eyes boring into the back of my head, I wonder whether I should take the old, direct route over the grass around the foothills or make the trek up and down on the mandatory detour. Defiantly, I choose the former option, exchanging sympathetic looks with Sisyphus and waiting for a "Moo-oooo – get off the grass, you moron!" from our lord and master.

In fact, I hear nothing more from him until the end of break when I am wandering back to my room again.

"'Ere, 'scuse me, guvnor," squawks a strident quasi-Cockney voice. "I got anuvver free ton o'fresh topsoil for yer. Where d'you wan' it?"

"Headmaster," I respond, "why don't you just open my drama room door and tip the whole lot in? Don't mind me."

"Precisely, another load of shit in there won't make any difference."

Tosser.

Wednesday

Despite my various travails, I am in a forgiving frame of mind, a little less 'on edge' as Dr Thorpe puts it. The sun is out, my young thesps are almost up to speed for the Visiting Examiner and I drop Piers an email to inform him that all is finally set up and could he please keep his furniture-movers at bay for a day or two? "Also," I add cheerfully, "what about a nice little 'Drama' sign for my door?"

His response comes winging its way:

I've already made a sign: 'Moody old tarts this way'!

Oh god, he's bloody well forgiven me too. I'm doomed to remain here forever.

Friday

For me, there is something unnerving about Visiting Examiners, especially those of the female persuasion.

What happens is this: after the introductory phone conversation with the exam board's appointed harridan, I immediately form a favourable mental image of her. Her voice is rounded, her vowels pleasingly trained and BBC, and so naturally I imagine a tall, blonde, beautiful, smiling woman, not too slim, not too comely, and invariably unattached. However, up to and including today, I have always experienced a twinge of disappointment when the Visiting Examiner turns out in the flesh not to be a fairy-tale princess of stage and screen, but merely a spinster Box-Ticker from Bognor, always ready to fix me with a gimlet eye and the obligatory smile which says *I've done the training so don't mess with me.*

Today's specimen turns up an hour early and I track her down to the wrong room to which she has been directed by a well-meaning Brazilian prefect. I find her unpacking her paraphernalia onto a chipped formica table. At first glance, I know I am not to be disappointed in my anticipated disappointment. Is the root of the problem to be found in her regulation hair, slightly too big for the head provided, bouclé blonde, dyed, sternly moussed and sculpted to brook no argument? Or is it something more sartorial? Her twin-set is an alarming forty-thousand volt blue confection and, glancing briefly down towards her pedal extremities, I notice that she is raised four inches aloft upon fluorescent pink shoes (complemented by appropriately electric blue tights). Only an examiner could get away with it. With a deep breath and steely determination, I curtail my scrutiny of this apparition and concentrate on not flinching at the firm sunbed-bronzé handshake. We make eye contact – it's what we actors do – and yup, I'm getting the Smile. *But don't worry, love,* I think to myself, *you're quite safe – I can read the signs. I'll not be making moves to swap the remains of my relationship with Valerie for a brand new one with you. You don't do men. It's fine.*

We set off towards the correct room, she dragging a little blue wheelie suitcase behind her. We follow a meandering path through a tiny apple orchard and approach the main thoroughfare. I spot the man himself sauntering up the slope wearing a maroon baseball cap; there being nowhere to hide, and realising that we are on a collision course, he visibly accelerates as we approach. "What are you doing, you madman?" he mutters rhetorically as he sweeps past, ignoring my companion.

"That was the Headmaster," I whisper. It's best not to

introduce visiting professional females to Piers. An A Level art moderator once asked him very politely for directions to the staff toilet and was told quite sharply that here we tend to pee behind a bush at the edge of the sports field. Most of that group failed their A level. "Bloody fat-thighed lesbian," he had moaned to me afterwards. "Where do they find them? And what was with the limp? She walked as if she'd got a cucumber shoved up her arse."

I sense that VE is beginning to freeze over. She has become pensive and taciturn and I know she's wondering when it was precisely that she fell down a disused rabbit-hole into a long-lost masterpiece by Lewis Carroll. I lead onwards, past Oscar the horse, negotiating the occasional piles of his dung that bespatter the pathway in this rural region of Piers' realm. Crossing the raked topsoil outside my room, I throw open the door with a triumphant smile to allow VE to stalk in. I'm guessing she will need five minutes alone.

The candidates are waiting in the adjacent classroom. On a desk is an enormous bread-basket of packed lunches.

"Toby, what are these doing here?" I hiss.

"Chef give 'em to me when I went for the examiner's coffee."

"But we don't need packed lunches, do we?" I patronise. "We are not absent on a school trip. We are here." I suppress an urge to take Toby by the ears and shake him until he dies. "Look, Tobes, just take them back."

"No, sir, Chef said I was to take 'em." A little voice tells me to leave well alone. As Marie-Antoinette would have said, had she been in my position: "Let zem eat zee packéd lûnch. Est-ce que j'en donne une tosse?"

I knock on my door. The electric blue Ice Maiden is nearly ready for curtain-up. She reminds me of Valerie, there now being a crisp Force Eleven chill factor pouring off her. To thaw the old bird (and I'm nothing if not a consummate flirt and bureaucrat), I proudly present her with the reams of required exam paperwork which I know to be in perfect order because

I've checked them. She riffles through them for a moment and then looks up at me with a well-practised half-Smile. *Squalls off the port bow, Cap'n.* An icicle is dislodged from her chin and tinkles onto the desk. She turns up the Smile to Full and enquires whether I have read the *Guide for Teachers* which states perfectly clearly what I am supposed to have done in order to gain a Distinction for Having My Paperwork Absolutely In Order. I say that in my line of work I have to read so many opaque *Guides for Teachers, Teacher Assessors, Teacher Examiners* and *Teacher Assessor Examiner Moderators* that I can't actually remember which exam board wants which bit of information when, in what order and on which bit of paper. All I know, love, is that I'm here, you're here, my pupils are here and we are both in possession of a) our faculties and b) a pen. The paperwork can be filled out correctly as we go along if necessary and don't say to me, *darling*, that you aren't allowed to tell me these things on the day because c) you are doing, d) we're all under pressure here, e) my Headmaster is mad and by the way, f) don't patronise me. Oh, you'd like me to *label* the pupils now, would you? That certainly isn't in any handbook. Right, I'll go and source some. Or would you prefer me to brand their little botties for you?

I bump into Dr Thorpe on the way to the office and offload some VE bile at him. He wonders how I could possibly be so wound up yet again when he's having to contend with a series of International Incidents: a group of twelve-year-old Russians with no clean laundry, a gang of tiny female Colombians with no coach-driver to take them to Legoland and four members of staff out on a Professional Development Course. "I've got no cover for anybody," he snarls, "including you."

The Chef approaches as Dr Thorpe stumps away.

"You got my packed lunches down there?"

"Indeed. Do you want them?"

"Course I bloody well do. There's a mob of Nigerians or Peruvians or something waiting to leave."

I promise Chef that I'll kill the thief, but upon returning with the labels to the waiting room I find that Toby (who missed his breakfast) has already consumed one packed lunch and spilt most of its packet of crisps onto the carpet.

"Toby, get these bloody packed lunches back to Chef."

"But, sir..."

"NOW, Toby!"

A little bell (or another icicle) tinkles from the examination room. Oh god, here we go. I spotted earlier that Ice Age 3 has actually brought a small brass bell with her; it sits on a pad of red velvet at her side and she dings it lovingly with a tiny beater to summon her next victim. I send the first duo in and, feeling a little calmer, take the opportunity to check on how the later candidates are doing. Alex is muttering to himself in the corridor, Zach is gazing in despair at a dog-eared photocopy of his script whilst others are rehearsing outside. Oscar the horse is grazing under the chestnut tree while, six feet away, Algernon and Jack from *The Importance of Being Earnest* are arguing about muffins amongst little volcanoes of horse-poo. Further off, Millie and Lisa are realising that they should have used the five hours in a coach to the Houses of Parliament and back yesterday to learn their lines, and Alexey and Juan are uncomprehendingly massacring a chunk of Ayckbourn with the aid of a balaclava helmet and two plastic water bottles. I feel good; this is what it's all about. Energy and performance commitment. Theatre in the raw. An experience for the children.

At 10.45 precisely, 'Coffee' being marked on VE's schedule, out she pops looking more benign now but in need of the loo. Keeping a weather eye out for Piers, I accompany her to the staff facilities, skirting carefully behind the horse. I explain the equine presence before she asks any awkward questions: "The Head won't hear of sending him to the knackers' yard," I say. "He reckons the old nag can wait right here outside Drama until he conks out. He expects the rest of his employees to do the same; it's cheaper than running a pension plan. This'll be the staff graveyard one day."

VE gives a snort, or Oscar does (I can't tell which). Nearby, the Head of Music, belabouring an old accordion, is cavorting maniacally around Matron in an effort to serenade her with an arrhythmical version of *Je ne regrette rien*. I hurry VE onwards, but as we approach the staff loo, I am hailed by Alan, a small Chinese boy who knows me well enough not to approach when I have an examiner in tow.

"Aaaah, SO, Sah," he squeaks, "Are you awrigh', Missah Wobson, sah?" Why does he choose this moment to take the piss out of his compatriots? He doesn't normally speak like a cartoon Chinaman; he was born in Basingstoke.

"Aaaaahh, I quite awrigh', Aran," I reply in overtly racist tones learnt years ago from the proprietor of a Chinese take-away in Pimlico. "One number for'y-six, one seventy-four and eggfryrice, please, youn' man."

"Bout twenty minute OK for you, sah?" he responds. "Thank you for your custom, sah." And, weighed down by an enormous black school-bag, Alan skitters away, waving and giggling.

"All very good-humoured here, then?" comments my companion without moving her lips.

"Rather."

"No political correctness, I see."

"No, the Head doesn't encourage it."

After VE's ablutions we are almost back within the confines of the Drama Room when we are approached by one of the School dogs, a dirty brown and white beast attached to the Riding Stables.

"The dog's name is Oscar too," I say, reasoning mistakenly that she might have been a doggy person. "Same as the horse. And the boy who wins the prize each year for looking after the dogs: guess what his name is."

"Oscar?"

"Right in one", I smiled. "You're getting the hang of this place."

"Isn't all this an appalling health and safety issue?" she queries, side-stepping the canine's affectionate nuzzlings. "A horse and a dog, wandering loose on campus?"

"The Head doesn't hold with health and safety either," I respond cheerily. "In fact, there's another equally smelly dog who'd love to meet you; he'll be with Matron somewhere."

"The School Matron is in charge of a dog?"

"Of course. She's besotted with that animal. As are the children. She's also the school's designated peacock keeper. Keeps them supplied with chocolate cake."

"Is that so?" My charm offensive is falling flat on its face. It's as well she is only an examiner; imagine what a School Inspector would make of it all.

"We have rats too," I add, warming to my theme. "Usually dead though – in the wall behind the accounts office." Another snort, but this time both Oscars are definitely out of earshot. "Mice too, but we don't mind them because we need mice to feed the snakes."

"Snakes?" she crackles.

"Yes. Two. I held one the other day. I'd always thought snakes were soft and squidgy, but it was surprisingly hard. Have you ever held one?" *Is this the sort of question to ask a lesbian? Oh god.*

"No."

"Matron freezes the mice they catch," I persist. "She defrosts two every week and feeds them to the snakes."

The examiner stares up at me for a second: "Christ alive," she says, and goes back into my room.

I wonder how my pupils will fare.

17

Nomenclatures Anonymous

My letter to the Adoption People bears unexpected fruit in the form of a cancellation. This allows me to jump the substantial queue of inquisitive orphans which normally stretches from the Aldwych to Tower Hamlets.

A week later, passport in hand, I am ensconced deep within the bowels of the Births and Deaths Building at the southern end of Southampton Row, London WC1. An emaciated pale creature with acne and a receding hairline appears from behind a screen and ushers me towards the inner sanctum, a yellow, windowless space with a false ceiling. Behind a battered oak desk is a small woman labelled Marjorie. She sports a bob of grey hair, a black trouser suit and a sympathetic, concerned smile. She looks benignly at me as if she's known me for a very long time, since before my birth in fact. Is she about to reveal herself as my birth mother? Such service would indeed be startling. I am unnerved by her and when she begins her well-rehearsed questionnaire about precisely why I want to find out my real name, I respond with a voice that I don't recognise.

"It's me age!" I roar in broad Bristol, omitting to mention my lover's crucial input. "I'm well over halfway to me three score years and ten, so it's time to probe me origins!"

Marge has seen thousands of cast-off children doing battle with birth-name anxiety syndrome. The fact that I have suddenly morphed into Long John Silver or Worzel Gummidge does not faze her. She merely gives me the look, pulls a yellow piece of paper out of my file and places it firmly face-down on her blotter. "This sheet," she declares confidentially, "reveals your birth name. Before I turn it over I have to be completely sure you're enquiring for what we regard as the right reasons, and quite ready for any shock you may receive." I suppose she is legally bound to warn me off my habitual fantasies about being the much-missed son of Peter Sellers, for example, mislaid after a hushed-up perambulator incident in Kensal Rise.

"I'm as ready as I'll ever be," I say.

With a gesture of some solemnity, Marjorie pushes the paper towards me. I reach out and turn it over. On dots printed for the purpose in the centre of the page someone has written my birth name in neat blue capital letters:

DAVIES, KEITH STEPHEN

I stare at the paper, absorbing the disappointingly dreary and humdrum reality of the information imparted.

Keith.

Not a Geoffrey or a Howard, a Frederick or an Edward; not a Philip or a Sebastian, a William or a Timothy, but plain old *Keith*.

I look up at Margarine who is sitting neutrally before me. *I'm not a Keith*, I want to assure her, *because I do not fit the image of Keiths I have known*:

Keith 1: A farmer, brown moustache, ploughing the fields and scattering; a burly, beery and boisterous son of the sod who spends his life high up on the pastoral idylls of North Dorset cooped up in the cab of a John Deere tractor with only a stack of *Fiesta* magazines under his seat for company.

Keith 2: A swarthy O Level French teacher; black moustache and stringy saliva between his lips.

Keith 3: A diminutive troglodyte who dwells in a dank cupboard under a university stairwell; grey-brown moustache and beard; an aficionado of Webern, Boulez and atonal music various.

Although I did once grow a fine Keithly moustache for a rôle in *Hedda Gabler*, the general consensus at the time was that it made me look like a homosexual second-hand car dealer and so was removed after the run. This proves that I am no Keith but a Henry through and through. 'Stephen' has no connotations for me: it's a name. And I'm fine with 'Davies': a solid, dependable nomenclature. Keith S. Davies – not as resonant perhaps as Keith P. Sellers but I'm sure my career will blossom despite this set-back.

As I thank Marjorie and rise to leave, she reminds me of my entitlement to a copy of my original birth certificate. "It will cost you another twenty-five pounds," she says apologetically, "but it might contain details of your birth parents. Do think about it."

The next screwed-up adoptee, a wiry lad in a green hoodie and a brave attempt at a ginger moustache and sideburns is already waiting in the corridor. Old casting habits die hard but I manage to refrain from pumping his hand and wishing him a hearty 'Good luck, Keith'. His blank stare confirms to me that if anyone deserves to possess *that* Christian name, then he does.

The mealy-mouthed utterances of *Mr Fairweather and his Family* had fallen miles short of preparing me for the feeling of elation now welling up within my new dual personality. In the street outside I want to throw wide my arms and shout: "Finally, I know who I am and who I was! I may be no celebrity love-child," I add, vaulting over a taxi and onto the roof of a double-decker bus, "but I am so happy to be here and I love you all!"

The applause of two thousand extras ringing in my ears, I saunter down the Aldwych. In my pocket nestles confirmation of my former identity and short life before the adoption shop. But the yellow paper raises a myriad new questions: what had happened during those first six weeks, and who had loved or hated Keith Stephen Davies so much that they had handed him over to the local authorities, never to see him again? Who were these courageous or cruel parents? And what did I feel about them? Am I yet an orphan boy and, whatever the answers to these questions, is Valerie right about my being 'screwed up'?

I stop and lean against a tree because I am crying. Now I've started on this adventure, I suppose I had better stump up the twenty-five quid to move on to the next stage.

18

Fudging it in Fake Ermine

Although the end of term is still eons away, the grand old British institution of Sports and Speech Day is upon us.

I spend the afternoon hiding in Matron's Pimm's pavilion, trying to keep a low profile whilst watching the arrival of foreign dignitaries in Piers' Rolls Royce. I have taken some care in knotting one of my more flamboyant bowties, but the garment is a magnet for a tipsy Zeppelin of a German mother intent upon a close-up inspection of its construction; she stalks and molests me with marauding Teutonic fingers under my chin until I am forced to take cover with the smokers behind the scoring tent. Here I submit to twenty minutes' polite French conversation with an overblown sun-tanned father whilst his wife simpers at me from under her Absurdist Simone de Beauvoir hat.

Equally disconcerting is the spectacle of my normally sedate and indolent pupils being coerced into physical activity by the Head of Sports, a fierce Norwegian bachelor who takes inordinate pleasure in megaphone bullying. He pits the unwilling inmates against each other in unwonted competitive spirit, forcing them to run round a track, jump over a horizontal pole into a mattress or throw heavy objects as far as they can – all for reasons that elude me. The parents sit proudly in neat rows and applaud when their neighbours do.

When enough people have won and lost the main events, Piers takes a group of the smallest children and patronisingly explains to them the rules of that great English tradition, the egg and spoon race. With the aid of a blob of blu-tak, a tiny Ukrainian lad cheats and wins but this is all right because he is Piers' Favourite; the child's parents (eternally grateful to Mr Halliday for having taken the excitable little sod off their hands) have recently presented the school with a black and gold embroidered priest's vestment presumably looted from a church; it now hangs halfway up the main staircase in a prominent position between the Samurai sword and a stuffed weasel. There are rumours that Piers swans about naked under this robe when he's alone here at Christmas, but the only witnesses would be Horatio the obese School dog and a poltergeist (resident on the first floor and prone to hurling chairs about), neither of whom can be trusted to express a reliable opinion.

Sports mercifully at an end, all that remains for us to endure is the speechifying. In the old days, I'm told, we would waft over to a marquee or into the Sports Hall to be treated to strawberries and champagne from Matron before taking our seats and dozing off for an hour or two. However, as I have discovered, Piers spends his insomniac hours deciding which bits of his train-set he can randomly move around today, because after all it's *his* train-set and he can do with it what he will. The station has been on that bit of line long enough, so without telling the station staff, he'll move it and replace it with an engine shed. That signal box has been useful by those points, but let's whip it out and put it by the tunnel. The plastic leylandii can go by the hill and the horse can go there by the bridge.

It follows then that although the marquee or Sports Hall options have been tried and found to be pleasant and satisfactory, Piers has decided to bus everybody four miles into Bridlington and have the speeches in an old church on the seafront. This entails pissing off the locals by booking out half the limited car park spaces in town for the parents' four-by-fours, and forcing staff and pupils to swelter on hot coaches in our glad rags as we crawl through the Saturday afternoon traffic. A normal Headmaster would arrange for us to be delivered to the church itself (wherein Matron is primed with her strawberries and champagne), but Piers has teasingly instructed the bemused coach drivers to deposit the school next to the fairground at the far end of the esplanade. In a PR exercise of jaw-dropping proportions, it is his whim and wish that we are to be displayed for all to see marching the last half mile along the sea-wall.

Lined up in amazement to observe us and draw their own conclusions about private school education will be not only the occupants of the large plastic swans on the the pedalo pond and the innocent crazy-golfers further along, but also the red-and-yellow painted ladies and gents of the town revving up for an important local football match due to kick off later in the afternoon. They will be nicely tanked up on fish and chips and beer and will be vastly entertained by the sight of a bunch of bleedin' toffs strutting their stuff along the seafront; pupils in bizarre school uniform, prefects in lime-green gowns and staff in flowing black, with Piers, like a medieval King, striding ahead in red and gold, his ermine collar fluffing around his ears in the sea breeze. To complete his inflated self-image, he would really need to be side-saddle on a white charger, but mercifully the local authorities have drawn the line at horses. The constabulary, however, did allow one thing to slip under its guard: at the head of the procession, in full regalia of kilts and sporrans is the School bagpipe band.

When rumours of this surreal and potentially humiliating

event were beginning to percolate through the staff-room some weeks ago, one of my colleagues reacted simply by saying "*I'm not fucking well walking through the town.*" How wrong he was. How wrong I was also to think that I would be able to duck out of wearing a gown in public, but such is the power of the employer that I find myself alighting, bat-like, from Coach Number 6 and joining three hundred and fifty unshowered school children fresh from the running track.

I'm not sure this has all been thoroughly enough thought through, though, for we are spectacularly effective in our blockade of the pavement in front of the fudge and sweetie stall. An invalid chair nudges its way past and one or two small pupils are pushed off the kerb into the road. Piers spots this hitherto unforeseen health and safety hazard and becomes exercised.

"Will you all get BACK! Move BACK, you morons! Staff, don't let them bunch here. Move them BACK!"

My young charges are looking at me, imploring me to rescue them somehow, to lift them from this living hell and take them away to the safety of a cream tea shop; but I am powerless.

"Revel in true toe-curling embarrassment," I hiss. "It's character building. Mr Halliday wants us to look like wallies, so like wallies we will look, alright?"

RJ sidles up to me brandishing an enormous Pentax, his most inane Californian grin etched across his face. I want to slap him.

"Hey, Robson, this is, like, *real*. Wait till I tell ..." he tails off, his eye caught by one of our more sensuous seventeen year-old girlies sashaying ostentatiously up and down the pavement, flashing the purple soles of her Manolo Blahniks. Removing his lens cap, RJ scampers after this vision of loveliness. "Hey, Georgina," I hear him holler, "it'd be like real cool if I could like take a couple o' shots of you on the sea wall!" I turn away in case I become implicated.

A small boy approaches. "Sir, could you please buy me some fudge?"

"Don't be ridiculous, Charlie," I snap, "how can I possibly do that? Go away."

"But sir, here's the money. It should be enough."

"I said 'go away'!"

"Thanks, sir." The money is in my hand. "See you in church."

Above the hubbub of traffic, wolf-whistles and seagulls, I discern the unearthly strains of bagpipers letting rip two hundred yards ahead. The procession is moving off at last.

"Looks like you're rear-guard, Mr Robson!" a colleague shouts as the column begins to snake off. "Sweep up any stragglers!" As if: to lag behind here would be suicide. Who would be that stupid? And what are these coins? Oh, *Christ*. Charlie's bloody fudge. I spin around and duck under the awning.

"Hullo, do you have any fudge?"

The face of someone who has elected not to pay for her children's education looks at me for a second, weighing up the wisdom of engaging in conversation with an individual attired as I am enquiring after fudge at the counter of her fudge shop.

"Yeah, love, all along the front there."

I grab blindly for a pack and hand over Charlie's cash. Turning, I see the tail end of the procession negotiating the corner by the crazy golf. I am suddenly alone, dressed in a weird gown, a straggler. Panic rising within me, I set off as fast as I decently can without actually running after the platoon, but the pavement is blocked by two plump and bronzed mothers with buggies loaded with shopping.

"Ere, whass all this about, then?" one addresses me. "Got some graduation ceremony or summat?"

"Um, yup, it's Speech Day. And I'm out here wearing this lovely gown. D'you like my tie?" I sound like a man about to commit some highly newsworthy crime.

"Yeah, it's great. Fancy a chip, my lover?" A chubby brown hand proffers a bag.

"Too kind," I say, refraining from adding 'my good lady'.

"Well, see yah, then. Wave bye-bye, Kyle. Wave bye-bye, Charleen."

I wave to the two pug-faced little beasts partially concealed under shopping bags and stride on, my cape flapping madly behind me.

I am soon abreast of the cabin selling tickets for train rides. An elderly couple and their grandchildren are gazing after the procession as if they'd just woken up and found themselves employed as extras in a Harry Potter movie. I ignore their stares, but the way is barred again by three simian lads quaffing beer. What to do? They aren't going to miss six foot five of me in a black gown accelerating past them, are they? If I try the I'm-too-grand-for-you approach I am surely opening myself up to any amount of comment, mockery and possibly even assault. I can see it all:

"Oy, Dracula!" I'd stop and turn. "Arrr! YOU! Where d'you think you're goin' in such an 'urry? Fuckin' vampire convention?" I attempt a dash across the road. "Stay where you are, you TOSSER!" One grabs me by the lapels and pulls his meatloaf face up towards mine. "Wha' you goin' to do? Bite me to death? Eh? Eh? Eh?"

I draw alongside them. They are wearing T shirts and trendily scuffed jeans, crotches clinging under butt cheeks. I grin cheerily and start in straight away with pre-meditated self-deprecation:

"What do you make of all this, lads?"

"Bloody mad. What you doin'?" says the leader.

"Prize-giving. D'you like my tie?"

"Yeah, it's alright," he admits. "Like them bagpipers better though." There's no accounting for taste.

With the pipers giving it large in the middle of the pavement by the narrow church door, the Gussage Court pupillage is now backed up five deep over the zebra crossing. The lights patiently change from red to green and back again, smiling down at the traffic as it forms a queue from Dover to Penzance. Nauseous with embarrassment, I hear car horns sounding their Saturday frustration. A white van driver shouts "Wankers!" and someone throws a beer bottle. Will there be a policeman soon? Oh god.

Finally inside the church, a vast Georgian theatre of a place with a balcony, I head for Matron's alcove. Champagne (imported from La Cité Europe during last week's Form 2 French trip) is served in a plastic beaker and the strawberries are dispensed on a kebab stick alternating with pink marshmallows. I pass mine immediately to the nearest hungry teenager just as Charlie sidles up and relieves me of the fudge and 20p change: "Cheers, sir."

Good news opens the speeches as we learn that we are to be spared the usual foreign dignitary's offering because thankfully he is stuck in Moscow with a slipped disc. Eager to get it over with, Piers delivers his forty-minute tirade as if he were driving a tank into a crowded market place, adopting that special stentorian voice reserved for the School Prayer and taking full advantage of having complete power over a captive audience. He blethers on about working as a team and being part of a community, but this is all immaterial because the audience isn't listening, either because they are foreign and have lost track or because they are teenagers and are thinking other hormone-fuelled thoughts. On the rostrum behind Piers, the senior staff become comatose amongst banks of flowers and silver cups.

Only when Piers goes too far do we wake up.

"We have an infinite variety of talent here at Gussage Court, ladies and gentlemen. An infinite variety of individuals. For example, who is the only gay in the School?" The audience sits up. "Yes, ladies and gentlemen, all the way from Germany, it's Gunter! Stand up, Gunter!" There is a putter of applause from Piers' Pimm's-soused mother and an uncomprehending Mexican parent. Gunter gives a little wave and slides lower into his seat. "We have tall pupils", he continues remorselessly, "and short pupils, thin ones and fat. And who is the fattest boy in the School, Johannes? Up you get!" A frisson of horror passes around the auditorium and people look earnestly at their programmes or flex their kebab sticks. Staff exchange glances. The academic administrator has bottled out and is feverishly texting. The Head of Business Studies is sitting with his eyes shut, beads of sweat rolling down his cheeks and into his moustache. The purgatory ends only when Piers brings his speech to an inconclusive close and the foreign parents begin a subdued round of applause. No-one can say what the speech has been about, but we are all left with a nasty taste in the mouth.

It is time for the presentation of the silverware, a cup for the fastest runner, the best scientist, speller, dog-lover, English-speaker; for the pupil with the most Character or house-points. And finally, the leavers, dressed in brand new orange acrylic gowns and mortar boards, receive a certificate for having made it to the end of their school career. Then, on a signal from Piers, they throw their headgear into the air, a photo-opportunity of the highest potential, and a good way of killing a junior. A loud cheer and then Yuri, our diminutive Head of School, presents the Samurai sword (smuggled in by Matron) to his successor, a stolid Bulgarian named Nikolay.

"And now," Piers intones, "all that remains for me to do is to award the Head of School prize". A blue wooden box is produced, about a foot tall. Piers invites Yuri to the front of the stage. A polite, serious and sensitive pupil, Yuri's patent leather shoes have always impressed me, as has his modesty and calm authority.

"Yuri, there is a plaque on this box on which is inscribed a quotation from Sir Arthur Conan-Doyle, author of Sherlock Holmes." Piers gazes proudly down at the box and then looks back at the audience, smirking. "It says 'The little things are infinitely the most important'".

My stomach lurches. *No. Please – NO!* Surely Piers' lust for dispensing public humiliation has been sated for one afternoon? He has lashed out at homosexuals and at the obese and he has sneeringly paraded the entire School in front of the inhabitants of an impoverished Victorian seaside resort. Since Yuri is by no means a tall person, I am guessing that the Head's *coup de grâce* has been reserved for the vertically challenged. The church is hushed; something truly appalling is about to befall this young Chechen, and it won't be a vote of thanks. Nothing short of a gunshot from the dress circle can avert this unfolding horror.

"Stand on the box, Yuri."

The boy obediently steps onto the box and, decked out in his absurd robes and still holding his rod of office in a trembling hand, he looks out at the five hundred. His face is grey with shame. I am willing him to deliver Piers a fatal blow to the back of the head with that stick; Chechens are not known for lying down in the face of adversity. Legend has it that two years ago one pupil became so enraged at what he perceived to be a slur against his national honour that he hurled a desk through a stud wall. It earned him immediate expulsion but he had made his point.

"This is the only time in your life I'm allowing you to be taller than me," says the Headmaster, "so make the most of it." Yuri forces a grimace. "I want you to bring the proceedings to a close for today." Yuri makes as if to step down. "From the box, Yuri. From the box."

Yuri lifts his chin, looks out at the sea of horrified faces, raises his stick, bangs it down on the floor and cries "School!" in a voice broken with mortification.

We file out into the evening sunshine. It is over.

Upon my return to school an hour or so later I spot the retired Head Boy, now dressed in shorts and a vest, sitting alone on a bench.

"Hullo, Yuri, may I join you?"

"Sure, Sir. No problem." He is tossing his mobile phone disconsolately from one hand to the other.

"Are you alright?"

"I'm fine, Sir."

"I take it you've spoken to your father?" Rumour has it that Yuri's Dad is the Chechen Chief of Police.

"Yes."

"What did he say?"

"He said he would deal with Mr Halliday if I wanted him to. But I said him No, I'm fine."

We are silent for a moment, watching a gang of small boys kick a football about on the cricket pitch.

"Listen, Yuri, I for one am truly shocked and utterly embarrassed by what he did this afternoon. I'd like to apologise on behalf of the school and indeed on behalf of the whole of the English Speaking Peoples. It was a truly appalling scene."

He turns and looks me squarely in the eye. "It's OK, Sir. Really it's no problem. In my country we have known far worse. Thank you anyway. Have a good weekend."

19

Shortcomings of Chocolate Spread

In an arguably vain or even foolish attempt to keep alive some of the original and pastoral excitement of our relationship, and knowing the pitfalls of trying to spend nights together, Valerie and I sometimes take the Salisbury road north out of the Village of the Damned and turn right down a dead end at the top of Gibbet Hill. We then drive for five or six minutes down the lane, through a tiny hamlet and gingerly onwards along an aged and now abandoned thoroughfare o'erhung with elder, oak and hazel into the very heart of the countryside. At the end of what dwindles into nothing more than a rutted track, we arrive at our destination, an ancient flint church nestling peacefully at the bottom of a valley on the edge of a wood of once-coppiced chestnuts. The place is lost to the outside world and, judging by the tattered cabinet which houses the Parish noticeboard, pretty much abandoned even by its decrepit Christian congregation. (I did once scrape the moss off the cracked glass of the board to read the one remaining scrap of paper pinned there: it stated that a jumble sale would be held in the church on July 21st 1987.)

All this bears witness to the fact that many centuries ago, well before the advent of the ballcock and antibiotics, some bright spark concluded that the best way to escape the ravages of plague was to dismantle the village and trundle it away up the hill to where the air was sweeter, leaving the church behind to fend for itself. Now that such pestilence is departed, this hidden spot is ideal for lovers, far away from prying eyes and the noise of traffic. Valerie and I often pick our way through the graveyard, climb over its crumbling wall and spread a rug in the grass at the edge of the trees. This is probably our Number One Venue for practising a spot of Naturism (and there is hardly a field, orchard or woodland in Wessex that we have not sampled), and here we tend to make our love and afterwards lie in the sun, looking south over the downland and wondering how the rest of the world is getting on without us. Neither Piers nor Agent P can reach me here because there is no mobile phone signal; those Normans knew a thing or two about privacy.

What they knew little about, however, is the relationship between the ambient temperature of Nutella and its consistency. Neither they nor I appreciated how you really need at least partial heat to soften such an excellently firm chocolate spread before attempting to smear it around the nipples or into the tummy-button of your mistress. Today, for example, the weather is not quite warm enough to facilitate this erotically charged taste sensation and the more I try to slather the paste sensuously amongst Valerie's erogenous zones, the less it will allow me to succeed. Even in the watery sunshine of an English summer, almost a year to the day since we first made love, the Nutella defies the promises

141

on its own label by declining to spread. Instead it pushes Valerie's flesh into unsightly hummocks and remains intransigently plastic. This has been Valerie's idea of fun, a nutritiously pornographic way of perking up our love life, but the chocolate seems determined to revert to something akin to a Belgian truffle as I push it and roll it stickily around her body. Licking it off neither stimulates the male nor cleanses the pores of the female and in the end, Valerie resorts to wet-wipes to finish the job. By this time I am feeling simultaneously hungry and sick and our meagre picnic of tiny prawn mayo sandwiches does nothing to improve either my gut or my mood.

"Come on then, my gorgeous lover," she says, taking a sip from her water bottle and uncharacteristically cupping her left breast at me. "You'll have to do better than that. A girl can't wait all day."

"Lie down then, beautiful," I say, hanging my glasses out of harm's way in the lower boughs of an adjacent ragwort. She does so, closing her eyes and allowing me to straddle her, lowering myself over her body to kiss her nose, her eyes, her lips. Then, with my chest hairs brushing her nipples, I move slowly up and down her naked form until hands on my shoulders tell me it is time. I settle myself between her legs, stroke and squeeze her waist and hips and thighs, hungrily following the contours of her bottom with my hands until she spreads her legs a little more for me to assume a position comfortable enough to perform some labio-lingual acrobatics for her. The world goes quiet for me until suddenly she gives a little cry of ecstasy and pushes my head away. She lies back breathless, grinning and giggling, her hair a joyful tangled mass on the rug.

A twig snaps in the woodland to our right and makes me jump. I swivel round and screw up my eyes, trying in vain to focus on the undergrowth. "What the hell is that," I whisper. "Someone's in there, I'm sure of it."

"Don't be silly, Henry," she smiles. "It's probably a deer or something. We'd have heard anyone coming."

"I'm sure we're being watched," I mutter. "Didn't you see anything?"

"Of course not, Henry, I've been busy." She sits up and kisses me on the lips. "Mmmm," she purrs, "my fabulous lover. That was *goo-ood*. Now, what about you?" I am still peering into the greenwood, my mind no longer on the job, my imagination whirring with potential horrors. The sun glints on something amongst the foliage. I'm becoming paranoid. "Come on, Henry. Lie down next to me."

I force myself to concentrate, but the moment is gone. Having tried and failed to don the latex, she lies by my side half-heartedly stroking my chest as I battle with myself.

"Nutella, Henry?" she enquires.

"I'll be fine, thanks."

"Well, hurry up and sort yourself out," she sighs, displaying just the tiniest flash of impatience.

As if watching a pornographic film, I try to ignore the conviction of being observed and focus instead on the contours of the naked body lying dispassionately beside me. She is looking at me struggling with myself, clearly not on my wavelength: how pathetic and foolish I must seem to her. "This love-making we do," she'll say, "it's so liberating, so fresh. It takes people with real imagination to break away from the routine of the missionary position and penetration, doesn't it?" I am somewhat discouraged by her point of view.

I stop for a moment and peer up at the fuzzy outlines of the branches above me. Any pervasive doubts about whether this is normal sex must be banished if I am to be able to perform like a real man and reach the longed-for orgasm in front of her. The thought suddenly occurs to me that we may not meet again for days and this causes a flutter of panic somewhere under my diaphragm. I force myself to ignore my aching arm and concentrate on the present, to make the most of this *al fresco* adventure. Surely I can winkle out some semblance of arousal. Henry, I chastise myself, for god's sake make an effort. Here you are lying naked and free in the sunshine, caressed by gentle breezes. Ignore the wafts of wet-wipe, Nutella and the spermicidal lubricants of the unused condom discarded in the grass! Put your arm around her shoulders and hold her tight against your side!

Even the consolation of a few inches of Valerie's tummy warm against my hip fails to ignite the dying embers of my passion because someone distinctly clears his throat in the woods to our right.

"Surely you must have heard that?" I moan, sitting up and reaching for my glasses.

"No."

"Well, I did." I'm sounding petulant. "Let's forget it. It's like bloody Piccadilly Circus round here today".

"Suit yourself," she sniffs. "I'm getting dressed. The sun's going in."

Another more distant commotion echoes from the wood. This time we both hear it.

"Stop fussing, Henry, for god's sake," she says. "It's bound to be some wild beast of the forest." She pauses, a second too long. "Just like you," she sniggers.

"Thanks," I say, accepting a fleeting kiss on the temple.

As I collect up the detritus from our pastoral idyll, a small fallow deer breaks cover and bounds across the corner of the field below us.

"Drive me home, Henry," she says in a voice steady enough to brook no argument. "I need a bath and an early night."

As we walk slowly back to the car, a Foundation Level GCSE Maths equation worth two marks pops into my head:

$$\frac{a + 1 = b - x}{y}$$

where **a** is an Out-of-work Actor, **1** is the Other Man's Estranged Wife, **b** is Boredom and **x** is the One Left Behind. Given the lack of joy emanating from these sporadic encounters with Valerie, the only Question remaining is **y**.

20

Carry on up the Grapevine

I am proud to have been the recent inspiration for one of Piers' more grandiose and short-lived whims. Taking me aside a couple of weeks before Speech Day, he announced that he intended to build me a four hundred-seat theatre. I naturally, nay, *naïvely* made enthusiastic noises and in return he declared that the new facility, to be built almost entirely of weatherboard, would be up and running by the end of the summer holidays. He and his tame architect had already designed the building (would I be interested in seeing the drawings?) and copies of same had been distributed to delighted yet credulous parents on Speech Day. Marketing went briefly mad. 'The Year of Drama and Music' had dawned and for a day or two my star was so much in the ascendant that I actually left the Earth's gravitational pull.

The accountants, however, taken somewhat by surprise (as

one always is by sudden frenetic activity in Piers' whim-mill), took a more cautious view and suggested that he think again. Which he did, the resultant shortcut to the Gussage Court Arts Centre being one of more than usual ticky-tackiness.

Roving across the campus in search of an affordable or cheapskate mega-botch solution, Piers' eye had fallen upon the Sports Hall. This is in reality one of those utilitarian grey barns which under normal circumstances would house five hundred tons of straw, a collection of obsolete Massey-Ferguson engine parts and endless scrumps of oily orange and blue baler twine. This particular one has a green-painted concrete floor suitably marked out for various indoor cardio-vascular activities with the suffix '-ball' in their titles. Piers' idea, one of commendable theatrical inventiveness, was to glue a wooden box onto each end of the barn: one poses as a foyer, the other houses a stage revealed through a rectangular hole hewn in the corrugated wall.

The builders encountered one problem, though: the barn had been dug into the gentle slope of the original walled garden. Would a few yards of topsoil be scraped out to create a level stage? No, the expensive digger-hire option was rejected, and, in a manner befitting Ramses III, Piers commanded his architect instead to design a stage which spanned the slope on three levels. This bargain-basement solution both causes the performance area to look completely bizarre from the audience's point of view, but also offers extra challenges for impassioned thespians flouncing offstage.

I relate this because I woke up this morning in a bit of a sweat after what I suppose must be described as an erotic dream. Regrettably, I cannot report that the thrust of this nocturnal fantasy features a delicious soft pink wish-fulfilment production on the topic of Valerie because she is (bless her little cotton socks) notable by her absence from the *dramatis personae*.

The dream stars instead Piers and myself and is set in this

very Sports Hall (or Theatre) during a School Assembly. We are 'ably supported' (as they say in amateur theatrical reviews) by a cast of three hundred and ninety unpaid extras, played for us today by the pupils and staff of Gussage Court.

In my dream, the lowest of the three stages accommodates a vast hydraulic platform capable of raising performers ten or twelve feet aloft (a feature reminiscent of expensive West End stage machinery employed in Lloyd Webber finales). Positioned on the platform is a grubby pink double mattress; on this are displayed two recumbent figures, Piers and myself. He is clad in his assembly regalia of crimson gown, gold trim and fake ermine; I am in my lounge suit and, if I may pursue the Lloyd Webber comparison, my tie of many colours.

Someone offstage presses a button and the platform begins to rise slowly towards the ceiling of the barn. *Au moment donné*, and despite the staring faces of the academic populace spread at our feet, I slip my hand down the front of my boss's trousers. Dimly aware even in my dream that I am dabbling in advanced homo-employeroticism, I am surprised in my rummagings to encounter a distinct absence of headmagisterial proboscis. The more my fingers examine the locale, the less they find. Pubic hairs abound, but of the male member there is no tangible sign. Something is amiss.

I raise myself onto one elbow. "So, Headmaster," I purr, "this explains nearly everything: you're a woman. You only had to say."

I am beginning to suspect that Piers is living rent-free in my head.

In other news, I must disclose the bitter-sweet information that RJ has been given his marching orders.

According to Matron, who dwells at the very taproot of the School grapevine, my fellow-thespian's demise is linked to nefarious goings-on amongst members of the boarding community. During RJ's quality-control inspection of a late-night pizza delivery ("d'you guys like actually eat this shit?"), our Meisner disciple was astonished to 'discover' small sachets of illegal substances secreted beneath jumbo-slices of pepperoni. Unconfirmed rumour has it that this contraband was destined for consumption (or onward sale) by inmates from far-flung outposts of the former Soviet bloc, exiles who are presumably too homesick to know any better.

Another incident involves sweet little Vladimir, an eleven year-old Russian with a mullet hair-do, whose stealthy digits have earned him the sobriquet 'Vlad the Bad'; he had been fingered by the ever-zealous RJ for making away with a hundred quid of a Spanish lad's birthday money and – even more daring – three hundred and fifty quid's worth of petty cash from Piers' own desk. RJ had assiduously amassed statements and DNA evidence (taken from discarded half-eaten doughnuts to which Vlad is known to be addicted) and had dutifully booked an appointment with Piers to spill the beans.

Knowing the Headmaster's views on thieves, RJ was unsurprised to learn that Vlad's parents had been summoned to the meeting to discuss their son's future in the burglary business. RJ had mentioned to Piers that you didn't have to be a mathematical genius to work out where Vlad might suddenly have found the cash to order a taxi to PC World and acquire a four hundred pound laptop. "Look on the bright side," Piers is alleged to have said, "at least he paid for the bloody thing."

Accordingly, a black stretch limo arrived one morning and Vlad's grim-faced parents were escorted to the Throne-Room from which they and the larcenist's luggage would doubtless be ejected after Piers had passed judgement. Poised to crack open the Appletiser and festoon their dormitories with celebratory bunting, Vlad's small colleagues awaited the moment of expulsion.

Instead, RJ himself was ordered to produce *his* laptop prior to being shouted at and summarily fired.

Matron assures me that it was Vlad the Bad's Dad who was

instrumental in persuading Piers to peruse the iPhoto section in RJ's laptop; it transpires that, as I feared after seeing RJ snuffling excitedly after Georgina on Speech Day, a selection of our most beautiful and scantily clad sixth form girlies had been helping our Creole comrade to air his proclivities as an amateur portrait photographer. The glorious array of glamour shots, once brought to light, caused Piers to question the young American's suitability as a resident housemaster. RJ was also bound over to keep the peace and apologise unreservedly to Vlad for the implied slurs on his character.

Late that night, under cover of darkness, the popular young man was unceremoniously bundled into Piers' BMW and transported for life to the nearest airport whence to secure a connecting flight to Sunset Boulevard and beyond. I hope RJ took expulsion philosophically. Speaking as a fellow actor, and purely out of concern for the poor old boy, disappointment and perceived injustice will be good for him because his portfolio of Meisner Method Acting Skills will now be brimming with freshly experienced and immeasurably useable emotions.

I suppose I have only to tell Piers about my dream to find myself following RJ down the exit drive.

21

A Summer Break

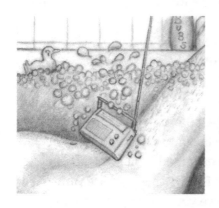

"Hell's tits! Why must it *always* ring at bathtime?" Snatching at the dressing gown I'd left on the floor, I wrestle the phone out of a pocket and press the receiver to my right ear.

"Hullo?" Foam squelches and fizzes in the earpiece.

"Hi, gorgeous, it's me."

"Valerie! I was just going to ring. How are you?"

"I'm good." *Good at what?* demands my inner pedant. "You still okay for our picnic? I've bought some Somerset Brie and organic tomatoes. I'm feeling great today."

"Listen, Valerie, I was going to ring because – oh *SHIT!*" I have caught the transistor radio aerial with my elbow and, with a small splash and a gurgle, Schubert's Eighth Symphony is silenced, terminally unfinished. "Shit!" I repeat. "Bugger!"

"Are you done?" she enquires, her tone perceptibly colder.

"Hang on a mo." I flip the radio out of the bath and shake it upside down. "Bastard thing!"

"Henry! Language, *please*."

"Sorry." I am pressing the radio into my dressing gown.

"Are you in the bath, Henry? It's nearly eleven o'clock."

"No, I'm washing up. Just knocked the radio into the sink."

"I told you about men and multi-tasking, Henry," she sneers. *Do NOT drop the phone.* I wedge it firmly under my unshaven chin in order to have two hands free to dry the radio. Something very remotely resembling orchestral sound squeaks from the saturated speaker. In deference to Radio 3, I switch it off. "Are you sure you're not in the bath? There's an echo."

"Of course not," I still lie. I lie still. "Fact is I've got to go up to London in half an hour. I've a casting at four." My mistress says nothing, milking her own theatrical pause. Yes, I am unnerved. "Maybe you can come with me," I jabber. "We could go for tea at Fortnums."

"You know I can't come. I've got my Yoga at five."

"Of course," I say. "I'd forgotten. What about the weekend? I'm desperate to see you." A pink button mushroom shifts dutifully under the waterline.

"Not that desperate by the sound of it," she says flatly. I know what's coming. "You're the one who suggested we could meet on your next day off. You promised." She is not wheedling. Valerie does not wheedle. She throws toys out of prams – ask any local baby. "I cannot believe you're doing this to me," she snaps. "You say you love me, so why am I always the one having to fit in around *your* hectic schedule? You know perfectly well that Millie's home for the weekend. Can't you think of me for once?"

"Oh, for heaven's sake, that's not fair." I sit up too suddenly and water sloshes over the end of the bath. "Agent P only rang yesterday evening. I can't *not* go. I'm the one having to try and earn a bloody living round here, aren't I?" Silence. "Valerie?" The line is so quiet that I wonder whether she's rung off. "Valerie, are you there?"

"Aren't you going to ask why I'm feeling so good today?"

No. "Why are you feeling so good today?"

"Because I've booked a holiday."

A gale of remorse blows through the bathroom. "Oh god, I'm sorry I got cross – I mean, that's great! Where are we going?"

"Well, the thing is – I was waiting to tell you face to face."

Something is amiss and I know Valerie to be the sort of person to save a bombshell until she has me naked and at her mercy. I brace myself against the end of the bath.

"So, tell me. Where are we going?"

"*We* aren't going anywhere," she states with no trace of irony. "It's a girls' trip: just me and my sister." *I knew it.* "Kitty's paying. Her divorce money is through and she really wants me to go with her to celebrate."

"And Millie? What's happening to her?"

"She's going to her cousin's in Vermont."

"Oh well, I suppose that's fine." I can be magnanimous; it could have been worse. "Maybe you and I can clear off somewhere afterwards. Where are you going anyway? Volcano-hopping in Iceland again? Rio? Weston-super-Mare's nice in August, I'm told. Or what abaaht Madge-orca?"

The eloquent silence is broken only by the regular dripping of the cold tap.

"Please don't take the piss, Henry. Or are you acting again? We've talked about that before: it makes you sound so very churlish." She allows a moment for her reprimand to bounce like bathwater off a rubber duck's back. It doesn't. "Australia for three weeks, New Zealand for two, a week in Fiji and then back via Indonesia. Finishing up in Bali. Nine weeks in all. The chance of a lifetime. Aren't you pleased and excited for me? We're off in ten days."

My insides churn as her news sinks in.

"So, you're going away for nine weeks during the time when I shall be off school for seven? Is that it?"

"The timing's not ideal."

"No, it isn't." I am about to lose my temper. "You know

153

what, Valerie? Millie becomes suddenly unavailable as a chaperone and you immediately come up with another plausible excuse for not having to see me. But don't worry, old girl, by the time you come swanning back from your trip of a lifetime, you and I will be history. Just saying."

"Don't be so bloody childish."

"Alright, how about this? I think it's time anyway for us to draw a line under our relationship because for me at least the stress of our love-life is beyond endurance. You really think it's OK for you to bugger off around the world leaving me – your *lover* – all by myself for an entire summer? You cut up rough when I can't see you for *one* fucking afternoon and yet I'm to give you my benediction as you sod off with your rich divorcée sister for a nine-week junket. Is that it?"

"Tell you what, Henry," she retorts, "while I'm gone, why don't you see if you can get yourself a life? Go and find somebody else's wife who'll put up with your moodiness, your rages and your very specific sexual needs."

"I'll do just that. Thanks for the idea. In the meantime, give your sister my love, will you?"

In no mood now to waste my life at a fish-finger commercial, I text Agent P and tell him there's been a 'train failure' at Woking and I won't be able to make it.

22

Testing Times and a Merciful Release

Monday

With Speech Day, the Marching Season and my relationship with Valerie all things of the past, it is now time to assume the mantle of misery and concentrate on important world events such as the End of Year Exams. Piers has ordered Sisyphus to apply some four inch screws to all the windows in the Sports Hall so that they can no longer be opened; the stifling heat, lack of oxygen and smell of defunct vermin in the wall cavities conspire to stultify any academic prowess amongst the punters. Blazers may be removed, but for the sake of propriety, waistcoats must be retained. It is a time of stress and moist armpits. Mandatory ink pens will be stolen from friends, mobile phones confiscated if spotted and literally put under Piers' hammer, and a vacant stare will be assumed by the two hundred as they settle down to scratch away at exam papers. Staff, who would rather be sitting by a pool in Tobago sipping cocktails and being nibbled by a nubile young person of their choice, are instead parading about in black gowns pretending that all this is a) normal and b) very important.

Glancing up and down the serried ranks of disgruntled youth, I begin to wonder how I can make them smile, live a little and encourage them to jump off the conveyor belt of civilised educational policy and to swing about in the trees like their ancestors. Should I rip off my suit and gown and run starkers amongst them? Would the pupils appreciate my self-sacrifice and visit me in prison or would they run screaming from the hall and into the arms of their therapists? It must be the heat; I am forgetting that I too am a part-time paid-up component of the British Educational Machine and that, as a professional civiliser and child tamer I am required only to tick the box, not to think outside it. I am here to invigilate, not to titillate, my remit being to confine my activities to a phantom-like glide between the desks whilst keeping a beady eye open for cheats and those more industrious captives requiring extra lined paper. Nothing more.

A hiss to my left and a tug on my gown.

"What is it, Tara?"

"Do you know anything about geography, sir?"

"I know where Africa is."

She turns her paper towards me. "Is this the Hudson River?"

"Is it in Africa?"

"I don't think so, sir."

"In that case, how'm I supposed to know? Get on with it!"

"But, sir ..."

"Shut up, Tara!"

A cough from my right. "Yes, David?"

"Can I go to the toilet, sir?"

"You should've gone in break. No."

"But, sir, I'm bursting."

"Put up your hand when you need a mop, then."

Let it all be over.

Meanwhile, in the parrot-shit green Nissan hut which passes for a staffroom, vital piles of academic bureaucracy are stacked along every wall and in every corner and pigeon-hole, and on every flat surface. Panic has permeated the confines of the only adolescent-free space in the School. Grown men and women wear hunted and harried expressions, glancing warily behind them as, heads bowed, they scurry about clasping piles of papers to their chests. Behind them, always just out of sight, the Beast snaps at their heels, a Beast whose dread purpose is to reveal which teachers have failed their pupils this year; failed to teach the right syllabus, to enter them for the right module of the right exam with the right Examination Board; failed to assess their coursework correctly having failed to apply the correct assessment criteria. The Beast, slithier even than the Jabberwock and certainly a deal more manxsome as a foe, grips in its claws a dreaded P45 from Piers marking the end of employment at Gussage Court. We all recognise the power of the Beast at this time of year, and we fear it. These are, in short, testing times for all.

Aware of a certain tightness in the back of my neck, I approach the staffroom in the hope of break-time coffee. However, I am prevented from entering by an impediment consisting of a sweat-stained T-shirt straining across the broad back of Sisyphus who is endeavouring to reverse out carrying one end of an enormous piece of furniture, namely a set of book-lockers used by pupils when leaving their prep for marking. Squashed between the door-frame and the other end of this practical piece of equipment is the grizzled little face of Lev, our Estonian (or is it Latvian?) School decorator, spattered as usual with parrot-shit green paint, tempered today with flecks of dark red. His beseeching grunts seem to be imploring me to give them a hand, which I do, and we lug the offending article up the slope and slide it onto a rickety farm trailer attached to the antediluvian School tractor. I assume the lockers are destined for the bonfire; odd, then, that they are still choked with paperwork.

Inside the staffroom, I find a hornets' nest of outrage. It seems completely bizarre, it is suggested, that Piers should have chosen this point in the term to remove the book-lockers. Obviously, we know it is on the cards: anything is on the cards when Piers is playing with his train-set. Although we are dismayed, we are *au fond* unsurprised by the sudden demise of this useful item of pedagogic furniture. But just as we are nodding and tutting knowingly, we spot Sisyphus and Lev coming back down the path. We watch with increasing consternation and disbelief as the gardener produces a three-foot jemmy and, with a determined lever action, wrenches the staff pigeon-hole unit away from its moorings against the plasterboard. They then take it, together with supporting table and all its contents – staff memos, essays, timetable changes, rotas, packets of sandwiches, exam papers (both sat, unsat, internal and public) – and dump it on the trailer. White plaster dust trickles down from the two holes left in the wall.

Coffee being now definitely required, I enter the laughingly labelled 'Staff Kitchen', in reality a pestilent corner cupboard containing an empty biscuit tin, a broken-down 1970s sink unit, a defunct microwave, and an occasionally functioning white plastic kettle with a frayed lead. I forage amongst the puddles of water and brown piles of tea-soaked sugar on the draining-board but the staff teaspoon has gone again and some arse has perforated the only remaining polystyrene cup with a pencil. Abandoning any hope of refreshment, I watch my colleagues scrabbling around rescuing piles of paperwork as Sisyphus and Lev continue their demolition work.

Over the next five or six minutes I observe the removal of the one staff computer, the eight chairs from around the table, the table, all the admin files, and then as many of the extraneous boxes and remaining piles of papers stowed on the floor as can be grabbed and shoved into a bin bag. The standard lamp, an armchair, the bookshelves (and their contents) and the low coffee table soon follow, leaving only a grubby beige sofa. The workmen will leave this until last because seated in it, his arm draped over the back, is Piers. He has come to spectate, brandishing a cup of expensive percolated coffee in a porcelain National Trust mug. He is wearing his best grey suit, pink shirt and tie and, lurking behind the short stubble of his goatee, a supercilious sneer. His comb-over is glued triumphantly into position and I have the impression that he is challenging someone to approach and ask him The Question. Part-timers, wary of the precariousness of their contracts and mindful of employment in the autumn, stay well clear. Senior and full-time staff fume and glare, avoiding eye-contact, bustling about gathering up armfuls of paper before heading for the door. A bell rings and, as the room empties, I incline my head.

"Good morrow, my Liege," I begin with the mock obeisance I have found effective when dealing with Piers. "What is happening?"

"I'm moving the staffroom."

"Evidently, Sire. But why now? Why four days before the end of term?"

"I'm showing the buggers who's boss."

"But we're in the middle of ..."

"I am fully aware of what we're in the middle of, Mr Robson. But what are staff for if not to piss off? I hate them. They hate me. They piss me off. I piss them off. Simple, really." He takes a sip of coffee and barks an order. "Lev, just shove it all in the stable block!"

"Yes, Headmaster," comes a grunt from behind a teetering tower of yellow lever-arch files. "But there may not be room in him enough."

"Well, take the bloody horses out first, you moron, and then stuff the whole lot in. I don't care what happens to it." He turns back to me and grins amiably. "The politically correct brigade has seen fit to whine about the content of my Speech Day address. This is what happens when people complain behind my back."

"Well, you were perhaps a little near the mark with…"

"Oh don't you bloody start now. The day you're politically correct is the day you're fired. Fact is that Gunter *is* gay, Johannes is *fat* and Yuri is *small*. End of."

"But couldn't you just have waited another week?"

"Another week? What would've been the point of that? Everyone would've gone home!"

"But, my Lord …"

"Oh shut up, you bloody Drama Queen!" And with that, he gives me his empty coffee mug and stalks out.

Thursday

Almost there. Apart from a few stragglers, unloved by their parents and condemned to remain improving their English at the Gussage Court Summer School which starts tomorrow, most of the pupils have now scarpered, whisked away in silver Porsches and black Discoveries with tinted windows. Reports have been laboriously composed, photocopied and stuffed into envelopes; classrooms have been tidied and dormitories emptied of lost property. The resulting treasure trove has been dumped into a large yellow skip through which, ever environmentally friendly, I have assiduously rooted. A life-long adherent to the philosophy which declares that you don't know you want it until you see it, especially if it's free, I am frequently to be seen rummaging through the most fecund-looking dustbins, dumpsters or trash-cans to satisfy the urge to scrimp and save, to be able to rant at what I see as wasteful behaviour.

Today has been a triumph and I have come away with a brand new balalaika, a Gussage Court waistcoat (slightly too small), a desk lamp and, best of all, two small pieces of corrugated perspex with which I intend to repair my shed roof, should I ever possess a shed. I stow my haul behind the cedar tree for imminent collection and am sidling off towards my car when I am hailed.

"Mr Robson!"

My stomach lurches. Valerie's naughty schoolboy has been caught pilfering and trying to sneak through the hedge to freedom.

"Ah, Dr Thorpe," I squeak guiltily, "what can I do for you?" As usual, he is holding a piece of paper in his hand; on this one will be the proof that I have somehow failed. The Beast is about to sink its fangs into my rump.

"Would you like an end-of-term glass of wine, Mr Robson?" I let out my breath slowly but the tone of Dr T's question leaves little room for manoeuvre. "Perhaps you could find some glasses?"

"Certainly, Dr Thorpe."

Having no idea where to find glasses, I set out on my quest and spot Piers berating Lev outside his paint store. The decorator is shuffling dejectedly from foot to foot, holding a paintbrush in each hand.

"Excuse me, Headmaster," I interrupt, genuflecting slightly, "but have you any idea where I might procure some wine glasses?"

"Try Matron," he replies tersely, "but I'm warning you, she's pre-menstrual."

The thing about the Chief of Domestic Staff at this time of term is that the nearer you get to her, the stronger the stench of teenager laundry. Even without my olfactory senses, I home in by following the trail of duvet covers, pillowcases and the occasional off-white Adidas sports sock, feeling my way through the dingy rabbit warren which meanders through the bowels of the old house. Breathing gingerly through my mouth, I approach the dark and airless zone which is Matron's gloomy domain. As I draw nigh, I step over Horatio, the obese and somnolent School hound (I was going to say moribund, but it seems unkind) who is lying across the narrow passage. Displaying signs of having once been a black labrador, he loves Matron and thrives on being physically and verbally abused by her. As does Piers – or so it is alleged by the more puerile members of the staff room.

Peering into the murk of the laundry, I can just make out the once elegant but now rather plump Mrs Tiggywinkle-like creature rooting amongst aromatic piles of boarder by-product.

"Ah, Matron," I project over the din of washing machines, "any idea where I might find some wine glasses? Piers said you might know."

"Did he indeed?" Matron's accent is, like her hairdresser's skills with the peroxide, slightly disappointing. "Why the bloody hell should I know, Mr Robson? Are you lot all getting pissed now the kids have buggered off?"

"I think that's the general idea," I rejoinder with one of my most winning smiles. "Will you be gracing us with your presence, Matron, or are you enjoying yourself too much down here?"

"Sod off," she retorts and catapults a slightly soiled diamante G-string at me. I dodge the pestilent item and it pings behind a drier. "I've got enough on my plate what with that idiot Hector having washed his hair in the Round Pond and now all the bloody goldfish are dead." (I know Hector to be thirteen, Greek and destined for a career sweeping airports, but my thoughts and prayers are with the families of the goldfish.) "Why Piers should think I'd have wine glasses, I have no idea. Do I look like a girl who drinks?" She winks slyly at me. "Try the kitchen, Mr Robson! Mind the dog ...!"

A canine yelp as I crush Horatio's offside rear leg under my size thirteen brogue.

"Oh, bugger! Bloody animal!"

I consider bending down to stroke him but think better of it.

"Ooh, Howatio," croons Matron, "has howwid Mr Wobson twodden on your toe? Say go 'way, Mr Wobson. Go 'way!" Horatio gazes balefully up at me.

"I'm very sorry, Horatio", I dissimulate. (Bastard dog. Shouldn't have been lying there anyway. Someone should put it out of its obese, arthritic misery; a diet of discarded muffins out of litter bins wreaks havoc on a hound's health).

"I thought you was goin', Mr Robson," chastises Matron idiomatically. "You've caused enough trouble down here. Poor Horatio, look at 'is 'ickle face. He's all sad! Ye-es, he's a howwid man; I know he is. *Howwid* Mr Wobson."

I beat a hasty retreat and leave Matron to administer a vigorous consolation rub to the voluminous nether regions of the School mascot. Five minutes later I am armed with a tower of plastic beakers and back on the terrace near what is left of the staff-room, only to find wine being poured into actual wine-glasses procured from elsewhere by someone more competent than me. A few staff are gathered round under starter's orders awaiting the moment of release into the summer holidays. Dr Thorpe stands to one side and thanks us all for our hard work and says a few well-chosen platitudes about a departing member of the geography department who is off to do "I don't know what, actually" and we all drink her health as she unwraps her bottle of Tesco Chablis. Piers is lounging in the evening sunshine, leaning back amongst fronds of wisteria leaves and doing his camp Yacht Club Commodore impersonation: navy blue blazer, white trousers, green and blue tie, slip-on brown shoes and an alarming pair of white socks with blue stripes.

"Well, ladies," he drawls, "Miss Walter's exit means that the Head of the Lesbian Department is up for grabs once again. Any offers?"

During the ensuing breathless pause, our ears are assailed by the sound of pins dropping all over southern England.

"Headmaster," I hear myself saying, "surely the only visitor from the isle of Lesbos is you, judging by those socks. *Très, très Alice in Wonderland.*"

"Mmm, I know, Mr Robson. They were all I could find in the drawer this morning. Matron's lost all my pink ones."

At this poignant moment, a small and by any standards, dreamily pretty Portuguese lad appears on the terrace.

"Ah, Pepe, my little man, what a relief to see you!" cries Piers, leaping to his feet. "I thought you'd gone. And your passport's still on my desk. Come on!" And without a backward glance, Piers disappears.

Dr Thorpe coughs gently and raises his glass.

"As I was saying, ladies and gentlemen, thank you for your hard work and professionalism this term. Nine weeks' holiday will do wonders for recharging the batteries before we return to the fray in September. Cheers."

Nine weeks of holiday. Ample time to sort out my love-life and secure some acting work. I empty my glass of plonk through the decking and notice with some relief that my colleagues are beginning to edge towards the escape hatch. A dozen cursory pecks on the cheek, a plethora of promises to meet up during the holidays and I am hurtling homewards through the country lanes to spend the evening alone, mastering the balalaika.

23

A Single to Weymouth

According to my copy birth certificate, it appears that my First Mother, my natural mother, the mother – not to put too fine a point on it – amongst whose loins I was conceived, was called Pauline.

At the time of this venture into procreativity, Pauline worked in Salisbury as an 'Omnibus Booking Office Clerk', a phrase which conjures up an image of a cavernous and largely silent bus station with pigeons fluttering high up amongst dusty steel rafters. Half a dozen green omnibuses emblazoned with gold lettering stand gleaming side by side whilst a gangly conductor called Len, his mouth full of Rich Tea biscuit, wanders between them, subconsciously stroking his fingers across the green plastic buttons of the ticket dispenser which hangs round his neck.

He saunters towards the half-glazed door at the back of the booking office and peers through the window. Beyond a barricade of heavy black filing cabinets he can make out his beloved Pauline sitting on a high swivel seat at the public counter. Len watches her as she engages effusively with a customer. "One adult return with two children to Weymouth," she is saying, pulling two pink and four green tickets off their reels. "Oh, that's a lovely part of the world, my dear, are you staying long? Not taking your worse half with you this year?" She turns to answer a telephone and, seizing his moment, Len taps on the window. She looks up and waves to him with a thin smile of tired politeness.

Disappointingly, I can't imagine Pauline's features; all that comes to mind is the cliché 'fifties face painted on the front of *Girl's Own Stories* in antiquarian booksellers. I assume she will be pretty, with short mousy hair, but she'll let herself down with her clothes; her blouse is cheap, a dreary mustard-coloured turtleneck, and her skirt is plain brown, slightly too tight. I expect she's wearing sensible shoes and those stockings with the pencil line down the back of the leg, or am I barking up the wrong era?

Despite any sartorial deficiencies, however, Len worships her, and that's all that matters. Is he destined to become my father? There is no mention of male contribution on the certificate.

If it's not Len the indolent mechanic, then might it be Derek the horny bus-driver who has it away with booking office clerks on the top deck of his bus when the manager's gone home? I can see Derek now through Len's envious and uninitiated eyes, a cocky little sod, a younger, stockier version of me, rather pleased with himself in his driver's uniform and peaked cap. He whistles *Colonel Bogey* with a loud tremolo as he swings himself down from his cab. He's made it up from Warminster three minutes early and when Len hears him approaching, he hides behind a tall petrol pump from where he can spy on and try to learn from Derek's enviable courtship techniques. Len watches his rival sneak into the booking office, creep up behind his prey, blow tantalisingly on the nape of her neck

166

(which makes her shiver and jump) and whisper "'Ere, Paula, five thirty-five, alright? Upstairs on the Number Eleven. Don't be late, darlin'." And, there being no-one at the counter, he cups Pauline's right breast briefly with his hand, squeezes her nipple and skips out of another door and down the corridor to the staff canteen.

Presumably Pauline resigns from the exhaust-filled chasm of the Salisbury Omnibus Depot shortly before my birth. Did she hang her head in shame and rattle slowly southwards to Weymouth on the Number 137 like a frightened guinea pig, or did she walk out with her head held high? And then what? Was I born at the dead of night in a dark alley behind the docks in Weymouth, my greasy little body slithering into a brown paper bag and then being passed clumsily into the eager hands of Mr Fairweather and his gang? Or was there a hospital involved? Crisp white sheets, a sunny maternity ward and smiling midwives busying themselves around the black and white image we have of a fledgling NHS?

Pauline's address in Salisbury (convenient for the omnibus depot) is inked untidily onto the birth certificate. Still undecided, I report my progress to Donal again; he sighs deeply and announces that it's obvious what has to happen next and that he'll call me back in five minutes. It takes many adopted children years and years to discover absolutely nothing about their origins; thousands of pounds lavished on the best ex-police tracker dogs and private detectives only to confirm that the scent went cold and was eventually lost. Why should my case be any different? To conceal my increasing anxiety, I grab my secateurs and involve myself in hearty amateur attempts at rose-pruning for the benefit of tourists to the Village of the Damned. I don't know what I'm doing with the roses, but it makes me look useful until the phone rings again.

Judging by Donal's enthusiastic and succinct opener ("Well, I think I feel able to say that I may have been instrumental in the development of certain events which might, in all humility, be termed progress on the part of Yours Truly"), I know that the vocable-munching Irishman has once again succeeded in moving on my life a square or two. A combination of serendipity and the services of Directory Enquiries have revealed that even after a lifetime such as mine there is still a Davies listed at the address mentioned. "If you'll permit me the liberty," he continues, "I will pen this Pauline individual an epistle."

"Be gentle with her, won't you?" I urge.

"I will employ all the kindly lyricism afforded me as a result of regular bi-labial union with the Blarney Stone."

Only a day or two later, the phone rings again. This time I'm tying up a profusion of yellow hollyhocks by the front door. "Henry?" bellows a voice full of laughter and mischief. "Ken Davies. Why did you wait so long?"

Two Friday mornings later, I head for Salisbury and at three minutes to eleven enter the Cathedral and step quietly down the north aisle towards the transept. Stopping behind the font, I observe an elderly gent looking up at the alarming curvature of one of the four massive pillars supporting the tower. H.G.Wells or Dr Who might have been undaunted, but I find it unnerving to encounter a passable impersonation of myself forty years on. I am bald and bespectacled, wearing a white shirt and black trousers.

My heart pounding, I sidle up behind the spectre and cough theatrically. He turns and I see straight away that we share those extraordinarily pronounced facial wrinkles and furrows which have begun to concern me in the shaving mirror. Laughter springs to my soul but the soft warm echo of the cathedral constrains our desire to shout salutations across several decades; we resort instead to loud stage whispers.

"Well, well, well, it has been an age, Keith – or I suppose I should call you Henry!" He seizes me by the wrists. "Let me look at you, boy! Where've you BEEN all this time?"

"I was about to ask you the same thing!"

We are becoming manly and physical, shaking hands and slapping each other on the shoulder. A plump little verger scuttles crossly towards us and so rather than having to face down the Church of England with improbable tales of lost sheep or prodigal sons, I usher Ken out of a side door and into the Close where we give full vent to our mutual enthusiasm.

I am surprised, so early in our acquaintance, that Ken and I have no qualms or embarrassment about being natural and ebullient. I am not used to this with family members. My father's idea of physical affection has long been pursed lips, a nod and a fierce handshake. My mother (my second mother, that is) will always present me with a portion of her upper cheek adjacent to her left ear for kissing, and woe betide me if I accidentally dislodge any of her hair by overshooting the approved spot during the love-in. Ken's strong workman's hands seem to have a life of their own: one grips my right hip and the other is employed in pinching my cheek. My hands, I note, are long-fingered and effeminate in comparison. People are hurrying past, giving us a wide a berth, but I ignore their stern sidelong glances because I realise that although Uncle Ken and I have probably never actually met, I have known him all my life; I am already beginning to understand that I have just barged my way back into the lives of those who thought they had lost me decades ago. I am about to be re-adopted, but this time by my own family. By the tenor of his welcome, it seems that my Uncle Ken is pleased to have me back.

I'm already feeling less 'screwed up'.

24

Bathing with Beauties

I am about to relate two bath-time incidents. One is dream and one reality. But which is which? As Alan Bennett so aptly enquires: *What is truth and what is fable? Where is Ruth and where is Mabel?*

Bath-time Incident No. 1

Piers and I have become so close that, despite the entreaties of Matron and the laws of common decency, we decided in the last week of term to take our relationship to the next stage. We plumped therefore to perform some mutual ablutions and accordingly ensconced ourselves naked in a large white enamel bathtub in his flat at the top of the house. The air is laden with steamy possibilities that I am determined to avoid by eschewing physical contact with my boss; Piers is splashing happily with a rubber duck and his comb-over is looking matted and damp. Has this all been a terrible mistake? I strike up conversation.

"Piers, may I make a personal observation?"

"If you must, Mr Robson. But speak not to me of Matron."

"I wasn't going to, my Lord, but the thing is this: I've worked out why you only walk in circles."

Piers' blue eyes open wide with horror. I can see the whites around his irises. He lurches suddenly away from me, scuffing his ribs on the cold tap and causing a minor tsunami to slosh over the end of the bath: "What are you drivelling on about, you bloody luvvie?" he snaps.

"You know how you can't walk in a straight line?" I persist, (cut away to a shot of Piers trying to walk towards the Sports Hall but swerving inexorably away and finishing up at the back door instead), "well, what I've realised is that your left leg is far shorter than your right."

Piers says nothing, but submerges his duck, holding it beak-downwards on the bottom of the bath until its tail stops bubbling; he seems to be attempting to drown it.

"Obviously the leg isn't really shorter," I persevere, "that would be absurd. But the fact is that your hips are twisted and make it appear shorter. I have therefore asked Carola to book you an appointment at the osteopath's on Monday morning."

Piers stares at me as if I am mad, as well he might. Intimidated by his gaze, I glance down: amongst our legs I notice that my companion has been circumcised.

Bath-time Incident No. 2

As promised, I have been proactive in my attempts to repair the hole in my appalling love-life whilst at the same time attempting to find some worthwhile employment as an actor. I have therefore agreed to play a smallish but vital character rôle (Ajax II) in a provincial performance of Offenbach's *La Belle Hélène*. I have succumbed to this at the insistence of an old university flame of mine called Christine. "You must come and do it, darling," she trilled down the line, "we can't find anyone else"

Of the four beauties I can honestly say I wish I'd kissed, the first is married and living with twins in Surbiton, the second has recently embraced lesbianism and lives with her children in a civil partnership with a prison warder from Gloucester, and the third was last heard of working for Oxfam in India. The fourth is Christine, the first real unrequited love of my life. When she calls me, I am uncertain of her current marital status; word on the street has it that she recently loaded her children into the back of the car and left her first husband, but whether she has any availability at the moment remains to be seen.

Perhaps I should explain.

Not unlike Peter Rabbit's drearily compliant siblings, I was a good little bunny at university and therefore a stranger to nocturnal revellings. Imagine my horror then when I was awoken one Friday night two decades ago by a gentle tap-tapping on my study-bedroom door. Fearing a little black rabbit with a basket of carrots (wasn't that Beatrix Potter's intruder?), I scrabbled to find my glasses, stumbled across the room, unlocked my boudoir and peered out. On the threshold was a Faerie Queen.

"Good god. Christine."

"Hullo, darling," she simpered, melting me with her famous knee-trembling smile and batting eyelids. (Was she slightly tipsy?) My heart leapt: how could she be here? By what miracle could she have evaded the all-seeing eye of Dennis the Glaswegian night watchman eight floors below? I knew also that at this very moment she was supposed to be attending a prestigious college ball where inevitably she would be seduced by some music professor, or lured away by any bloke with a deep baritone voice and a talent for flirtation. Having neither of these attributes, I stood in the doorway with my mouth open.

"Henry," she giggled, "you do look funny in those pyjamas.

Were you asleep? It's only half past twelve. I thought I'd pop up for a cup of tea. The ball is so dreary."

She was wearing a mouth-watering silk confection in plunging apricot, an off-the-shoulder ball-gown revealing more of Christine than I had ever dreamt of seeing. Even in the wildest of my nocturnal teenager fantasies I had never imagined anyone so devastatingly beautiful and so throbbingly sexy. I was stunned and dazzled by this voluptuous and buxom apparition and overwhelmed by a profound yearning in my soul that I attributed to eternal love. She continued to smile knowingly, her delicious body undulating under what little there was of that dress. She employed her breasts to best advantage, thrusting them forwards and upwards whilst gazing seductively at me from under long lashes, her eyes sparkling and flashing with studied eroticism, her curly black hair cascading over her shoulders.

"Can I come in, darling? It's cold out here."

"Of course, sorry."

I stood aside to let her pass. She stroked my cheek with an index finger and floated into the darkened room. "Wait!" I squeaked. "No!"

In this split second, the course of my life changed irrevocably. I could not invite her in. I could not entertain her to a midnight tea-party in a manner befitting a lady, befitting the girl I must marry and remain with for the rest of my days; this was not to be the beginning of a lifelong love-affair with the goddess who would initiate me into the joys of an uninhibited and acrobatic sexual partnership, and with whom I should make tall, happy, musical babies. And why could this never come to pass?

Because there was a man in my bed.

No, I have not been failing to mention something; I had not taken desperate measures and been lured into homosexuality by some pappy-fleshed member of GaySoc at the student union bar. No, soundly asleep in my bed was none other than my old bachelor friend, Donal. (To mark this, Donal's most irritating appearance in the narrative, I have chosen to enhance the image of the twenty-five year old Irishman by saying that his appearance for a late-night beverage clad in maroon silk pyjamas and dressing-gown did nothing to camouflage the Jeeves-like dome of his forehead.) Donal had been passing through London and had requested to stay the night with me because there was no room for him at the inn. Indeed, there was no inn at all, not in Lewisham. We had spent the evening gossiping like two old farts and had indulged in a döner kebab from over the road followed by a tin or two of mandarin segments and double cream. Simple as that. A sleeping bag on the floor was good enough for me whilst my guest availed himself of the best springless bed that Student Accommodation could supply.

I grabbed Christine's hand and tugged her back outside again, shutting the door behind me and gasping for breath. A whispered and devastated Q & A session did little to increase the romantic potential of the moment and so, for a tense minute or two, Christine and I leant against the common-room table and shivered. She was chilly because to all intents and purposes she was naked, and I was trembling in a cold draught of furious disappointment and frustration. I plucked up enough courage to tuck my arm chastely round her waist, but I was left only to imagine what it might have been like to curl up in bed with her.

Although Christine knew perfectly well that I had worshipped her from the moment I first spotted her singing on Day One at university, she had regularly spurned my inadequately expressed feelings for her, always maintaining that a wiry bloke called Kevin from Streatham Hill was the man of her dreams (until they had broken up a few weeks ago). Now, even the dancing lights of south-east London twinkling eight floors below us failed to ignite what might have been, what *must* have been, had my virginal bed been vacant.

I had long ago consigned this missed opportunity to the dustiest corner of my mental archives and had even forgiven

Donal for his untimely interference in my midsummer night's dream; at the time, however, accompanying Christine downstairs and into the sodium glow of south east London, I took a less than generous view of his presence.

Christine and I meet outside the country house hotel in Berkshire in which the cast are roosting, and in whose ballroom the performance of *La Belle Hélène* is to take place the following evening. My Faerie Queen still looks absolutely ravishing, throwing herself laughingly at me and kissing me firmly on the lips.

"Darling Henry, thank god you could make it!" She stands back to appraise me. "Do I detect just a few grey hairs, *mein Liebling*?" She has none. "What have you been up to?"

"It's a long and boring story," I smile, unexpected tears welling up at such effusive simplicity and directness. "There is indeed much to discuss." I am still holding her against me.

"Can't wait," she giggles, detaching herself and waving at a colleague. "But we'll have plenty of time to natter after the rehearsal."

At first embrace, Christine seems to have become an even more succulent and curvaceous soprano than in days of yore. Her creamy Mr Whippy attributes, as yet untasted by her oldest admirer, have been enhanced rather than diminished by the passing of years; although I am now older and hopefully wiser after my recent torrid experiences at the hands of Valerie (from whom still no postcard), Christine still holds pride of place on my mental mantelpiece, effortlessly managing to set my insides jangling with visceral anticipation.

"Bring that bag, could you, mein Engel?" she smiles. "I've arranged for us to save the company money and share a bedroom."

*

In an ideal world, the production weekend in Berkshire would result in my seducing (or being seduced by) Christine and being able subsequently to delete Valerie from my life. However, amongst the snags in my plan are the facts that firstly, I live three hours from my Prima Donna (thereby turning practical adultery into a logistical nightmare) and secondly, I have scant experience myself of singing on stage. Certainly I can *sing*, but I have never sung in an operetta.

What I realise during the next three hours, namely the first rehearsal (of one), is that the songster fraternity learn their part in advance; they then turn up and do it in front of the paying punter after perhaps only one low-energy run-through dedicated to ensuring the performers clock where the on-stage furniture is without falling over it. As an actor used to the expansive indulgence of having time to discuss a rôle with a director, to rehearse and repeat it and change the moves and try it another way this time without the script, I am stressed out of my face with fear because it soon transpires that I am the only cast member who knows neither a) his part nor b) what he is doing. Christine can do this sort of thing swinging naked from a chandelier (and would, if asked) and is looking forward with great good cheer and anticipation to the two performances.

This goes hardly any of the way towards explaining why I am in the bath with la Belle Hélène herself on the morning of our opening night. I am therein with Christine because, as planned, and *in sensu strictu,* I have just slept with her, but like Tristan and Isolde on their forest floor, we slept our four hours together with an invisible sword (and two pairs of chequered pyjamas) between us to protect my lady's honour. As a result, erotic historical precedent remains intact. Despite entertaining Christine to the point of tears of laughter with ribald tales of my recent sexual exploits, the ardent Byronic lover in me is doomed to be thwarted once again.

Not long before sparrow-fart, after hours of giggling and canoodling which, in my gormless masculine way, I mistake for foreplay, she rolls onto her back and takes my hand. She explains that after so many marriages, divorces, remarriages and re-divorces (she is now back with her second ex-husband having lived with her first one twice already), she is currently frigid and sworn to a life of chastity. "I've done my bit towards populating the planet," she murmurs, kissing me softly on the tonsure. "I'm all arid and dried up." I pause in the act of nibbling the top button of her skimpy nightshirt in the hope of a surreptitious lick of nipple. "I'm sorry," she adds.

Anyone less arid and dried up I cannot imagine; what she really means is "I don't want nookey now" and I can only conclude that I just don't smell right to these women. Or are Christine and Valerie in league?

"But I love you, Christine," I mumble, the button still between my teeth. "I always have".

"I know, darling," she says, slipping a warm hand under my pyjama jacket and caressing my back. "I love you too, but not in that way. I can't sleep with you." Inadvertently kicking over one of the vats of putrid chemicals normally reserved for use by Valerie, she adds: "You're free to sleep with anyone you want. Just not me."

It has been a discouraging night.

The bath is not particularly spacious, but there is just about enough room to fit the creamy frigid body of Christine between my legs if we both face the same way. Taking a bath with her makes a night of physical rejection hard (amongst other things) but when her pyjamas drop to the floor and I am treated to a heart-breaking view of la Belle Hélène's glorious behind ('Is this the *fesse* that launched a thousand ships?'), I am not strong enough to resist her entreaties to join her in the tub. Although in some ways Christine and Valerie seem cut from the same cloth, I cannot help but notice, even without my glasses, that although she is by no means overweight, there are no hard corners on her. She is endowed with a physical softness that is entirely absent in Valerie's yoga-firm body, and it makes me ache all the more for her. But Christine has spoken and who am I to disobey? What joy it would have been to be enveloped and protected by such maternal warmth and tenderness. Knowing time to be running out, I hug her tightly against my damp chest and wonder whether she will feel and be swayed by the arrhythmical juddering of my heart. I am too excited to consider myself to be in Purgatory, although actually, as on so many occasions with Valerie, Purgatory is precisely where I am. There is a review of me online at www.googlehades.com where the punters favourably compare me to Mount Vesuvius in AD 79, but unlike that petulant and thoughtless volcano, I am a professional performer, aware of what I will derail and possibly destroy if I erupt. I couldn't do that to Christine – not on her opening night, darling: it would be tantamount to rape.

What is it with me and women? Is there a girl out there who will permit me to flirt with her, kiss her, touch her – even make love to her in the normal way? Is anyone in the market for mutual adoration, celebration of life and either gentle or epic but above all *passionate* love-making? It's now Christine's turn to make everything complicated, and she isn't even playing the 'But-I-don't-want-to-hurt-my-second-ex-husband' card; why can't she be like the eponymous (and married) heroine of our operetta? Why can't my Hélène give in to capricious Destiny and be seduced by her Trojan Prince? We might indeed cause a ten-year siege (or its modern equivalent in the divorce courts) because, until last night, I had been sure that I knew Christine, that she was *la plus belle femme du monde,* that she loved me and would be an infinitely kinder and more doting partner than Valerie could ever be. But now even that hope has been stripped down and exposed as nothing more the workings of the warped fantasy-world that, in my desperation, I inhabit. I am in the bath with *another* another man's wife, *another* woman who doesn't want me. I am repeating my patterns. In an effort to be loved, I have behaved impeccably as the gentleman-adulterer to Christine, obeyed her decrees, and am left for my pains in the bath with her, with my body buzzing through lack of sleep and too much coffee. I am also doomed to crash and burn in an unrehearsed show in eight hours' time, and now I want to make love so badly that I don't know what to do. What a bloody fool I am.

The bathroom door opens and in comes Ellie. Ellie is pretty and doll-like with short black hair. I recall that she is Christine's best friend and another soprano. Under normal circumstances I should have been mildly alarmed at the intrusion of a virtually unknown woman into my bathroom, but Ellie is undaunted, as is Christine, and so I put it down to normal Saturday morning behaviour amongst singers.

As Ellie disrobes, climbs into the bath and settles down between Christine's legs, my frigid friend has an attack of the giggles and declares gamely that she'll hop out and leave room for Ellie and me. (Despite the prestigious five-star rating of this hotel, the architect had not thought to include bathing facilities suitable for threesomes.)

"Hi, I'm Ellie," says Ellie, as she leans back against me, putting an intolerable strain on my Vesuvian resolve.

"Hello, yes, we met briefly yesterday," I smile. We shake hands awkwardly over her shoulder.

"Henry and I have known each other for over twenty years", says Christine as she towels her pubic hair eighteen inches from my right ear. "We were at university together."

"I've heard so much about you," lies Ellie, sighing contentedly as I lower my arms over her. Someone's hands are gently rubbing her tummy. They are mine.

Now that I am not entwined with Christine, but with someone else of whose carnal strictures I am unaware, the situation seems to ease slightly, and the naughty schoolboy in me relaxes into a state of quiet ecstasy. Although I had originally applied for the position of Lover to Christine, I am now adjusting to the fact that she has appointed me Court Eunuch instead and as a consolation prize I am now bathing with her Deputy, the second beautiful soprano to wedge herself against my bewildered pudenda within ten minutes. Are these experiences that every man has? I think not. These are Man Adventures to be relished and ticked off, once-in-a-lifetime masculine escapades to recount to my manly friends in the manly surrounds of a pub or in a four-wheel drive at the top of a muddy track. Something to swig brandy to and yell "Ha-haa! That was a bath-time to remember!" And, scarcely able to disguise their envy, my friends will throw back their beardy heads and roar "Fuck me, Henry! You was the man!"

Christine has kissed us both goodbye. She is going to pop home to check that her second ex-husband has walked Mollie, her dog. "I'll be back at five," she says, with what I interpret to be pure Chekhovian subtext of the most encouraging kind. Ellie and I dry ourselves and sit coyly and fully dressed on the bed. Christine's things are scattered all over the room, a pink bra tossed artfully over a bed-side lamp, a boot hurled into a corner. Ellie looks me in the eye and asks whether Christine and I are 'an item'. I sketch in for her the delicate historical balance of our relationship and, with evident relief, Ellie leans against me and, as Dornford Yates would have it, *puts up her mouth and an arm slips round my neck*. I kiss her back. (By which I mean that I kiss her lips in return. I am not such a dumb-arse as to reach round and kiss her in the lumbar regions at this stage of the game.) We fall back together on the bed and I roll on top of her, pressing myself into her and feasting hungrily on her lips. Her skin is waxy and unyielding compared to Christine's. I wonder how many more unhappy wives there are in this part of Berkshire.

"Shall we meet back here after lunch?" I hear myself asking.

"OK, but don't tell anyone," she replies.

"Not a word."

"What about Christine?"

"She'll be fine," I whisper, pulling on my shoes. "I don't need her permission. She said I'm free to do what I like."

When we hear Christine's key in the lock later that afternoon, I am by no means so certain that the strength she draws from her self-imposed sexual abstinence will sustain her through the shock of seeing us lying in post-coital bliss amongst those rumpled sheets. I am right. Christine comes in, takes a view, smiles icily, picks up her show bag and closes the door again.

It is late. There is now no trace of Christine in our bedroom. She has moved out. *La Belle Hélène,* incidentally, has been an unmitigated disaster for me owing to my being unable, as predicted, to perform a solo part without rehearsal, especially when the leading lady is glowering at me whenever we share the stage. I am humiliated again, angry and mystified, but as alive as I have ever been and fabulously on heat. The phone by my bed rings: only one person knows where I am.

"Is she with you?" Christine's tone turns my *joie de vivre* to ash.

"Yes." It's true. She is. We've been at it like squirrels since curtain down.

"Come to my room. Now. First floor. Room 14."

Ellie is aghast at Christine's imperative but we think it best that I obey. We do not kiss each other goodbye and tearfully she lets herself out into the darkened corridor. I force myself to delete the image of Ellie climbing the stairs to her bedroom at home and slipping into the marital bed. I make my way to Room 14 and warily knock on the door.

"Yes?"

Christine is sitting up in bed, pretending to read, her dark curls tied back to accentuate a profile as hard and white as marble, any trace of softness chiselled away. I am reminded of my worst moments with Valerie and I know I am about to be hopelessly outgunned.

"Well done tonight," I simper. "You were fabulous. They loved you."

"Shut the door," she snarls without turning her head. I do as she bids. "How dare you?"

"What?"

"Don't play the fool with me. How dare you sleep with that woman, Henry? How *fucking* dare you?"

"But you said –"

"Shut up, you wanker!" Her voice is like steel on granite.

"But –?"

"Don't you understand anything, Henry?"

"I thought –" I flounder, "I understood from what you said last night –"

"You understand nothing at all. Get out. Go back to your frigid Valerie and stop fucking up other people's lives."

She opens her book again. The interview is over. I am spent, and before the lashings of her serpent tongue can inflict further horrors on me, I creep back to my room, my ardour now a hollowed-out mockery of what, barely a day earlier, had been my *raison d'être*.

I brush my teeth and flop onto the cold emptiness of the double bed, the rumpled sheet still redolent with the mingled scent of two glorious women. My mind is racing with impotent indignation: "You're free to sleep with anyone you want," she had said. "Just not me." Her devastating little speech had left scorch marks on my forehead. So, what happens? – I take her at her word and all Hell breaks loose.

Very well, I think, if that's how the harpy wants to play it, I'll resume my role as the eternal unrequited lover. "Screw you, Christine!" I screech. "And you, Valerie! What's the *point*! I'll just remain a fucking bachelor until the day I die!"

An irate thumping from the bedroom next door and a muffled yell of "Do you *mind*?" is the last straw, and in a sudden surge of masculine rage, I seize the bedside lamp and smash it against the wall.

25

And never called me Mother

To take my mind off my inner turmoil, and in particular after a conversation with Donal during which he accuses me of almost pathological indolence in the maternal bonding department, I ring my new Uncle Ken and suggest a way to bring about a semi-clandestine rendezvous with Pauline. Although I have taken tea with Ken and his wife Beryl, Pauline is obstinate in her desire to avoid me, unwilling to revisit the ancient emotions buried when she sacrificed motherhood and gave me away to a better life so long ago.

My plan revolves around Ken being a lawn bowls champion, a force to be reckoned with in a white coat on a summer afternoon. To celebrate this talent, and to wassail with like-minded folk, Ken and Beryl occasionally pootle (given Ken's nearly eighty years) down the A303 to a bowls tournament at Torquay. They stay for a week in a hotel boasting in its bowels four indoor bowling greens teeming with elderly enthusiasts glaring at each other's balls. On a prearranged afternoon during this week of festivities, Ken's little sister Pauline and her husband Len drive over for an annual family reunion tea party. It gets them out of their flat in Exmouth where they have lived over a second-hand car showroom for forty years and where Len still keeps his hand in for three days a week despite being fifteen years beyond even the most generous of retirement ages.

I have been to the considerable trouble of arranging with a) the Wilton Bowls Club c/o my Uncle Ken and b) the hotel management to come and give 'an interesting and amusing talk' to the assembled membership during tea-break. I am to titillate them with tales of my failed acting career. It's a dead cert and I'll have them rolling in the aisles.

In no mood for pootling, I hurtle to Torquay. At the appointed hour and experiencing an unwonted nervousness akin to stage fright, I am led by my somewhat flustered Uncle up a sloping corridor past the indoor pool to a table set for five. The atmosphere is chlorinated and clinical and, to a backdrop of permed grey or bald heads gliding slowly up and down the pool on the other side of the plate glass, we all sit down to tea and biscuits. Ken, Beryl, Len, Pauline and, unbeknownst to her, her son Keith.

"Paula!" roars Ken, erupting in laughter. "This is Henry. He's an actOR. Old friend of mine. Met him on a cruise years ago." I lean forward to shake hands with my mother, but she pulls me in for a peck on the wrinkliest of cheeks. She looks just like me.

"Nice to meet you," she giggles. "Come and sit next to me. Len won't mind, will you, Leonard?"

Len, husband of four decades and alleged erstwhile bus conductor, is caught off guard with a dunked digestive biscuit poised over his cup. "Not at all. Lovely to meet you, Henry," he says, as half the biscuit plops into the brew. He appears to have the use of only one eye.

I look back on my childhood and adolescence as a period of continuous sunshine and love, and it is perhaps because of this felicitous upbringing by adopted parents that I have instinctively considered it to be disloyal even to give much thought to my First Mother. Until falling under the influence of Donal and his own curiosity about my origins, I had accepted and embraced my post-Fairweather life and had suppressed any curiosity about myself. But what takes me quite by surprise is that the passing of the years do not seem to have obliterated a fundamental physical memory. I absolutely recognise Pauline as my mother. Here I am sitting next to her for the first time in decades, and all I can think of is how very normal it would be to make up for lost time and demand a cuddle, maybe even sit on her knee. I'm sure it would surprise *her* a very great deal (not to mention Len and the passing swimmers) were I to clamber onto her lap, but yet I feel it would be the natural thing to do.

She chatters and I gaze. She is quite the boniest seventy-nine year-old I have ever seen; thin to the point of skeletal, her skin hanging from her bare arms in closely wrinkled hanks like miniature hammocks. Her hair is grey regulation swimming pool, cropped very short to facilitate regular visits to the local baths, and I am fascinated by her lively, most mischievous green eyes and her extraordinarily animated mouth which constantly twitches and twitters as she giggles, full of the joys of a coquettish bonhomie. She is above all a tactile old bird with enormous, cool hands constantly touching mine and gesticulating wildly at her family as she mocks them. (I can see from their faces that they are used to her antics and Len tolerates her flirtation with a younger man with a wry and private grin.)

When she puts her hand on mine and leans towards me, something about her, her ancient pheromones perhaps, seems to re-ignite some primal bond. I refrain from leaping to my feet, knocking over the tea table and catapulting the company through the plate glass into the swimming pool; I do not throw my arms wide and cry "Mother! It's ME! How *could* you have given me away?" Neither does she throw herself into my arms weeping "Oh, my darling Keith, I'm sorry I abandoned you, babes." Nor do I sniffle "I forgive you, Mummsie!" into her boney bosom. But I want to. I really do. And the reason I don't is that, having the advantage of her with regard to Who's Who round this table, I am finding it a little disappointing, even a tad irksome that she does not seem to recognise *me*; after all, I am the youthfully spitting image of her brother Ken sitting opposite. Maybe I'm not being *filial* enough. Maybe I'm treating her with that particular well-behaved condescension that I have always reserved for Grandmothers.

Looking over the rim of my teacup, I catch a glimpse of myself in the glass and see me, twenty-five years ago, politely smiling the same Aged Relative Smile I employed to pander to my Grannie in her enormous Edwardian house in Sudbury. My father's mamma was a fierce and spherical lady with pink hair and a demonic technique with a croquet mallet; my siblings and I suspect that she never really took us to her heart because, having been acquired at an adoption emporium in Weymouth, we were not her blood descendants. Is this why she fed us mouldy lemon sponge cake when we came to visit, or was it simply that her catering skills were somewhat under-developed? I remember perching politely on the edge of a capacious armchair while Grannie served tea and blue-flecked cake on a Coalport tea service. I can still hear the trolley trundling through that cavernous house on its way to the 'drawing room. How times have changed, I maunder, sipping the hotel's tepid industrial tea out of cheap white porcelain.

Thus brooding, I feast my eyes upon Pauline, reminding myself that she is my Mum, not a Grandma. My position is unusual; I am not merely guzzling three-in-a-pack custard creams as if I were passing the time of day with a coach-party of pensioners from Taunton. No, I am in the midst of an experience for which most adopted people would give their eye teeth. And yet I am calm, almost contented, my mind full of other, more practical historical queries: have I, for example, ever suckled at this sadly depreciated and deflated breast, gazed up at this kindly face in adoring and intense concentration – daring her not to dislodge me from her mountainous mammary until the last drop of milk is drained? Have I, in short, nestled in the one place where even as a grown man I still long to be, where warmth and tenderness combine with a gentle heartbeat and a two-course meal?

Further questions present themselves: what happened after I was born? Did I stay with Pauline for my first six weeks or was I fostered away before adoption, bottle-fed by a cold State spinster in a strange halfway-house far from the maternal scent I had so briefly known but so very much loved? Had the Adoption Shop people come and whisked me away in a grey Vauxhall Victor even before the distraught young mother could cuddle and form a bond with me? Was I then disposed of sensibly and clinically, an illicit, shameful little bundle disallowed by an unforgiving society?

Few of these questions will ever be answered but at least I am understanding that my First Mother and I share an affliction: the urge to entertain, to show off, to be appreciated. Within Pauline I have detected the spirit of Bad Behaviour and outraged ego. She seems to embody the living ruin of a retired actress, a gossipy old thespian perhaps now running a B&B in a faded seaside resort not unlike Exmouth. Once her life-blood, the local repertory theatre has long since been replaced by a multi-storey car park, but she still craves a sympathetic ear, darling, someone to regale with tales of famous actors behaving badly in the good old days.

This is all arrant nonsense, of course, because Ken has already told me that his sister worked for decades as a cycling post-woman, but nonetheless, after half an hour of verbal romping with her, I see that Pauline is precisely the sort of woman whose waters *would* break as, according to Beryl, she danced a sailors' hornpipe to entertain the other disgraced single mothers-to-be. I am thrilled and warmed by the thought that I actually emerged from within this eccentric, brave and spirited woman, my little squished head peeping out, appalled, between her legs. And as I look at her smiling face, the very tiniest glimmer of what might one day develop into an inner peace (heaven forfend) creeps into my soul, for now I understand a little of more of myself, a little of the paranoia and the sense of the absurd, of my tendency to the extrovert, of my longing to be loved and cherished, held and consoled. This is where I came in.

"Darling man," says Pauline conspiratorially, "you don't *half* remind me of my boys at the swimming pool."

"I do? You have boys at the pool?"

"Many, dear heart, many," she whispers. "They're lovely boys. So very kind to me. We have a laugh together." She raises her voice suddenly. "Len doesn't mind, do you, Leonard?" Len shrugs benignly. *He does.* "Silly old sod," she adds, *sotto voce.*

"Are you saying that you actually flirt?" I probe. "*You?* With boys? I'd never have thought it."

"Yes, dear man," she replies, squeezing my knee under the table.

"In your swimming cozzie?" I raise a disapproving eyebrow. "Is this appropriate behaviour for a girl of your age?"

She beams at me and pours more cold tea into my cup. There is already a bond, a relaxed understanding between us, as if we have known each other a very long time and have no need to explain our idiosyncrasies, no need to apologise. She asks about my parents, where I was brought up, where did I go to school, am I married, do I have a girlfriend? "Do you like reading, dear heart?" I pull a copy of *Darling Buds of May* out of my bag. I've had enough of Dornford Yates for the time being. One's love life has to be optimistic if Dornford is to be taken seriously. I show Pauline the dog-eared paperback and notice that it was published in 1958. "A good year", I say, feeling the ice crack beneath me, but she does not pick up on the coincidence. Has she deleted 1958 or is she, like her son, acting a part, deftly not revealing to me that she knows perfectly well who I am? I look into her eyes but detect no suspicion. Luckily she omits to ask when my birthday is.

Described by his sister-in-law as 'only a biscuit eater', Len sits quietly and indulgently opposite us. The plate before him is indeed empty, but I can see what Beryl means by that curious turn of phrase; there seems to be something satisfied and a little cosy about him, a lack of energy and imagination; no evidence of get-up-and-go. I'm surprised that Pauline hasn't got up and gone before now.

Beryl has already filled me in about Pauline and Len.

1955
As I suspected, Pauline meets Len on the buses.
1956
Pauline and Len step out together. (No Derek, then.)
1957 i
Len's Mum interferes: "'Ere, Len," says she one breakfast time, "you don' want ter be seein' that Pauline no more. She's far too hoytee-toytee for the likes of you. You mark my words. Too hoytee-toytee. You dump 'er, Len, there's a good boy."
1957 ii
Pausing only to grab a final garibaldi, Len dumps Pauline.
1957 iii
Pauline declines to whimper into her bus timetables but strikes out for pastures new.
1957 iv
Early May, Pauline meets a soldier boy whose genes and DNA I share. I imagine the two of them canoodling and cuddling somewhere under a furze bush on Salisbury Plain, or on the top deck of a green bus parked at dusk in a lay-by near Fordingbridge.

1957 v

Late June, with me indisputably on the way, Pauline goes unto the soldier boy to enquire as to whether he is going to marry her or not. She encounters four flies in the ointment as she approaches the white wicker fence surrounding my father's dreary army-issue house: her lover, his wife and their two snot-faced children playing Happy Families in the garden. Heartbroken and devastated, she creeps away.

1957 vi

July. Pauline goes to Len and pops the question: "Leonard, will you marry me and bring up this unborn infant of mine?" Len says "Nope."

1957 vii

October. Despite the entreaties of the extended Davies family, Pauline courageously insists on exile in distant Weymouth, climbs aboard one of those green buses and is carried away out of sight of gossiping neighbours, Len's mother and the inevitable scandal.

1958 i

February. I am born.

1958 ii

April. My Grandma tearfully watches my parents leave for Weymouth. Pauline hides behind a frosted glass door and watches my parents arrive, pick me up, place me in that empty carry-cot and, with smiles of joy, take me away and out of Pauline's life.

1958 iii

September. Len's mother capitulates. Pauline and Len are married.

1959

Len puts it to his wife that it might be a good time to start a family. Pauline replies "No. You didn't want my child so I don't want yours."

*

4.30: time for me to entertain the assembled bowling enthusiasts. A flustered manager tells me that they have refused point blank to sit in a neat semi-circle of chairs laid out especially on the dance floor. The Wilton Bowls Club declines to move, preferring instead to remain at their accustomed parallel tables under a balconied area cluttered with four-foot wide concrete pillars. Try as I might, I can only maintain eye-contact with about a third of the punters at any one time, peering from behind pillars and darting about in their midst like the increasingly desperate loon that I feel myself becoming. I've done these talks before, but this lot, about a hundred of them, are really not in the market for the self-deprecating personal reminiscences of a Nobody. They want filth and Names. They want beery mother-in-law jokes and a seasoned stand-up comic bussed in straight from the end of the pier. One or two of them perk up at the mention of dog-shit in Camden but after two minutes and four anecdotes, I begin to sweat; panic sets in after three minutes as I waffle on about sheep dogs in Derbyshire and after five, I can't think of anything much else to say.

Smelling the fear from my own armpits, I scrabble feverishly in the bottom of the barrel marked 'Vastly Entertaining Stories' and find nothing but useless scraps of egotistical anecdote. Simultaneously, I become aware that I am no longer the only one talking. The Wilton Bowlers have resumed their conversations as if I wasn't there.

I glance at Ken. "Don't worry about it, mate," he says. "They're a bloody rude bunch of tossers and you're wasting your time. Sit down with us."

Nobody notices that the entertainment has stopped, but all this is fine by me because I am wasting valuable mother-time. There is no applause, no vote of thanks, no plenary. It has been quite the worst performance I have ever given, but am I bothered?

Ken, Beryl and I accompany Pauline and Len to the rooftop car park and, as we climb the slope, Pauline takes my hand and says "Dear heart, I could quite fancy you." I put my arm around her bony shoulders and give her the gentlest of squeezes. Her comment is fraught with more dilemma than the average Greek tragedy: imagine structuring a play around the tribulations of a young man embarking upon a torrid affair with a seventy-nine year-old woman who happens to be his own mother; it would make even the stoutest tragedian blench.

As I drive home, incest, adultery and enormous petrol bills are but three of the Oedipal imponderables I decide to leave unpondered.

26

Damp Towels

Of the two tales of bath-time depravity discussed previously, I would love to be able to report that I dreamt them both, but in reality it is only the account of watery intimacy with a Headmaster which bubbled up from the warped and twisted recesses of my nocturnal subconscious. (Whether it is meet and right – as they say in the Sung Eucharist – to suffer from recurrent homosexual dreams about one's employer must remain a moot point.) The saga of wet naked sopranos, however, was no dream, and despite reaching its nadir in Berkshire, it continues unabated during a second and unexpected rendezvous with la Belle Hélène a week before the beginning of the autumn term.

For reasons that will become clear, Christine and I meet in another hotel with a delightful view this time over Lincoln Cathedral, near which edifice she is performing something unspeakably modern in a disused warehouse. My visit will be a short one because I decline to stay and weather Harrison Birtwistle in a drafty shed; nevertheless I zip up country and stow my car in the underground parking reserved for patrons, whence I emerge, somewhat dazed, to ascend to the second floor.

What I behold in Room 217 causes me to stagger against the door-frame: the curtains are closed, a subtle warm light bathes the room and upstage centre, Christine is ensconced like the Helen of Troy of my dreams on an enormous double bed wearing nothing but a single pink rose between those creamy breasts and a look of lascivious anticipation written all over her beautiful face. I have seen that expression on no-one since that night long ago when she materialised as a Faerie Queen demanding midnight sustenance. This time, there being no surplus Irishman with whom to contend, I feel it incumbent upon me simply to leave my clothes where they fall and set about at once disposing of that rose with my teeth. "Let's make up for lost time," she says. And we do.

Allow me to boast that, in stark contrast to most of my more recent escapades with Valerie, I am positively encouraged by Christine to explore with her as many erotic postures and possibilities as I can. In short, if I may be allowed to misquote Julius Caesar, "I see, I conquer, I come," and what should follow will be a night of affirmation and reaffirmation for an ageing Lothario making love with the girl he has always adored.

Very late that night, however, I lie pinioned to the bed, by which I do not imply that we have succumbed to instruments of sexual endeavour such as manacles and leg-irons, but that Christine is fast asleep, half on top of me, her legs entwined with mine and her head resting on my chest. I do not move a muscle because I have no wish to awaken her and, in so doing, end this warm, supposedly magical moment. I am unable to sleep because I am trying to work out precisely why I am beset with Doubt. Dare I allow myself to imagine, for example, that after all these years this beautiful goddess is the love of my life?

Does she truly love me? Why has she so suddenly cast off the shackles of frigidity? It all seems too precipitate, although a man in my position is not going to slough her off onto the bedside rug and start asking questions.

What I remember is that after *La Belle Hélène*, I returned home very late and spectacularly angry to find an answer-machine message from Christine informing me in no uncertain terms that I was so stupid that it made her eyes water. "Call me when you get in," she concluded.

With my heart in my mouth, I dialled her number only for her take up where she had left off the night before. "Don't you understand anything, Henry?"

"Evidently not," I said. "Being a mere male, I'm too stupid."

"I love you, idiot man, I love you," she sighed, scarcely audible over a fortissimo D major chord for full orchestra plus triangle *ad lib*. "Yes, Henry, I do. Why did you wait twenty-two years to make me understand myself?" I was speechless with joy. "Meet me in Lincoln next week. Come on Friday. I've got a concert on Saturday night."

Did it simply take the sight of me cavorting in bed with Ellie to make Christine realise that maybe I was the man for her after all? Were these the machinations of that much-maligned green-eyed monster? Is this how love works?

Christine sighs in her sleep and turns over to face the window. I pull the duvet over us and, just as I submit to maudlin thoughts to which I am prone at this time of night, Destiny pokes me in the ear with its bony, omnipresent digit and I hear an ethereal quartet of voices singing the last number from *Don Giovanni*: "Mend thy ways and mend them well," they chorus. It is a finale of irritating simplicity (especially in translation) and one to which I might have paid greater heed had I been more of a Mozartian virgin and less of a serial adulterer.

A low whine and a snuffle issues from the floor at the end

of the bed. This unusual sound does not unduly alarm me and is explained by the fact that my new lover has come north in the company of Mollie, a bloody great dog of no particular merit. Christine has travelled fore-armed with all the paraphernalia of a seasoned dog-owner: the sack of 'Bakers' Dog Food, the stinky rug basket and the device for raising a water bowl. Quite what the point might be of a dog that can't bend its own neck to drink I have no idea, but maybe she is Christine's personal Cerberus, employed to guard her mistress against unwanted amorous advances. If so, she fails because she is an indolent and slothful creature more interested in snoozing than patrolling the perimeter of her mistress' virtue; and once I get used to the idea of the hound balefully gazing upon my more than usually imaginative antics in bed, I forgive its presence – for the time being.

The dog's nocturnal rumblings (coupled with the Mozart) have the effect of unlocking something in my head, something which reveals the unpleasant truth of my situation, and the reason for my doubts. The fact is that Mollie is not the only canine presence in the bedroom. Christine's hound is in reality playing second fiddle to a consummate lap-dog with whom Valerie too is well acquainted. In my desperate need for approval, I am willing to be petted, stroked and admired not so much out of love, but out of what is, I suspect, a need on Christine's part to *own* me, to be able to pick me up and put me down when she wants. I am again part of a selection process, back to being that pot of marigold matt emulsion that the shopper can leave unwanted at the cash desk. I am an acquisition added to Christine's collection, a commodity, a fresh victim. I know this because she has been thoughtful enough to compare me to other lovers: "You're very good in bed, you know," she said, smoothing my ego as she might a little dog's head. "I would never have guessed." Even in the midst of the most exciting love-making of my life, I am dogged (I use the word advisedly) by the notion that my mistress is appraising me, observing my behaviour, gauging whether her finely-honed charms are still working their seductive magic; whether her oldest lap-dog is still firmly on the lead.

The following morning, Christine leans out of the window and has a short but ferocious row on her mobile with her second ex-husband on the topic of travel insurance for a forthcoming holiday. I am in full denial about my latest conquest being a twice-married mother of two, but am savvy enough to be painfully aware of how seamlessly she adopts that terrifying edge to her voice when emasculating her menfolk. Mired in hypocrisy, unseen and unsuspected by the hapless husband, I actually pity the man.

I am so shocked by this scene that I consider testing Christine's powers of irony by humming the Mozart finale as we stand in the lift down to breakfast. But, being unable to meet her eyes, I think better of it.

And so it comes to pass, as we return to our room, that the Finger of Destiny makes its final move, hovering momentarily over Mollie's bladder before pressing down decisively and hard upon it. The ensuing expulsion of liquid waste represents so vile a moment in my life that I can hardly bear to report it. A fountain of evil-smelling urine spurts from the bastard dog's rear-end and splatters and splashes all over the carpet.

"Oh, Christ!" screams Christine, half-laughing at the sight of so much Lincoln green gunk gushing out of the wretched mutt's arse. "I forgot to take her out for her walk, poor thing." She hoists the dog's posterior into the air in a vain attempt to hold the waters back, the only result being that the fountain, now nearly vertical, becomes more effective in soaking the environment for yards around. "It's alright, Mollie-wally," she cries, stroking the bloody hound, "Mummy's not cross. Henry, fetch some towels instead of standing there gawping!" *Mummy's not cross? Well, I am – I'm fucking furious.*

I fetch towels. I mop and I dab and I squeeze. I use up all

six of our fluffy white ones and then hurl them into the bath to try to rinse the stench out of them. Avoiding the mystified gaze of Far Eastern cleaning staff, I run cursing down the hotel's corridors grabbing other people's used laundry from outside their doors. But despite our endeavours, the reek only increases and so in desperation I pant out of the hotel into the street to hunt down industrial-sized bottles of detergent. Having cleared the shelves of all the local stockists of Febreeze and Dettol, I spray the entire room and stamp more towels into the stinking stain. Then, while Christine stows the disgraced animal in the back of her car, I throw open all the windows and check out expensively at Reception.

"Thank you for a lovely night, darling," says Christine, still out of breath from wrestling the dog over the tailgate of her Volvo. "I'll give you a call when I'm back from Morocco."

"Don't be late for your rehearsal," I reply, wishing only to make my escape and be able to think. She holds the front of my trousers with her hand until she feels the requisite involuntary movement.

"Good boy," she murmurs before slipping her tongue deep into my mouth. I'm sure I still smell of disinfectant.

"Good luck tonight." I give her a final hug. "Give 'em hell."

It's me, isn't it? Do I fall for these frightening and beautiful women – these mermaids – in order to become their lap-dog, or do they turn me into this cowering, subservient creature as a result of something in me, a yearning for unconditional love which manifests itself in a yapping and salivating little monster deservedly destined to be kicked under the sideboard?

As I head back down the A1, I wonder whether it is entirely wise to vault out of the Valerie frying pan and hurl myself into the fire that licks around the pedestal upon which I placed Christine twenty-two years ago. During our two trysts I have spotted traits in her that I was too blind to see when I was a mere sapling; when it comes down to it, even after a night of such Vesuvian sexual activity, I am probably as frightened of her as I am of Valerie. I have witnessed both the loving gaze and the man-eating scorn in her eyes and I am sure that a future with her would be fraught with danger and unhappiness. I must be careful to avoid becoming Christine's third ex-husband.

Short of getting into bed with Piers, it looks as if I am to remain alone until well after the cows have come home.

27

Cream Tea and a Biscuit-Eater

It is the prerogative of even benign Destiny's digit to reserve its imperious prodding for a moment most inconvenient to the recipient. So it is that in the midst of the general brouhaha of the beginning of a new academic year, Agent P lands me a short television job. A triple starburst of excitement follows his phone call because this will be a) prime-time telly seen by trillions of Sunday evening viewers, b) a BBC sheepdog-free zone and therefore unlikely to be cancelled and c) filming in Devon, hardly a stone's throw from where my First Mother Pauline roosts with Len. Having heard nothing from her since Torquay, I have accepted – not without a rumble of primal disappointment – that she hadn't recognised her own son. It is therefore up to me to make another move or I'll have Donal breathing down my neck again.

We are filming on the Saturday and Monday (something to do with market days, apparently) and so I call the ageds and arrange to meet for cream tea on Sunday afternoon in Otterton, a tiny village somewhere near Budleigh Salterton, wherever that is. I buzz down to Exeter and check in to a brassy hotel in the cathedral close. At my beck and call is a constant stream of black BBC limos and an awfully nice man pressing cash into my hand for subsidence, or subsistence, or whatever the word is. Too, too glamorous.

However, on Saturday night, after the first day of filming, I am preoccupied, more nervous of what I must do on Sunday than I had been acting a country solicitor buying jam at a market stall. I had acquitted myself reasonably well in front of fifty BBC crew and extras, remembering all three of my lines to the satisfaction of the director whilst simultaneously walking in the prescribed arc over the cobblestones towards the camera without tripping up or dropping the jam pot.

I sleep fitfully and, with an overweening sense of anticipation, drive slowly to the appointed rustic Cream Tea-ery. The lane meanders away beyond a narrow high street of thatched cottages, but I swing my motor over a bridge and come to rest in the Mill car park. I have spent an hour feverishly pacing a bridle path overlooking the Exe estuary, but my guts are churning. Today is the day when Keith Stephen Davies must reveal himself to his birth mother if his own Chapter One is not to remain forever incomplete. I am even feeling sick at the thought of those well-meaning piles of scones. And this I regard as a really bad sign, for I am normally Mr Guzzle, King of the Cream Teas.

I climb out of the car and glance about. There, waving to me from a table under a white buddleia is Pauline. Len, the benign old biscuit-eater, lurks behind her, perusing the menu. I paste on my Grannie Smile and wave back, take a deep breath and stride onto the terrace. Like long-lost friends after decades of incident and turmoil, we fall enthusiastically into each other's embrace. Pauline is very sunburnt, even thinner than I remember, her waif-like frailty emphasised by a bright pink shirt, white shorts and trainers; she is as fragile as a Chinese lantern I must take care not to crush. I can imagine those hunky lifeguards, her 'young men' at the Municipal Baths, teasing this inveterate swimmer as she ploughs her way up and down the pool. They will be aware that their brawny physiques are being inspected by this elderly stick insect, but they know nothing of the dark and brave misadventures of her youth and will snigger and whisper behind her back as she steps gingerly along the side of the pool towards the changing rooms.

For well over an hour the talk is of Piers and Valerie, twin peaks of chaos in my life. Then, with Len largely silent, Pauline regales me with tales of Davies family adulterers who flailed for decades before starting afresh with new partners. From what she intimates, I suspect that were I to prod about with a long stick, I would dislodge dozens of other village Lotharios like me from the mud at the bottom of the Davies gene pool.

"Is there someone else, Henry?" she enquires, grabbing my hand, her motherly instinct on red alert. "You don't seem very happy with this Valerie." Not wishing to burden her with my most recent adulteries, I assure her that there isn't but that I'm open to suggestions. Pauline gives me a meaningful look and despatches Len for more cholesterol. She leans towards me, gripping my hand even more tightly. This is it. She knows. My throat tightens and my tummy, now fully laden, attempts a partial rotation but fails. I am braced for an early *dénouement*, but need not have worried, for my First Mother is merely on a roll, determined to show me that she understands parlous love-lives. "There's a lot of it about, Henry. But, dear heart, when it comes to Len, I could have left him so many times. I've been with him decades – centuries, darling, but he's so boring, Henry, he drives me nuts. Sometimes I just have to walk away. And there are times when we sit there in silence for the whole evening. Don't get me wrong, Henry, I'm not talking behind his back; I tell him to his face. He lacks spark, Henry, imagination.

Listen, his idea of a holiday is to go down to Plymouth. He means well, but we never do anything or go anywhere, do we Len?" The gent under discussion has rematerialised, having done the noble thing with the teapot. "But, do you know what I say, Henry? I say 'Bottoms! *Bottoms* to it all!' Have another scone."

We sit cosily around the tea table with the butterflies flickering overhead in the afternoon glow of the fading buddleia. The terrace gradually empties of its elderly clientèle and we settle down to enjoy some gossip about her brother Ken and his relationship with Beryl; how he once 'buggered off with another woman' and how Beryl relented and took him back and, reading between the lines, had been exacting revenge ever since. "Families, eh?" muses Pauline. "Of course, we've never had any children, have we, Len? Don't know why not, but there it is, we just haven't."

This might be the moment to say: "Now, Pauline, is what you've just said entirely accurate? Haven't you missed out a teensy-weensy detail here? Does the phrase 'illegitimate son' mean anything to you? Does 1958 ring any bells? Beryl's told me the whole story and – how can I put this delicately? – I am that child. D'daaa! Hi, Mum."

This sounds good in theory, but how am I going to tell her in practice? How do I separate her from the biscuit-eater who spurned me in the womb without arousing his suspicions?

"Well, Henry," Len pipes up bang on cue, "would you like to come back to our flat for a bite of supper? It won't be much, just a bit of salad and cheese and biscuits. We could show you Budleigh on the way back."

A plan begins to ferment.

"Thank you," I say slightly too loudly. "Here's another idea: why doesn't Pauline come with me in my motor? It would make a nice change for her."

Thus committed to a brief car journey, a ten minute once-in-a-lifetime opportunity to do the deed or miss the moment for ever, we bumble off with Len leading the way at a septuagenarian Sunday pace down narrow country lanes; the late afternoon sun glares in my eyes and I flip the visor down, waiting for inspiration to strike.

"Pauline, listen," I begin, when it does, "if I had a secret to tell you, would I tell you in front of Len or would I tell you alone?"

Her response is swift and decisive: "Oh no, don't tell him. Tell me. What is it?"

My mouth is dry.

"Well, you know who I am, don't you?"

She glances at me. "No," she says, smiling nervously, a hint of alarm in her voice. "Are you a detective?"

"No, I'm not a detective," I reply. "But, come on, you do know who I am, don't you?" How could she not know? I have convinced myself that all this time she has been egging me on, dangling me over the snake pit, trying to make me come out with it first.

I notice with a jolt in my abdomen that we have arrived somewhere, presumably Budleigh Salterton, and that Len is indicating left off the main street. I follow, beginning to panic, my heart in my mouth. Two hundred yards more; he turns right, indicating his intention to pull in. I have about thirty seconds.

"Are you ready for a shock?" I ask, the tension in my middle becoming unbearable. Len will be turning off his engine, undoing his seat belt, reaching for the door catch. I stop a good distance behind him; reverse a few yards. Handbrake on. Engine off. I take Pauline's cold hand in mine and look straight into her eyes.

"Yes?" she murmurs.

"I am your son. Keith."

She stares at me, her face unmoving, eyes wide.

"I had no idea," she whispers.

Footsteps approaching along the pavement.

"God bless you." She pauses, her lip trembling slightly. "Nice to meet you."

A fleeting kiss on my left cheek and Len opens her door.

We have walked along the promenade at Budleigh, Pauline holding both her men by the hand – "You don't mind if I hold Henry's hand as well, do you, Len?" – and we have returned to their flat over the car showroom in Exmouth. On the way, Pauline vouchsafes me only one wistful recollection: "I got on quite well with your father, Henry", she says, which I suppose is good news although I understand from Beryl that their acquaintance only lasted a night. "We won't talk about *him*, though. And we'd better not tell Len either – he's already had one nervous breakdown and we don't want to give him another."

Bearing this in mind, I am relieved to note how, during a supper of cheddar and lettuce tainted with beetroot juice, Len shows no outward signs of impending nervous collapse. Happy in his ignorance, he and I get on famously whilst Pauline, a little withdrawn, looks wide-eyed at me, alternately smiling, shaking her head, wagging a gnarled index finger at me, incredulous and dumbfounded, grabbing a furtive hug when Len isn't looking. She urges me to phone Ken, but speaking to him and being unable to answer a single one of his excited questions demonstrates painfully that Pauline and I are doomed to a life of whispered secrets unless Len is brought into the picture. Living in such a tiny space, the two are inseparable; and with Len constantly within earshot it will be impossible for Pauline and me to communicate with each other at all, especially by telephone. For once, however, I am warm inside, deliciously suffused with a heady cocktail of joy, relief, release and what amounts to a loving gratitude towards this woman.

Supper is over and Len is in his pinnie busying himself with the washing-up and a pot of post-prandial tea. Pauline and I are whispering together in the sitting room, holding hands between our chairs.

"What shall I do, dear heart?" She looks pleadingly at me. "D'you think I should tell him?"

"I think you must, otherwise we're stuck." I give her my handkerchief and she wipes her eyes.

Len potters in with a tray of tea and Hobnobs. He sits down and clasps his hands behind his head, armpits to the fore. This is evidently a familiar evening pattern, but Pauline sits I suspect more stiffly than usual in her wing chair to my right. It is her turn to feel Destiny's digit prodding her in the back of the head.

"Leonard!" she shouts, making us both jump. "Got something to tell you."

A grunt from her husband. His nearside blind eye is masked by his right elbow, giving me the impression that he's concentrating on the blank television screen and not listening at all.

"Leonard!" she repeats, "we've got a relation amongst us."

Another grunt.

"You know who it is?"

"Well – " Len puffs out his cheeks and exhales.

"Go on, say it!"

Len shifts a little in his seat, turning his teacup slowly on its saucer.

"Say it!"

Although assailed by an urge to stand on the coffee table and pull my own face off, I am unable to move because my torso has been seized in the vice-like grip of Destiny's other fist; I am being lowered onto the blade of a circular saw, imminently to be split from scrotum to cranium.

"Say it!"

"Well – " Len glances up. The blade is nipping at the stitching under my crotch. "Is it your son?"

"Yes, Leonard."

The blade recedes a quarter of an inch. My mouth gapes open in a silent yell of anguish, but Pauline perseveres, determined to see this one through to the end, whatever the cost.

"What d'you think, Len?"

Len's eye disappears behind his elbow. Is he regretting his decision of 1957? The blade begins to tear at my boxer shorts.

"Erm – well," he explains, "that's nice."

"Oh, he's a good man," cries Pauline with a sob. She leaps to her feet and seeks the refuge of the kitchen where we hear her blowing her nose and whimpering "they tricked me, the *swine*! Ken and Henry, they tricked me!"

I cannot move, but my torso is free and the blade is gone.

While Len procures fresh tea, Pauline and I sketch in the ground rules for a new relationship. We establish the absence of resentment and I promise that I am not out to fleece her of anything in the way of money or worldly goods. As I get up to begin my long journey home, she grabs my arm and, in a display of flirtatious affection evidently typical of our genetic make-up, huskily issues an unusual enquiry:

"Do you love me, Henry, with a fervour which threatens to unseat your reason?"

"Well, you know what, Missus," I declare as suavely as I can given that I am too dazed to feel anything at all, "I've never actually thought of it like that, but now you come to mention it, I rather think I do." She laughs and tweaks my chin and I wonder whether she is going to cry again.

Out on the pavement, under the sulphurous glow of a lone street lamp, I open my car door. Suddenly, Len's arms are about me, holding me like a bear; he is stronger than he looks.

"You're just as much my son as Pauline's, Henry," he whispers in my ear. "I mean it." He raises his voice. "Aren't you going to hug her goodbye?"

I turn to my first Mother. In the yellow lamplight her eyes are sparkling. "Come here, girl," I say, my throat tightening. She smiles up at me, throws open her arms and steps forward. For a long minute we hold each other tight while decades of uncertainty slip away.

Owing to some rather odd town planning decisions thirty years ago, having once driven away, I am obliged to pass their house again a minute later. On the verge there is a tall skinny woman dancing a jig, lifting her skirt and tossing her head back in a manner both theatrical and provocative; she couldn't be anyone else's mother. I put my foot on the brake and lower the window.

"'Ow much, darlin'?"

Her peals of laughter remain with me as I drive off into the night. A last glimpse of her in the rear-view mirror assures me that she is still dancing.

PART THREE

PART THREE

28

Huis Clos

Friday

After such a period of stress and emotional turmoil, it is with a heavy and arrhythmical heart that I turn my low-slung Vauxhall Astra once more towards Gussage Court to attend what I fully expect to be a soporific staff Inset day before the pupils' return. Huddled around the coffee urn are squadrons of bright-eyed new teachers to replace the ones who have been unable to cope with Piers any more and have escaped back to pastures predictable and professional; we are not to be vouchsafed an official introduction to them because, whilst they meet each other, we older hands are ushered away into an hour-long wankfest of a Child Protection seminar in another part of the campus.

The session merely aggravates the already festering sore of

my Sartrian despond. (After Dornford Yates, the French Existentialist philosophers are at the top of my holiday reading list.) Is it only failing actors like me who think that Powerpoint Presentations are the scourge of modern life and sound the death knell of public speaking? Or is it just that Denise, today's frumpy Geordie box-ticker, exceeds even the usual norms of unacceptability? Is it simply that, being an unreconstructed 'fattist', I immediately take exception to her barrel-like figure silhouetted against the white-board? Maybe the answer to my hostility lies in the fact that her own boredom is contagious, for as she flicks through slide after slide (reading off in her drear and patronising voice what we all absorbed at a first glance), eyeball-rolling begins in earnest and I am obliged to close the offending ocular organs to concentrate on not falling asleep and dribbling.

This ploy works so admirably that I am hardly disconcerted at all when I notice a shadow being cast across the white-board as I float in front of the overhead projector. Looking down, I see the tops of my colleagues' heads shimmering like fur balls laid out neatly in an egg-box. A soft snoring noise causes me to look upwards only to realise that I am teaching history to a class of obese purple pupils fast asleep on a high bookshelf. Like me, they have no idea who came first, the Romans or the Victorians. Piers is standing behind me complaining about my having parked my traction engine too close to the School buildings; he is afraid a spark will ignite the thatched roof.

My colleague Mr Lukins pauses the game of Spider Solitaire he's playing on his laptop and pokes me in the arm with his pencil, indicating the gob of saliva forming a damp patch on my shirtfront. Whilst applying the spotted handkerchief, I realise that by some strange osmosis, or unless I dreamt it, I have assimilated some of what the frump has been saying: apparently, a teacher must never touch a pupil, get into its personal space, block its only escape route by standing between it and the door, shout at it, throw board dusters or furniture at it or clip it round the back of the head with a complete Shakespeare. Drama teachers in particular should also avoid swearing, the removal of clothing, demonstrations of stage kissing and the defenestration of children of any age, even in jest.

The good news is that for luncheon there is Piers' speciality lumpy green soup with cheese sandwiches ideal for dunking.

Now that I am up to speed on my child protection shortcomings, I am allowed to join one of the tour groups being shown around to view Piers' summer improvements to the infrastructure. Once again, Mad Hatter's Tea Party Syndrome has swept through the corridors and everybody has moved on one place. History has gone to the staff room, Maths to History and Business to Maths. Geography and some English have gone to EFL and EFL has gone to Domestic Science. Domestic Science has been abolished altogether owing to rodent infestation; EFL is now the proud possessor of the twelve-foot conference table which used to be in the Junior Library, now the Girl's Common Room. The Junior Library is currently to be found in the former Sixth Form Common Room, and the sixth formers themselves are now permitted to lurk in a white weather-boarded café built on the spot previously occupied by the late-lamented School horse, Oscar.

During the tour we notice how Piers' art of painting over the cracks has risen to new heights of cunning and artifice; four enormous antique mirrors in kitsch faux-gilt frames now hang over damp patches in the more decrepit parts of the School. Under one, Piers has installed a golden Roman stool with a plush red velvet cushion. One of the mirrors still has its 'Antiques Centre £295' label stuck to it. "So that'll be nearly nine hundred quid spent on decorative tat," says an embittered young R.E. teacher whose new classroom until recently housed a sit-on lawnmower, surplus horse paraphernalia and bales of hay. "And he won't even pay me for coming in to do revision sessions on my day off."

No wonder I'm feeling Sartrian today. Also, it's raining and the green soup is repeating on me.

Evidence of fresh upheaval is everywhere to be found: I come across Karen, the Head of Modern Languages, who is at the end of a second box of tissues not because she has a cold but because the spacious new office Piers had promised her next to his new café has been given to one of his up-and-coming Young Men, recently promoted to Head of Sixth Form. Karen has been offered instead a former boys' lavatory. She is crying not only because of the implied snub but also because Piers has declined to furnish her with even an off-cut of old carpet to cover the cracked and stained tiled floor and disguise the recently-cemented patch where the loo had stood. Also, the only electrical socket in the wall has been removed, leaving the live cable sticking out of the plasterwork. To pacify Karen, I promise to hunt down Sisyphus (a reliable source of assorted junk including old carpet), but on my way to his dingy lair, I discover Janice, the Mad Media Woman wailing outside her classroom. I can't decide whether she is laughing or crying.

"Oh, Mr Robson," she simpers (or whimpers), "come and look at this." I peer through her door to observe that the Media Room is now dominated by a truly splendid conference table. This particular example is in two pieces, each the size of a helipad. "Has he gone mad, Henry?" she pleads, throwing her arms about me and sniffling into my jacket. "Why does he do this? How can I fit twenty-three Russians in here?"

"You'd be hard-pressed to fit *five* Russians in here even without their helicopters." She looks at me as if I'm mad. "And curiously, this is the second conference table I have come across today. Piers is plainly obsessed with them. Shall I bring in my chainsaw tomorrow?" I do not possess a chainsaw.

"Oh, please do, Henry," she sniffs.

I give her a hug and leave her trying to attach her ageing laptop to the overhead projector with the aid of what looks like a television aerial, the correct lead having disappeared over the summer holidays.

Round the corner I meet a distraught new female recruit struggling to drag a broken bookcase out of her room. As we tug at the remains and chuck them outside to swell up in the rain, she reveals that she is a little dazed at the informal and improvised nature of her employment so far. She draws my attention to her sumptuous teaching space, a small rectangular cupboard strewn with coke cans and a used condom, all snowed under with bits of broken plasterboard.

"The water feature is a nice touch," I say. She looks ruefully at the torrent of rain coming through the ceiling and I explain that it was only recently that Piers had attached this corridor onto the existing prefab as a sop to permanence and solidity. I place a waste-bin under the worst of the waterfall and explain that guttering is generally not favoured by Piers and his builders and that, as everyone knows, flat roofs are notoriously difficult to blu-tak together in this inclement British climate.

By the end of the afternoon I have assimilated well over one piece of good news: the first is that Matron has managed to keep alive all the wildlife left in her care. The second is that Marketing is happy because nobody has stolen Piers' vintage Rolls Royce. The car still stands guard by the front porch, albeit now looking a trifle forlorn and dusty. Sisyphus is diligently applying a strip of silver carpet tape to a torn section of its soft roofing material, and it occurs to me that the Rolls' heyday has passed, that its star too is waning. The beautiful and stately car is clearly to become, like astro-turf, an all-weather facility, doomed to become a hutch for one of Piers' future whims. Chickens and guinea pigs have graced the front garden in recent months, but I wouldn't be surprised one day to find a giant panda installed in the Rolls' faded grandeur. Piers might even hand the car over to the pupils so that it can become the victim of Installation Art, sliced in half perhaps, the front portion being propped against an old brick wall and filled with punctured footballs and a blow-up Homer Simpson at the wheel. I seem to remember spotting two rusting halves of a red Mini jammed against walls around the School, but I have no idea where they are now. Piers keeps moving them.

Wednesday

Break time, and I am sampling homemade cakes in Piers' new café. I bump into a shuffling mole of a man I have never seen before. He's probably a colleague and so I assume a friendly and concerned expression as he shakes my hand.

"I give it 'til the end of the week," he whispers. "If things haven't improved by then I'm off. Can't take this level of stress at my time of life. He's not paying me enough."

"What's the problem?"

"No classroom, mate. Spend my whole day dragging 3B English round the campus looking for somewhere to have a lesson. It's bloody chaos."

"Listen," I confide, "think of yourself only as an incarnation of the Flying Dutchman, cursed to wander for all eternity through Piers' kingdom. And look on the bright side, it provides some cardio-vascular for the children." He gives me that withering and piteous I'm-a-professional look and I haven't seen him since.

Lunchtime, and a Northerner with thick glasses and an intimidating black suit sidles up to me. I must have that sort of face. He may be the new Head of Maths but, having never been introduced, I can't be sure. "I'll tell you what, lad," he says, glancing furtively over his shoulder, "they can have these three days with my fucking compliments. I'm gone at tea-time. I've been grossly misled."

I turn towards the staffroom, gloom and outrage settling into my colon. "Ere, Mr ... er," says a dishevelled bloke who looks like a taxi driver. No point in hazarding a guess as to his rôle here. "Have you heard?"

"Probably not."

"I was introduced to a new IT teacher at five-to-nine this morning."

"Lucky you. I meet nobody officially. Sorry, didn't catch your name?"

"Bill. Nice to meet you."

"Henry." We shake hands.

"Nice to meet you too, Henry. Anyway, the bugger was gone by ten-twenty-five." Bill pushes his stubby fingers through a mat of unkempt grey hair. "Couldn't take it. Ninety minutes. Got to be a record." He stumps off, a forlorn figure in a baggy brown suit.

I call after him: "Gussage Court brings out the escapologist in all of us." The place is alive with misery and malcontents. I'm just beginning to think I can't take much more when I hear a shout.

"Guess what, Henry!" It's Louisa, a part-time art teacher. "He's taken away all my chairs; my cupboard has disappeared and he's filled the room with vast second-hand tables from god knows where and I can hardly move. Why does he DO this?"

"Because he's OCD, autistic, lonely and a barking control freak?" I suggest. "Or because he just doesn't like you, Louisa."

"He's certainly mad and absolutely knows how to wind teachers up. But why do we put up with it?" she demands rhetorically.

"Because we are unemployable elsewhere. At least I am. That's the bottom line."

Tea break, and I am accosted by Louisa's new Head of Department, a lady who thought that life outside a vast comprehensive would be a gentle and cosseted doddle towards retirement. She is not looking happy. "Are *you* all right?" I begin tentatively.

"Not necessarily," she says. Her voice sounds hoarse and her eyes are red. "I have no computer, no printer and no chairs. And I'm supposed to teach A-level art this afternoon." She pulls out a hanky. "Oh, and he's painted my room yellow. I went to complain this morning but he said if I didn't stop moaning he'd demolish the art block with me in it." She blows her nose. "This would never happen in the state sector. For Christ's sake, what has he got against me?"

"You're a woman, silly," I patronise. "But I can help you with the chair situation. He took all mine as well. You'll find them in the car park under a blue tarpaulin."

"But ..."

"Ours is not to reason why," I say.

29

In the Pink

One of the disadvantages associated with being the Village Lothario is that squadrons of curtain-twitchers, back-biters and gossip-mongers tend to gang up together in the village shop to discuss how best to shun the miscreant whose actions have so shocked them to the very core of their bourgeois respectability. Naturally, I despise them for this, justifying my venom by telling myself that these bottom-feeders are working from a position of envy and regret, only wishing that they'd had the presence of mind to become my confidant and walking partner instead of Valerie.

My neighbour Jo stands alone amongst the local burghers as being the only friend liberal enough in her views to ignore and forgive my misdemeanours and feel able still to invite me to her birthday parties. This year's theme is 'Pink' and so I have borrowed a curly wig, dressing gown, stuffed bra and feather boa of appropriate hue from the drama cupboard at school and am gazing upon my gloriousness in the bedroom mirror when I hear a knock at the door. A glance at my bedside clock tells me it's six forty-five; it can only be my hostess coming to borrow some serving dishes or tinsel and so I bound downstairs and, with a flourish of pink panache, throw open the door.

On the threshold is Valerie.

"Good god," I splutter, whipping off my wig, my heart leaping. "What the hell are you doing here?"

"Hi, Henry, I'm back," smiles my erstwhile lover. She is not particularly tanned, but there is something fresh and dangerously appealing about her which sends me into a tailspin of recriminations and regrets. "Have you missed me so much that you've turned trannie?"

"There's a party tonight at Jo's, ok? The theme is 'Pink'."

"So I see," she says in a tone which implies 'we'll see about *that*'. "May I come in or do you have company?"

"Alan, love," I call over my shoulder, "could you ask your Oriental dancing boys to keep it down for a bit!" She doesn't smile. "I've opened a Bangkok-style gay-bar since your precipitate departure from these shores. Are you coming in?"

"Actually, I brought you a present. From Bali," she says, handing me a shirt-shaped cardboard box. "I hope it fits."

"Thanks very much," I murmur as I unpick the Sellotape. Inside is an expensive-looking dark blue shirt which I like immediately. I glance at her as I shake out the garment, already feeling her tentacles entwining themselves around my lower abdomen, making me quiver. Her scent and sudden proximity are making me dizzy and I am already sensing capitulation and disaster. I want so much to kiss her.

The disaster comes first: "I forgive you, Henry," she announces. "I forgive you for all those horrible things you said to me before I went away. Kiss me and we'll say no more about it." She leans up and I capitulate – a short, lingually non-intrusive affair quite unlike the last kiss I had shared in a Lincoln car park. "I've thought of nobody but you for the whole trip," she goes on, stroking my cheek with her fingers. "My sister thinks I'm mad, but here I am, willing to take you back despite everything." Deftly untying my pink dressing-gown cord and slipping the fluffy excrescence from my shoulders, she takes a step back to appraise her wares. My stomach lurches but Valerie, never one to *carpe diem,* keeps her hands to herself. "Let's see what it looks like on," she says, indicating the shirt. "I had it made specially."

The shirt fits perfectly so she makes me go upstairs and put on trousers and shoes to see the full effect. "Mmm," she purrs, "I've missed you, Henry. Must you go to this boring party?"

I am torn between two manly desires: firstly to exact a terrible revenge and throw her out, and secondly to seize my own day and submit to the screaming of my body for the touch of hers. "Listen," I whisper, "I'll just pop round and tell Jo I'm going to be a bit late. Put the kettle on, will you?"

I dart next door only to be coerced into spending nearly twenty minutes helping Jo's husband hang some last minute fairy lights over the front porch. Jo is in the bath but a message concerning my late arrival is sent up to her; I know she will take a dim view – she has never cared much for my obstinate obsession with Valerie.

Rushing back as soon as I decently can, I lock the front door and go through to the kitchen. There is no sign of Valerie apart from her jacket slung across a chair but I can hear her voice from above. I climb the narrow staircase and distinctly hear Valerie say "Sure, I'll tell him you called. Bye." I push open my bedroom door. "Some woman called Christine from an opera company you worked for in the summer. Wanted to know whether you wanted a video of the show or something. I said you'd call back."

My heart stops. "Yeah, it was a job I did a few weeks ago. *La Belle Hélène.* You should be grateful you missed the show. I was crap."

"We have lots to talk about, then," she grins, slipping out of her blouse. "But first, there are some feet aching for the Robson Rub." She pulls the duvet off the bed and makes a nest on the floor under the window. I squat next to her and inhale that perfume I have so missed. I take her right foot in my two hands and gently raise it to my mouth. "My naughty schoolboy," she murmurs, unbuttoning her jeans, "it's been a long time."

In the morning, I awake to find Valerie looking at me slightly quizzically from a pillow adjacent to mine.

"I don't remember you snoring like that," she says, leaning forward on one elbow and kissing me fleetingly on the receding hairline before swinging her legs out of bed. "Need a shower," she says. "Breakfast in fifteen minutes, please, Jeeves. I'm picking up Millie at ten. Girls' day out shopping. She's going to buy me my birthday present!"

I watch her pale slim figure tripping across the bedroom and feel suddenly very tired. I would have liked to make love with her again, or at least been permitted a few moments' cuddle, but Valerie doesn't do morning favours and anyway, I'm clean out of condoms.

Toast preparation does not permit me quite enough time to decide whether reverting to some sort of obsessed and frustrated normality with Valerie is the bravest or wisest course to pursue, but I do have a dark foreboding that something is about to happen. Opening the curtains downstairs, I check that all is well outside; apart from a beer bottle smashed on the pavement, there are no obvious signs of imminent cataclysm: no alien spacecraft straddling the cricket pitch, no smouldering ruin where once the church had stood. Just Valerie's car parked in a proprietorial way right outside my house.

Nothing disturbs the view until a solitary female figure walking a Dalmatian appears through the lychgate and strides down the Green. Another hung-over Sunday morning in the Village of the Damned.

Having kissed Valerie goodbye, I stroll along to the shop for a bag of sustenance to last me for the rest of the weekend (an *Observer*, a small hard loaf of Teutonic long-life bread, three shrivelled courgettes and a pack of streaky bacon) and hear the phone ringing as I approach my cottage. How can it possibly be that the phone seems more insistent when Christine is on a mission to emasculate?

"Henry," she says, subtext slopping out of the earpiece.

"Christine!" I over-compensate, "how lovely to hear your dulcets. How was your holiday?"

"What the fuck was *she* doing in your house yesterday evening?"

"Who do you mean, darling?"

"Your new PA" she spits. "The person who answered the phone at seven o'clock last night when you were next door borrowing sugar. The saccharine and self-satisfied person who told me quite candidly – me, of *all* people – that she was your girlfriend. The person who was hot off the plane after a long holiday and presumably needed her feet rubbing. That person."

There is no point in dissimulating further. "Listen, Christine," I try, "she just turned up at my house, okay? I was about to go next door to a bloody party. Sorry to have a social life without your permission and all that, but –"

"Just turned up, did she?" I recognise a familiar metallic edge to her voice, an axe being sharpened. "I expect all the time you were with me, making love with me, you were busy counting off the minutes until you could get back to some really weird quality latex-time with her."

"Fuck off, Christine." I'm sunk.

"Oh, I shall, Henry, I shall. Don't you worry. How could I have been so stupid? It wasn't so much a question of you not understanding me in Berkshire, was it? It was me being too naïve to understand how you were just *using* me – me *and* Ellie! – as comfort blankets while your manic depressive, sexually screwed-up whore was out of the country. I understand it all now, you *bastard*."

"Christine, I'm sorry, but –"

"Goodbye, Henry."

I bang the phone back into its cradle, stomp upstairs and throw myself onto my bed where I lie glaring at the constellation of fly-spots on the ceiling until my heart ceases its palpitations. Phrases to the effect of 'You pathetic weak tosser' flicker through my thoughts until, as the church clock strikes midday, I feel myself dozing off.

I am awoken with a start by something moving on the opposite wall and find myself sitting up and staring at my Waterhouse *Mermaid*. This time, a smile of triumph is definitely playing about her seductive lips, and as I look, her tail gives a little flick of anticipation.

30

Plenary

All Lesson Plans must be submitted on Fridays. SIMPLE, REALLY. Piers

Very occasionally, and only after receiving a terse bollockatory email like this one, do I allow Professionalism to undermine my teaching, especially at the start of a new academic year.

The trick is to compose a superb lesson plan immediately after the lesson has been delivered. This is the only way I can be absolutely certain that the plan will meet the exacting standards of the Schools Inspectors industriously ticking their boxes at Ofsted HQ. It also means that I can still drive to school with my head devoid of anything except admiration for the purity of the mist in the valleys, a distant view of the Isle of Wight and the effect of the last movement of Sibelius 5 on the spirits. I therefore arrive serene in body and mind at Piers' Palace of Varieties and only then, as the final chords blast out of my quaking speakers, do I allow the very faintest gossamer outline of a lesson plan to form in my head. Minutes later, coat off and standing in the midst of the baying mob, I bring my first set of pupils to heel, confident that as a trained actor I'll be able to improvise the required *Lesson Introduction, Class Activity, Evidence of Assessment Criteria, Differentiation* and possibly even go as far as to slip in a *Plenary*, whatever that is.

"Enough, ladies and gentlemen!" I bellow. "Thank you. Rupert, off the floor! Daniel, on your own chair, not on Lee. Tania, disengage yourself from Howard – you know it's pointless: he's obviously not interested in girls. And put your phone away or it's over the balcony with it."

"But, sir, it's my LIFE!"

"Then you are a sad and deluded young lady." She gives me the look.

"Sir?"

I turn.

"Yes, Helena?"

"Is it true you threw Wai Kan Chu's mobile over the balcony last week?"

"Yes," (I have no views about disobedient Chinamen), "and I'm about to do the same with Tania's."

By way of an explanation about the balcony mentioned above I must interrupt this broadcast and announce that against all the odds, Piers has now upgraded Drama into an airy first floor space at the very epicentre of the campus. I haven't bothered to allude to my most recent room, an old tractor shed prone to flooding and dead rats – so brief was my sojourn there. I can say though that it has now been partially dried out and filled with stud walls and accountants.

Modesty tinged with expediency dictates that I suppress any outward signs of being overly pleased with my exalted status on the first floor of a brand new building. Judging from one or two barbed comments, I have the feeling that a handful of my colleagues suspect me of blatant brown-nosing, of somehow engineering my meteoric rise into Piers' favour through nefarious means. As I gaze down from my elevated position, I can dimly make them out scrabbling away below, condemned to teach in dingy rooms with neither heating nor functional windows. But I am innocent of all charges and can explain the course of events which has led to my current and doubtless short-lived supremacy.

Last winter, Piers' team of carpenters threw together a perfectly lovely wooden building on the site of an earlier staffroom. In style, it was not unlike the souvenir cuckoo clocks available duty free at Zürich airport: upstairs was Dr Thorpe's palatial office which boasted French windows onto the Khrushchev balcony from which Piers had mocked me on Topsoil Day; downstairs were the fierce ladies of the Administration.

The status remained perfectly quo until one day Piers came to see some drama in the tractor shed. He was surprised and impressed. "I feel inspired," he waxed lyrically, gesturing for me to join him on his favourite bench in the dappled shade of the cedar tree. "From now on I want Drama to be central to the School. I want Drama to be cool. I'm going to put you in there with Music." He nodded towards the Cuckoo Clock.

"Oh, right. Excellent." I stammered. "But what about Admin? They've only just moved in. Won't they be pissed off?"

"Don't give a toss," he grins confidentially. "If they don't like it, I'll put them in a tent on the front field or they can leave. Save me a salary or two."

One Sunday night at the end of half term three weeks later there was an incident: Administration burnt to the ground. All that remained was its outside casing and a mass of blackened sticks pointing skywards. What the fire hadn't consumed was reduced to a stinking wet pulp by the attentions of the firemen. I was standing behind the police ribbon considering the implications of this disaster when a voice at my shoulder hissed:

"I already told you the room was yours. You didn't have to burn the bloody thing down."

"It wasn't me, Piers." Rumours of an insurance scam were already rife. "It was you."

"It's what comes of having a dragon for Matron," he sighed.

I felt sorry for him; there was something fragile about the little man and I could tell that this jocular bravado was more of a mask than usual.

One of my flirtatious sixteen year-olds cornered a bloke from forensics and wheedled out of him the 'fact' that they'd found a melted petrol can in the ruins. This confirmed to the school grapevine that the fire had been the brainchild of Felix, the expelled and outraged Sheep Thief who had recently been spotted lurking furtively outside a seedy B & B round the back of Bridlington.

With Music and Drama safely installed in the hastily rebuilt Cuckoo Clock, it might seem paradoxical that I have just composed a resignation letter. I shan't email it though because the money is useful and Valerie would crow.

At the risk of sounding churlish or ungrateful, I'd just like to say that I might be feeling happier if Piers had listened to advice and thought to put any sound-proofing or insulation *at all* into any of the floors or walls of the rebuilt Arts Centre. From the music department below comes the constant jungle-beat of the drum kit, the reverberation of a bass guitar, the castrated corncrake squawkings of teenagers singing Abba a semi-tone flat. On bad days we are treated to the discordant wailing of a musically inept African prince being taught the bagpipes by a plump fourteen year-old lad who should by rights have been in Geography. Rehearsing Chekhov is out of the question in this aural maelstrom and so I tend to march my sixth-formers down to the staffroom where we can usually hear ourselves think, despite the presence of Piers' Filipino domestic staff supping pot noodles in the corner.

But this is not the end of the drear tale of aural punishment for, to complete the illusion and in a bid to rival Blenheim Palace or Waddesdon Manor, Piers has commanded that a stable clock be bolted to our roof. It boasts an elegant white casing surmounted by a *faux* lead pinnacle and four round faces with golden accoutrements. Photographs of the damned thing peeping picturesquely through apple trees are to be found in all the newsletters, and the School website can now boast another quaint English feature with which to bamboozle prospective customers.

The clock's chimes owe something to Big Ben, but unlike its famous forebear, Piers' clock remains conspicuously silent until it is time to ring out the hour. At this point, it cranks itself up into a positive frenzy of campanological activity; inside the drama room, whose exhausting cavernous acoustic puts me in mind of what it must be like to work inside a giant cello, the effect is staggering. Whereas Big Ben will chime four times before striking the hour, Piers' clock chimes no less than seventeen times (in three groups of four and a dyslexic group of five) in various combinations of ring-tone before striking a sonorous, single DONG. We are never treated to more than one DONG, whatever the hour; presumably the clock is quite run down after so much preamble. The entire performance lasts one minute twenty-three seconds and has left me on occasion prostrate and gibbering on the rug. But now for Piers' *coup de grâce*: for the benefit of the purist National Trust and English Heritage members amongst us, I hereby declare that the bastard thing is a computerised fake. The bell 'rings' through a series of internal speakers linked to Windows Media Player. And in the name of the 'Gussage Court Difference', Piers has instructed the volume to be turned up as high as possible in order for the virtual bell to be heard from a pub garden two miles away. Which it is.

I am worn out with it.

*

Despite my entreaties, Tania is still Facebooking her friends and so I sneak up behind her and pocket the offending accessory before negotiating a last minute no-balcony-tossing compromise. She surprises me by having the delicacy to blush a little, for I have caught a glimpse of her unspeakably hormonal screen-saver. But I am grateful to her because she has inadvertently provided me with the title for my burgeoning Lesson Plan.

"Today, I want us to work with the concept of humiliation."

I set them off to flush out some material we can work up into an Ofsted Triumph of rôle play and in-depth improvisation. And as they begin to flush, I find myself wondering, as they regale each other with predictable parental horror stories from their own lives, whether Piers has ever been humiliated. Perhaps something happened – or didn't happen – when he was small to make him behave as he does. I reflect upon my own recent sexual ignominies and upon the public shaming of Felix and Gunter, Johannes and Yuri, all of whom will remember their Headmaster with bitterness and embarrassment until their dying day.

"Sir?"

"Yes, Irakli?" Spookily, Irakli Kozhevnikov is the same Yuri's younger brother. He has big round eyes, curly chestnut hair and the same patent leather footwear. Butter wouldn't melt and he smells of money.

Scene 1
INT. DAY

Irakli: Sir, I sometimes a bit humiliate.
Henry: Humiliated.
Irakli: Yes, sir. Humiliated.
Henry: When were you humiliated, Irakli?
Irakli: When I drive to my house in mountains.
         I have problem sometimes.

Henry:	Do you drive, Irakli?
Irakli:	Of course.
Henry:	But how old are you?
Irakli:	I fourteen, sir.
Henry:	When are you allowed to drive a car in Chechnya, Irakli?
Irakli:	When we seventeen year old.
Henry:	Right. You say you were humiliated. What happened?
Irakli:	I have accident. I drive into, um, lump.
Henry:	Lump?
Irakli:	Yes, sir. In road with light on.
Henry:	Ah, a streetlamp. You drove into a streetlamp?
Irakli:	Yes, sir. Streetlump.
Henry:	And what happened?
Irakli:	My father, he come and I am humiliate. People shouting. I embarrass.
Henry:	Understandably. What happened then?
Irakli:	Ees no problem after. Ees good. My father, he fix.
Henry:	Excellent. You have a kind father. He wasn't angry with you?
Irakli:	No, sir. No problem for me. My father, he Chief of Police in my country.

Not knowing quite what to say next, I leave my charges to babble creatively over this latest tale and step to the window. What am I doing in this spawning ground for corrupt Mafia children? Should I report Irakli to Interpol?

My rêveries are interrupted by the word "prostitute". I distinctly hear it. "What did you just say, Jum?" I ask sharply, focussing my attention on a burly lad from Thailand.

Scene 2

INT. DAY

Jum: I said my most humiliating moment was when my Dad nearly caught me in bed with a prostitute. Sir.

Gemma: So, like what did you do?

Jum: I pushed her out of my bed when Dad opened the bedroom door. No problem.

A silence.

Gemma: Was she hurt?

Jum: Oh, yes. She banged her hip and her arm. She was like well pissed off with me.

Ethan: And this was humiliating for you?

Jum: Very. But it was OK, my father was drunk and he didn't notice.

Antonia: But, Jum, are you serious? Why did you have a prostitute in your bed?

Jum: To have some fun, of course. I often have prostitutes.

Henry: Erm, how often, Jum? If you don't mind my asking.

Jum: Four or five times a week, sir. Sometimes more.

Phil: But, fuck, Jum! How much - ?

Henry: Language, Phil!

Phil: Sorry sir. I wanted to ask how much a tart costs in Bangkok?

Jum: At the present exchange rate, about a hundred pounds a night.

Phil: But that's five hundred pounds a week? What the hell?

Jum: Yeah. That's right. *(He smiles round at his friends)*

Hannah: But, Jum, you're fourteen. You've got a girlfriend!

Jum: Yeah. And?

Hannah: But you said you don't sleep with your girlfriend.

Jum: I don't.

Hannah: Why not?

Jum: It would make her seem like a whore.

It us common knowledge in the staffroom that Jum has a girlfriend happily entitled Titaporn Bunnag, but in a rare moment of sensitive professionalism I decline to mention this linguistic irony. Maybe I'll save it for the 'Plenary' column on my lesson plan.

31

A Birthday Treat

As unavoidable as October mists, Valerie's birthday is fast approaching and I have reserved a table for two at the most expensive restaurant in southern England. This goes against the grain because I am by nature careful with my hard-earned cash. It's the lapsed Jewishness in me; my Uncle Ken's wife Beryl told me all about it when we first met. "Oh, she's a tight one, your mother", she had announced. "Ken's tight too, aren't you, you miserable old sod? It's in your blood, you can't help it, Henry. Your great grandmother was Jewish."

Ken had raised his hands and eyebrows in despair at this. An 'Oy vey!' was imminent. "You have to be so careful with these women," he exclaimed instead. "They're an expensive business." In the words of Dornford Yates (an anti-Semite of note, incidentally): *Be sure I agreed with him.*

I would not go so far as to describe myself in terms of being a 'miserly old curmudgeon', but I have oft heard unflattering comments bandied about by some of my ex-friends and relatives with reference to my unwillingness to step up on occasion to the fiscal mark. This is another reason for avoiding pubs, the thought of 'getting a round in' being as obnoxious to me as it is absurd in its generosity. Neither do I relish the thought of expensive holidays abroad and am rarely seen in clothes shops. I am loath to lash out substantial sums for what I do not – in my curmudgeonliness – deem to be worthwhile extravagances; shelling out eighty or a hundred pounds for a *dîner romantique à deux* that I dread in advance falls plumb into this category, especially when I know that at least one of us is witnessing the death throes of our love affair. Even if Valerie herself declines to read the writing on the wall, I am convinced that we are all but over bar the shouting. I know what is fast approaching in the bus lane: the 36B of Destiny, a vast, swaying red lump of a double-decker bus careering out of control, bearing down on me, smoke and fire belching from its roaring engine, its cadaverous driver hooting and cackling with diabolical glee. Passers-by leap for safety, but somehow my own feet are glued into molten tarmac in the middle of Camberwell High Street, a vision guaranteed to boost the symptoms of both arrhythmia and tinnitus.

As I drive to collect the birthday girl, I imagine the horrors to come. It is up to me to attempt to put a stop to this dysfunctional relationship, the altercations over the telephone, the acts of revenge, the insomniac nights of endless internalised recriminations. As I turn the Vauxhall under the willow tree outside her house, I wonder whether she will consider a mere eighty or a hundred pounds to be an expensive enough meal. *Is that all I am worth to him?* Perhaps I should have flown her to New York for dinner instead? There we could have quarrelled in style.

The restaurant seems draughty and bleak, the ceilings high and the apple logs in a distant inglenook give out no discernible heat. Valerie sits opposite me, rather prim and formal with her hands folded in her lap. She is behaving as if this were some professional business dinner on the company credit card, going through the motions of being polite to some fat bloke from Sales she has bumped into in the hotel bar and, both being alone in Swindon, they have agreed to eat together. So far, the evening is coming right down to expectations.

Although she has given her coat to the waiter, she is still wearing her aura of independence, a tight-fitting black body armour, visible only to the practised eye of a frustrated lover and designed specifically to keep him at arm's length and excluded from her intimacy.

"I need champagne," she says, "it's my birthday."

I had been on the verge of suggesting a little glass of something but she has beaten me to it. Having ordered, I tentatively reach over and stroke her menu hand with my finger. She withdraws it slightly. It is at this moment that I realise with regret that I have been sitting and looking at her for what seems like years thinking how beautiful she is without really seeing her. I am accustomed to telling her that she is beautiful, but is this withdrawn coldness towards me compatible with true beauty? I watch her across the wasteland of tablecloth separating us and understand with a spasm in my aching heart that I now consider her to be beautiful out of habit rather than observation. She was definitely beautiful for me at the outset of our adventure together and even now, her face and body boast a certain sculptural something, an elegance of bearing, an absence of excess fleshiness. In the very early days of danger and promise I had seen this beauty and in due course had complimented her upon it. She used to say that I was the only person in the world to appreciate her for what she was. The courtship ritual in all its transient glory.

"I am a beautiful woman, Henry," she remarks suddenly, as if reading my thoughts. "And now I need another glass of champagne."

She *never* drinks more than one glass of alcohol. She's

doing it deliberately to wound me where it hurts most: in the wallet. I order it for her and a J20 for me because a) champagne by the glass is absurdly expensive, b) I have nothing to celebrate and c) I'm driving.

I sip at my juice and, as I crunch an ice cube between my teeth, I experience a sudden surge of what might be called maturity: am I gaining a little objectivity at last, beginning to see this awful relationship more clearly? I am not going to find unconditional love, warmth, softness, companionship and a fulfilling sexual relationship with a woman I find decreasingly beautiful as the minutes go by. Valerie is a creature whose constantly reiterated sense of self worth obliterates a fundamental truth: that between us there is an absence of anything that might be termed *substance*. She thinks I'm cleverer, better educated and more cultured than she is. I am. She wants me to introduce her to classical music. I have. In return, she wants me to keep out of her space and learn to throw myself about to her vile rock music. I don't have the hair for it and anyway, how can she listen to such boorish and formulaic shit? Furthermore, as I tinker with this unmemorable but expensive food, I begin to wonder whether a firm-bodied woman is also by definition a vain one and if so, whether Valerie's heart is destined to remain as hard and unyielding as her abdomen. Perhaps, I think, as I push my steak around in a puddle of congealing pepper sauce, I should concentrate on casting about again for a companion a little more ample and giving and warm and loving. I had thought that I had found such a partnership in Christine, but I had been wrong.

Dark thoughts indeed for a birthday feast.

And now, the moment she has been waiting for: the shower of expensive and thoughtful gifts, ordered from distant lands, beautifully and tastefully wrapped by her adoring lover. There's nothing a girl likes more than the anticipation of receiving and unwrapping a really sensitive and feminine gift from her bloke, a little (or preferably big) something that isn't the thirty-five CD Complete Karajan box set *he* wants, but something he has bought at vast expense for her alone. A ring, a necklace, a tiara, a wrist-watch, anything suitably encrusted with sparkling stones; an evening gown, a diaphanous nightdress, an antique mirror lifted from Piers' upstairs corridor, a box of Milk Tray delivered by a man in black through an attic window at three in the morning, a personalised i-phone, -pod, -pad, -mac, -love you ... anything sexy.

I am no hypocrite when it comes to killing off a moribund relationship and so, ladies, I have to say that disappointment is in the air when I hand over a white plastic bag containing a collection of curiously heavy gifts, poorly wrapped in second-hand Christmas paper. Buggered if I was going to buy new birthday paper which would only get torn and crumpled up. I sit back and await her pleasure. Eagerly she begins to rip off the paper and I watch the expression on her face slip from suspicious excitement to surprise, from surprise to mystification and then from mystification to cold fury. The shiny new hammer comes as a blow to her, but the sight of a pair of orange-handled pliers, a set of screwdrivers and a small adjustable spanner result in a distinct pallor spreading across her already marble-pale features. (She reminds me for an instant of another very angry woman I recently encountered in a Berkshire hotel.) A bonus side-dish of picture hooks, nails and screws is received with a mixture of disgust, revulsion and utter contempt.

"How romantic," she murmurs without looking up. Hell freezes over. "You sure know how to please a girl."

The presentation has gone exactly to plan. On one level I had wanted her to have these useful items in her house because, in my manly and hands-on way, I am forever being required to bring my own tools *chez elle* to fix or hang something. I did it to please her so that she might love me. And now that I was about to move out of her life, she was going to have to learn how to hang a picture by herself, wasn't she? A practical gift, mindful of her future needs, especially considering how assiduous has been the recent hammering of so many final nails into the coffin of our affair. From her reaction, I gather that the irony of a toolset being offered to 'a strong woman' has not entirely escaped her.

"I *thought* you'd be pleased," I say, looking at the bill and out of delicacy resisting the urge to summon the management to query its enormity.

At her house an hour later I apply the match to the fuse under Part 2 of the Birthday Action Plan; it will take unusual courage to carry it off, and I am preparing to stand well back, having lit it. There will be great unpleasantness, but I am determined for once to give it a go. The tool-kit has merely been the overture to greater treachery.

Valerie has locked us in and we are sitting at the kitchen table, still in our coats, drinking glasses of water and digesting the implications of the birthday celebrations so far. She takes her tools out of their plastic bag and arranges them on the front page of yesterday's 'Times'. On the counter next to me is a card from her daughter: "Happy Birthday, Mummy. I hope this year will be better. Love you. Millie xxx". I look at the floor, adrenalin pumping through me, the vats of purple chemicals lined up ready to be kicked over. Out of the corner of my eye I see her look up. Chocks away.

"Shall we go to bed?" she asks.

"No," I reply quietly, "I think I'll go home."

I can almost taste the acid fumes emitting from the long, ensuing pause.

"Why?" She is as icy as a Visiting Examiner.

"I just think I'd better."

Her foot is on the first vat. It wobbles slightly and vitriol begins to slop over the rim. This is going to be twice as vile as I had anticipated.

"Oh, I see," she says, glaring at me. "This is all because you can't go to bed with me without wanting to have sex? Is that it?"

"Yes, of course," I whisper. *Perspicacity, thy name is woman.* She pulls off her gloves and begins to unwind her scarf.

"Sex isn't everything, Henry," she announces, embarking upon a well-trodden road of contempt for male carnal desire. "If you had a partner who wanted sex all the time you wouldn't be able to keep up." A low blow, but I am aware of a certain truth in what she says and so do not react by seizing the hammer and smashing her skull in. I am no spring chicken, no bantam cock, no stud. I merely wish to sleep with my lover now and again. Once a week would probably shut me up and keep me faithful. "Or is it," she continues, "that you still want me to *mother* you? Is that it, my little orphan boy?"

"I wasn't going to mention it, Valerie, but since you ask so nicely, I can report that I have both tracked down and recently met my First Mother. This has made us both very happy, believe it or not. I wasn't going to bother you with this most important moment in what you presumably regard as my mid-life crisis, because you have made your views on my adoption abundantly clear."

"You've actually done it, have you? Thanks for telling me. You are utterly incredible. What an egotist." She begins to unbutton her coat. "How dare you deliberately set about upsetting a harmless old woman? You have no idea what damage you might do."

"I'll always be grateful for your loving understanding and support, but I'm all mothered up now, thanks all the same." I get to my feet, tuck my chair under the table and step towards the front door to find my shoes.

"Penetration isn't everything either," she adds.

Had I not already been crouching to tie my shoelaces, this well-aimed and endearing remark might have sent me sprawling across the parquet. As it is, I merely lean my shoulder against the wall and gaze at the doormat. 'Welcome', it lies. I can think of nothing useful to say.

"It's my birthday, Henry. Why are you being so mean?"

"Because we're finished, Valerie. That's why. Unlock the door, please."

For a moment she looks child-like and broken, but I resist the idea of a last-ditch attempt at Dornford Yates chivalry because Valerie despises knights. She wants to be one herself and to ride out to do battle with the men who worship her. She is the living antithesis of a medieval hero. Perhaps she's a lesbian.

And now the guilty ache of being deliberately unkind to a fellow human sweeps through me. I feel selfish, foolish, belligerent and an oaf, but the little voice in my head insists that for once I do not cave in and risk another devastating "I don't want nookey now" scene under the duvet. I take a deep breath and look her full in the face.

"Goodnight. Happy Birthday."

"Goodnight, Henry."

There is no major explosion, but she has managed nonetheless to overturn a good half dozen vats of noxious chemicals. Utterly nauseous, I stumble away from the house and hear her lock the door behind me.

Once safely home, I banish the Waterhouse *Mermaid* to the bathroom and allow the chemical slurry to subside. What I have done will be for the best: I have faced down Valerie for the first time and have earned myself a reasonably restful night. Communication being something that she and I don't do any more, I haven't bothered her with the fact that I shall need my sleep if I am to triumph tomorrow.

32

Strutting in Suburbia

This is the big one. My long-awaited and, after all I'm going through, richly deserved break into the soaps; a chance at last to be recognised in the street, to be able to command squillions a week to play the baddie in panto every Christmas. The casting director has actually telephoned Agent P to demand my presence at an *EastEnders* audition for a small barrister part; 'small' as in having an insignificant number of lines; she knows full well I'm six foot five.

"He's just perfect for the part," she gushed. "He'll walk in and get it."

Smugness oozes from me. It slimes across the road, washes up the Village Green and laps at the church door. Playing upon my insider knowledge that my Headmaster religiously clears all visitors from his rooms at *EastEnders* time, I ring Piers to tell him where I'm auditioning and demand a day off. Armed with the Royal Assent ("Be extra vigilant, Mr Robson: lesbians at large!")

I head off on the long trek across the Home Counties and Greater London to the BBC studios at Elstree. Lacking a Duke of Edinburgh Gold Award in orienteering, I set aside many hours for this voyage into uncharted suburbia. I know what is liable to happen: true to my native *esprit de provincial*, I will become befuddled after my mad dash up the escalator and over the footbridge from Waterloo Main to Waterloo East. Then, assuming that I board a train which actually stops at London Bridge, I am bound to leap onto the wrong Thameslink service and will either hurtle southwards to East Croydon or will correctly head north but on a train that declines to stop at Elstree-Borehamwood. I must therefore factor in plenty of time to trundle all the way back from St Albans on the slow train and still leave an hour or so for fruitless peregrinations amongst the backstreets of Elstree. You can at all times see the top floors of the BBC studios in the distance, but even seasoned visitors to this desolate region have difficulties finding their way through the nightmare 'thirties sprawl which, as if sealed by some Harry Potter spell, masks the main entrance from an incompetent Muggle like me.

Eventually, I am signed in and appropriately labelled by a delightfully obsequious security man who gives me detailed instructions with regard to the final stage of my quest. I don't listen, of course, because I am far too excited and spend a longish while wandering lonely as a would-be star through the endless shiny corridors of glamour until I happen upon the casting suite. I am gratified to feel the old familiar sticky sensation in the back of my throat, something that manifests itself exclusively prior to a performance or a clandestine encounter with another man's wife. I read through the script handed to me by a young man who doesn't look up from his laptop.

```
Robert Morton for the Prosecution. I
understand you want to see me … Yes … And
so? … Of course …
```

We are not talking BAFTAs here, but I swallow my pride and learn the scene by heart over a cardboard beaker of glutinous BBC hot chocolate.

"Henry Robson?" I am summoned.

This casting being, as I have said, a mere formality, I have decided to risk dazzling them with some serious barrister acting. I have therefore attired myself for the nonce in my black pin-striped suit (a natty Oxfam number acquired for a fiver) and carry a battered black attaché case containing on this occasion not my latest legal brief but my jobbing actor's luncheon in the form of a Happy Shopper pork pie, a Yorkie bar and a banana in its Lakeland Plastic banana case (this last much mocked by all who behold it). I am under strictest instructions from Agent P not to play the clown for once because historically I have made sofa-loads of executives roar with mirth at no less than three failed *Casualty* auditions. Consequently, when I enter the fug of the hallowed casting chamber I am the very personification of Robert Morton for the Prosecution. Modelling myself on Piers' Assembly gait, I walk slowly and confidently, taking in all around me in the courtroom and acknowledging the fawning officials as I sashay to my seat.

Professionally speaking therefore, I am somewhat discomfited when an ebullient and curvaceous casting lady rushes at me, kisses me on both cheeks and says how lovely it is to see me again after all this time. Needless to say, I have no recollection of having encountered her before, and for a casting director has she not made the lamentable mistake of not noticing that I am 'in character'? I feel a little hoist with my own petard because I have tended to mock actors who attend castings in costume. I have openly sneered at pirates turning up in full regalia and false beards, but of late I have imitated them; in my efforts to nudge unimaginative production teams into visualising what I might look like in rôle, I have actually donned a solar topee and khaki shorts, a full ski outfit and once, a complete vicar's paraphernalia. (I did in fact get the vicar job and spent a happy half day driving a grey Morris Minor up and down the dual carriageway at Shepherds Bush reciting "Last night I dreamt I went to Manderley again" which is, as everyone knows, the opening line from *Rebecca* and something to do with braking distances. I can also say that I remained in Anglican garb until I had booked into a country pub for an afternoon of illicit shenanigans with Valerie under the assumed names of Reverend and Mrs Peter Simpson of Sheffield. It's a marvel how an assumed accent, a dog-collar and a wad of ecclesiastical tenners can pull the wool over the most worldly of landlord's eyes. Happy days.)

My efforts at today's characterful disguise are evidently going to cut no ice here at the BBC, but since my presence is a mere formality, I soon rally and perform the scene twice for the camera, once with and once without suspicion as instructed by the burly assistant director. We part on the friendliest of terms, he saying "Henry, that's really good, thank you so much. We'll see each other again very soon, I hope," by which he means the following Saturday when they're shooting the scene.

Once safely re-installed on Thameslink, I rip off my tie and wolf down my healthy snack, returning home buoyed up by the knowledge of success and imminent televisual glory: I shall be on *EastEnders*. Piers will love me. My pupils will worship at my very feet. Valerie will be grudgingly complimentary and everyone in the Village of the Damned will see me. My existence will be justified and explained.

The next day, however, nothing.

The following morning Agent P phones. "Greetings and all manner of hallucinations!" I jibber glibly. Has he arranged a BBC limo to collect me in the wee small hours of Saturday morning? Will I have my own Winnebago? "What news, O illustrious Agent?" I enquire.

"Henry," he begins, his voice peculiarly flat today, "you didn't get it. I'm gob-smacked. I don't know what to say. She said you were perfect, but guess what?"

"What this time?" There is lead in my soul.

"The producers were frightened of you." He pauses. "They've gone with someone else."

"Frightened of me?! But they weren't even there!"

"I know, Henry, I'm sorry. We'll land it next time." *I very much doubt it.* "Goodbye, Henry." I drop the phone into its cradle and automatically flick on the kettle. How much worse can things become? I hate this bloody business. I hate all the ups and downs and the hopes raised and dashed. I hate the fact of being constantly battered and bludgeoned by my lover and by both of my supposed careers. I hate my life. I hate myself. What's the *fucking* point?

Sitting staring at a cold cup of post-Existentialist tea an hour later, I consider whether I might have let any personal misery and rage creep into my interpretation of Robert Morton for the Prosecution. I must either be prodigiously talented or really angry to intimidate grown men and women at an *EastEnders* production meeting. I can see them now, big bruisers all, staring wide-eyed at my two little performances on their video player and then leaping from their chairs and running from the studio, their hoarse yells of terror echoing through quiet suburban streets.

But let's be positive here: perhaps – if they dare – when next they're casting a mass murderer, a bulgy-eyed paedophile or the Beast from the Swamp, they'll think of me again and give Agent P another call.

33

Tutorial

I come in from a quick dash next door for an onion to find my mobile phone flashing indignantly at me. I approach with trepidation and squint at the screen.

1 message received.

Oh god. Valerie has only been incommunicado for three days but I'm already beginning to allow myself to hope she's deleted me. My thumb and forefinger, as flaccid and dexterous as a pair of pork and ale sausages, reflect my apprehension; four attempts at unlocking the keypad result in a flash of temper and the hurling of the onion into the fireplace.

Keypad unlocked.
Message from 'Valerie'.

My stomach lurches. I hesitate to apply the quivering digit. The fantasy that her silence might have been terminal has dissolved into a shout of mockery and the message I open causes me to sit down so suddenly on the frayed arm of the sofa that I hurt my coccyx.

> Thx 4 a wonderful
> birthday meal n 4
> all my great tools.

I close my eyes against the pain in my bottom and fire up my computer. There's only one thing left to do.

Much, much later that evening, and bolstered by the knowledge that I have the final solution to Valerie in an envelope in my pocket, I climb into my damp Vauxhall and drive out of the Village. With great cunning and considerable thought for any future procreative activity on my part, I decide that if I am to deliver a letter and sneak away with my scrotum intact, I must approach Fortress Valerie stealthily and silently at the dead of night when I know she will be tucked up in bed with that lucky, *lucky* pillow wedged firmly between her legs. Accordingly, I stow the banger at a nearby pub and creep up the drive to the familiar picket gate, keeping to the grassy verge so as to make no sound on the gravel. Of course, the bloody gate squeaks (why hadn't I just hopped over the wall?) and a light comes on in the hallway. I curse under my breath. My plan to post the letter and run turns to dust: through the window in the door, I see her hovering inside, ready to welcome me in like Circe, poised to wave her magic wand and turn me into a pig. How did she know I was there? It's uncanny.

"Hi!" she says, cheerily, having grappled with the various locks and bolts. She is wearing only her dressing gown and I have already glimpsed the curve of her right breast as she bent down to pull back the bottom bolt. "Come in. Where's your car? Why didn't you drive up?"

"Left it round by the pub," I blabber. "Needed some exercise." My heart is crashing about again and I feel sick.

I know she knows I'm lying. All remaining vats of purple slime have been mustered from distant storerooms and are balanced on the edge of my sanity. I kick my shoes off on the mat and enter the kitchen. Same smell, same scene, same chaos on the table. I spot the tip of the adjustable spanner protruding from under a pile of newspapers and junk mail.

I cudgel myself into not noticing how fabulous she is looking by dint of thinking hard about rusty razor blades slicing into my penis (it's an old actor's trick I have oft used to stop a rising guffaw of laughter spoiling an otherwise perfectly moving scene on stage); the desire to undo the cord holding that tantalising dressing-gown together, to put my hands round her waist and hold her pale naked body against mine is overwhelming; something about her, her scent maybe, is – and always has been – utterly irresistible. Bastard hormones. She reaches up and lifts two glasses down from a cupboard. I am transfixed by the sinuous movement of her bottom and, despite urgently applied razor-blade imagery I still yearn for the impossible, to roll with her under the softest of white duvets, to run my fingers through her auburn locks, to stroke her slim body, to tell her how much I love her; and for her to reciprocate. I begin to crumple the letter in my pocket as I slide towards perdition, and as she fills the glasses at the cold tap I step forward, reach out and gently grasp her shoulders, pulling her towards me and gently kissing the top of her head. I press myself into her. Holding the two full glasses she wriggles from my grasp.

"You're in my space, Henry."

Right, that's it. Fuck you, Valerie! Just fuck you.

"I won't stay," I say. "I've just brought you this letter. You need to read it."

"Don't be silly, Henry. Sit down and I can read it with you."

"No, really, I must go. It's late." *Christ!*

"Just stay a few minutes. I've hardly seen you." She has smelt a rat and is damned if she's going to allow me to get the better of her. This was never supposed to happen. How could I have been so incompetent in my stage-management of something as crucial yet as simple as this? Have I really engineered the situation so that I actually have to sit in front of her like a dumb-ass pupil at a tutorial while she reads my letter as if it were an A-level essay? It will be just how it used to be at school with Keith the moustachioed teacher reading through and savagely correcting my pitiful attempt at translating Margaret Drabble into French. His red biro slashing the paper, my tormentor would turn and query: "And what should the correct ending be here, Robson? -e? -é? -ée? -és? Or -ées?" And at each incorrect answer, he would thump me on the shoulder and the fifty or so other pupils in the silent study-room would swivel their eyes and smirk at me behind their hands. The very idea is preposterous and revolting.

"Sit down, Henry." I sit. I despise myself.

Why can't I just walk away? She is carefully tearing open the envelope now and I grapple with a desire to snatch it from her and run for the hills so that she will never read my monstrous wail of self-pity and recrimination, a masculine vomit of verbiage best reserved for a private moment round the back of a pub. I sit, slumped, deflated and defeated, quite unable to bring myself to look up at her, preferring instead to gaze at the hole in my left sock. The tiles are cold and I yearn for my pair of sheepskin slippers. But I am not permitted to keep any clothing in Valerie's draughty abode and my feet will have to remain icy. Miserably I imagine the choice phrases she must be negotiating even now:

Sex and joy in each other's company are utterly entwined. I have tasted of the fruit and now that same fruit has become almost forbidden. Obsessive in my adoration, I have been a fool and I am sorry. I am sorry also to have 'held you to ransom over sex', as you put it, and sorry to have been so needy, and sorry that I have not been able either to make you understand me, desire or need me enough to want to move towards me rather than away. Valerie, I have never even met your daughter.

This is not a letter for public debate; it is a ranting epic, full of repetition and pain, the composition of which had left me in tears. Valerie, I notice, is not crying. She turns the paper over and reads the last line:

I will always love you, Valerie. Goodbye.

She pulls her dressing gown more tightly about her. "What do you mean by quoting this particular sentence?" she asks coldly. 'I will make love to you when I want to, not when you want to.' Did I say that to you?"

"Yes."

"I didn't mean it like that."

"Well, how else can you have meant it?"

"I meant that you think about sex all the time, Henry."

I know. It's a boy thing. "Have you not understood anything I say?" I rejoinder. "Read this bit." I grab the letter and point to a line.

"I wanted to know that we could make love together, gladly, willingly, lovingly, naturally, normally and of course, regularly. "

Reading it aloud to her makes my cry of anguish seem all the more pathetic (and anyway, there are far too many adverbs.) "And here," I drone on:

"I am not prepared to sit with you until Zimmer frame time screaming inside with sexual agony and frustration and not even <u>daring</u> to ask you if we can make love now and again."

I brace myself and look her into the eyes. She returns my gaze with a mixture of disdain, pity and genuine bewilderment. I plough on hopelessly, the paper trembling in my hand.

"Why should I be reduced to asking you? It has to be a mutual need, a compatible desire. With us, it is not. Nor am I prepared to stand there and masturbate at you while you dress. Did you not once tell me that this was one of your ex-husband's preferred pleasures? Nor will I lie with you and masturbate. No more masturbation, Valerie. Masturbation does not constitute love-making."

There is a pause. I am aware of the boiler switching itself off. Valerie is twiddling a screwdriver between her fingers. Why hadn't I just given her a set of thumbscrews?

"Henry," she begins, "I understand what you're saying, of course I do, but you've just got to loosen up a bit. Why must you get so heavy about all this? It's just sex. A shag's a shag."

Defeated by Valerie's mystifying yet implacable logic, the purple vats tip over again and a wave of self-pity engulfs me. I am done here; the mire can swallow me up.

"Then I don't know what to say or do," I mutter, getting to my feet. "We're finished and yet you won't leave me alone. I've tried to explain, but you don't or won't understand. Goodnight, Valerie."

How many more times must I hear that door lock behind me?

34

Beginning to lose the plot

Piers has been at it again.

I have spent much of the past week sitting in half-term traffic on the A303; my new mother is definitely not in the finest of fettles and I felt, correctly as it turned out, that a spot of filial butler acting would do us both good. Now, however, I'm back at the Madhouse, standing on the threshold of my room in the company of the enticing embodiment of another of Piers' whims. Sharon is a devastatingly pretty dance instructor with whom I am apparently to share my room and after whom, were it not for her tender years, fake tan and Estuary English, I would yearn. My nice new drama room (the aural torture chamber in the Cuckoo Clock) is now unrecognisable as a performance venue owing to the advent of a fresh chaos of second-hand office furniture: stacked high on Piers' highly polished, dancer-unfriendly, waxed plywood floor are the fourteen constituent parts of yet another conference table, a collection of square, low-slung blue chairs (ideal for an airport departure lounge but of scant relevance to Chekhov), two hardboard lecterns (one broken), a pile of disco equipment and a step ladder. No sign of the promised sound-proofing, and my plastic chairs have gone again.

A stickler for health and safety, Sharon leans against me and bursts into tears, overwhelmed at the thought of her lumpish charges leaping and pirouetting in such hazardous surrounds. "He can't expect me to teach in here with all this crap," she sobs. "I won't do it."

"Piers' priorities lie elsewhere now," I say, putting my arm around her shoulder in what I tell myself is an avuncular way. "He's moved on, darling. We in Performance Arts are so last term's news."

"Well, sod him," she says, erecting a pink umbrella which matches the stripe down her tight black leggings. "I'll go and see the old fuckwit."

Gazing wistfully after her, I recognise that in more ways than one, my day has passed. I am a lonely and lustful old tosser, spurned by women, reviled by casting directors and reduced to ogling the pert bums of pretty young dance instructors. My star in Piers' little firmament has been extinguished, sucked into a black hole of its own creation and leaving behind the shell of a once-great ego bombilating in the void. My whimsical and demoralising employer has passed me over and moved on to other things, leaving a cascade of useless furniture, broken promises and unalloyed misery in his wake.

I have become a fully paid-up member of The Sad Old Bastards League.

Currently the most demoralised of my colleagues is Piers' most dreaded *bête noire*, the Mad Media Woman. Referred to by her employer as "a figment of her own imagination," Janice is a tousled little blonde lady with a propensity for unseasonable décolletage, bright red boots and short skirts. In happier, more glamorous days she was, she insists, an air-hostess. We believe her because wherever she goes, she trundles behind her a little black wheelie suitcase, now sadly mud-spattered owing to having been dragged through the car park. Her teaching style is provocative, favouring (for example) episodes from *Blackadder* to illuminate the War Poets for A-level foreigners, and she is both vociferous and lachrymose in her outrage against Piers and all his doings. There's some problem with her contract, she tells us, and she has rashly involved a union in this dispute, thereby terminally upsetting He Who Must Be Obeyed and unsettling her less militant colleagues. To join a union is to declare war on Piers and will result in his finding some pretext for either sacking those in favour of employment law or making their lives so unpleasant that they leave of their own accord.

So it is with leaden heart that two weeks later I hear that the MMW's latest scheme is to form a United-We-Stand-Divided-We-Fall Staff Association where important matters of State can be discussed in open forum. Open to us but closed to Piers. Matters of great moment raised in her first agenda include the lack of distinction between the Ladies' and Gents' toilet facilities and the absence of a sanitary waste bin in the former. Could not Piers, she witters, be persuaded to fix signs to the loo doors? Emboldened by MMW's Association, the A-level maths lady of no fixed classroom now wonders whether a work table might not be provided in the staff-room. History frets about the excessive number of planned lesson observations this year. Business and EFL claim that there aren't enough classrooms to accommodate the pupils so efficiently provided by Marketing.

It is an idea doomed to disaster but, against my better judgement, I put in an appearance in the Media Room at the end of a lunch-break. Inside, I find a furtive group lurking around the conference table and nibbling sandwiches. Guilt and militancy are a potent mix. I spot Piers' mole immediately.

"Oh, Mr Robson," shrieks MMW, oblivious to the spy in her

midst, "how lovely to see you!" She is on her feet in front of her flock *outragé*, waving an order paper at me, evidently relishing her moment of power. "We wanted to ask you a little favour, darling."

"Uhuh?"

"Yes," she chirrups, "we want you to be our spokesman."

"I thought you might," I say. "Well, alright, but let me just tell you one thing."

"What, darling?"

I glance at Piers' mole (the young Head of Sixth form currently in favour) who is avidly polishing his glasses in the corner. "I *am* a double agent."

"Oh, you're so funny, darling," she laughs nervously. "We never know when you're joking. Thing *is*, Piers likes you and he doesn't like me." This is true, and despite many misgivings, I nod my assent.

The mole wastes no time in relaying what he has heard to his Master and within twenty-four hours I am accosted.

"Your new room should be ready on Wednesday, Mr Robson," Piers snarls menacingly.

"Ah, excellent," I enthuse. "That'll be great. Fantastic."

Proving once and for all that we are morphing into each other, Piers and I had dreamt up the same solution to Drama in the middle of the same night the week after half term. "What about putting Drama in the bodybuilding room?" we had gleefully suggested to each other. His cowboys could easily erect a lean-to against a spare wall where no planning permission would be required. Recruit a few hefty boarders to shift the weights, exercise bikes and running machines and *voilà!* Drama could move immediately.

(The current 'gym' is a flat-roofed double garage attached loosely to the side of Science, itself a flat-roofed extension of the original eighteenth century coach house. Until recently, it was the home of Trevor the Mechanics teacher. According to popular myth, Trevor was in fact a robot controlled remotely by his wife from their home outside Shaftesbury. He's gone now, of course, as has his subject; the reason being, or so the rumour-mongers have it, that his wife inadvertently pressed the 'Inflate' button whilst Trevor was shopping for her in Morrisons.)

Piers moves in for an early kill: "A *loyal* member of staff has been kind enough to send me a copy of the minutes of a secret meeting. Mr Robson, I cannot believe that you of all people are the spokesman for that woman's shambolic Staff Association."

"Oh, that load of toss," I say, testing the depth of his outrage with a fine display of moral cowardice *à la* double agent.

"It's not a load of toss, Mr Robson." He is glaring at me over his spectacles, doing his best to intimidate. "I am bitter, wounded to my heart." He strikes his chest with a fist in a manner too melodramatic to be taken seriously. "And after all I have done. What other Headmaster would spend twenty thousand pounds on a new room for you within two weeks of your mentioning it? And you repay me by becoming spokesman for that rabble. I am hurt." So that's his game, is it? Full-on manipulation bolstered by outrage and punctured *amour de soi.*

He rants on and on and suddenly, as I stand looking down on the comb-over glued immovably above his crosspatch face, something pink and fluffy comes whizzing round the corner and tickles me in the solar plexus. I am overwhelmed by an urge to giggle, for I am being belaboured by the soft feather duster of an epiphany: Piers is a nothing more than a paper tiger.

Fear evaporates.

He is powerless over me; time for the truth.

"Piers," I say, as we begin to walk slowly around the campus. "I have no views about that Mad Media Woman's dreary rantings and I care so little about the School that I could walk immediately. I told her then and I am telling you now: I am a double agent."

He ignores this. "Starting an Association without informing the entire staff is illegal," he pronounces. "I have passed the whole thing on to the school solicitor." *Marvellous. I shall soon be sharing a cell with MMW.*

We are approaching the nearly completed gymnasium 'complex', a rectangular wooden box attached as promised to the side of the Sports Hall (or Theatre). One of the builders is up a stepladder gazing disconsolately at a substantial puddle of water on the roof. The ubiquitous one-tool-solves-all hammer is swinging with attitude from his belt.

"Don't you think this is all a tad ironic, Piers?" I start in, looking at this jerry-built shambles. "Only last year, after Admin burnt down, you spent eighty thousand pounds on a purpose-built space for drama and music right at the centre of the School."

"Yes, and the insurance never paid up."

"Is this my problem? Did I humiliate a pupil so much that he doused the place with unleaded and applied a match? No. This was your doing."

"How dare you?"

"Listen, Piers, your own architect has admitted to me that you ordered the builders to finish the reconstruction as soon as possible. If you hadn't cut corners, if you'd just spent another couple of grand stuffing the walls and floors with some sound-proofing, I'd still be up there, happy as Larry."

"That room is a multi-purpose space; we need it for dance as well."

"That space is a repository for old furniture and a bloody death trap for dancers, and you know it."

"You're all so bloody ungrateful," he persists. "Is this why you've decided to rebel against me? Why can't people come and talk to me instead of starting secret societies? My door is always open."

"They don't come and see you because they are frightened of you, Piers."

"I'm not at all frightening. You aren't frightened of me."

"You are bloody scary, but I've grown used to you." Piers has begun to pick up litter. "Why must you be so bloody rude to everyone? Why do you have to run the School in such an adversarial atmosphere?"

"Meaning?"

"In an atmosphere of hostility, enmity, aggression and unpleasantness," I thesaurise. Does the man not speak English? "Not long ago you used to be in the staff room every break; there was cake and coffee and laughter and communication. Why don't you come in any more?"

"I don't want to. They don't want me there."

"They would do if you could be friendly and normal instead of Mr Angry sneaking round and never speaking to anyone except through an intermediary."

"I've said: I don't want to. There are people I don't want to see."

"But you're their bloody employer."

"But I can't trust them to follow instructions," he digresses. "They really piss me off. I ask them to do things and they don't. I told them I want posters up for the Open Day next Saturday and what has happened? Nothing."

"Are you really surprised, Piers?" I turn to face him before letting him have one I prepared earlier. "You're a micro-manager. As a result, you undermine everyone."

"I'm not. I don't even go to management meetings."

"Why not? You're the bloody boss!"

"I don't want to. I don't need to. The managers tell me what's happening and I rubber stamp it."

"Oh my god," I expire loudly. "Everyone knows that the opposite is the case. The *exact* opposite." I am beginning to shout. "You're the man who can dismantle a staffroom as an act of revenge! You do precisely what you want round here!"

"Whatever, Mr Robson."

The man is deluded. This is why I don't fear him any more.

I am wasting my breath and he isn't going to acknowledge a single point that I or anyone else will make. Nothing will happen here unless Piers has the idea first. MMW does not understand this and it will be up to me to persuade her to call off her dogs.

We have been bickering *sotto voce* outside the entrance to the Sports Hall (or Theatre) where Upper School Registration (or Bollocking) has been taking place. Two hundred pupils now file gingerly past us avoiding eye contact.

"I am definitely not a micro-manager, Mr Robson," mutters Piers sulkily, obviously hurt by my barb, "but if the staff don't put those posters up – and they were very expensive – I'll have to do it myself this weekend." And with that, he lets go his mooring rope and allows himself to be carried downstream in the wake of the last of the pupils heading off to Lesson Six. I follow a pace or two behind him, suspecting that the conversation is not quite over. A bell rings: my own Lower Sixth will be waiting for me. Let them wait.

As we approach the dining room, I hear the clatter of knives and forks and the subdued conversation of the Lower School at the trough. Piers puts his head through an open French window to make sure that no member of staff is surreptitiously eating in there with the children. "Come here, boy!" Piers snaps. The sounds of chatter and eating cease. "What the hell do you think you're doing with that banana?" A small Colombian is gazing up at Piers, a look of abject terror on his face. He is about to cry.

"I eat heem, sir," he quavers, a partly peeled banana clasped tightly in both hands.

"I eat IT, you mean!" comes the roar. "Has nobody taught you ANYTHING?" I can already imagine the contents of tonight's enraged email:

Polite Reminder. You are paid to teach these children. They are our customers. What are they paying for IF NOT TO BE TAUGHT ENGLISH? Simple really. Piers.

"Please, sir?" whimpers the diminutive stranger to these shores.

"At Gussage Court we don't eat bananas like that! We are not monkeys! You take a knife and fork and eat it properly, like a civilised human being and young gentleman. You!" he snaps at a junior prefect. "Show Alejandro how to eat a banana. You know the correct way. That is why you are a prefect."

The junior prefect mutters "Yes, sir" but the conspiratorial glance he shoots me indicates that he has in mind another, quite different use for that piece of fruit. I turn away to hide my smile. The banana routine is a perennial of Piers' and involves the partial severing of the stalk and the inserting of a fork across the loosened piece of skin. The idea then is that the strip of skin is rolled down with the fork as far as it will go. This hands-off process is repeated until the banana lies naked on the plate and ready for slicing up and dainty consumption with cutlery. I have it from a former pupil of a French catering school that this is the approved Eurozone way of approaching a banana. My own view is that life is too short, but I may merely be proving to the world once and for all that I am no gentleman. As Piers glowers at the silent multitudes, I am reminded of my father's declaration that a true gentleman will deploy the butter knife even when breakfasting alone. This has the ring of plausibility about it, but since I do not even possess a butter knife I am a failure. (I am also withholding from Piers the fact, recently told to me by Donal, that a true gentleman might know how to play the bagpipes, but declines to do so.)

Stamping away from the dining room, Piers continues. "The point is that if the staff don't like it here, they can fuck off and work in the State sector where there's a thousand times more paperwork and where everything has to be done by the book. We're here to make a difference to the children. They are the ones who matter."

"I agree."

"I sometimes worry, Mr Robson, what would happen to the

School if I went away? The place would fall to pieces. Nothing would get done."

This vote of no-confidence in his workforce brings me up with a jolt. Are we all in his view utterly incompetent and untrustworthy? I experience an internal flutter of something akin to a loss of temper, something the French call *je m'enfoutisme*. I hear myself speaking the truth aloud to my employer.

"What would happen, Piers? Do you really want to know? *Everything*. When you're out of the School, when you're taking the privileged few to Buckingham Palace or the Houses of Parliament or Ascot, do you know what happens? We all relax." Piers is silent. "We breathe a sigh of relief because there's no-one breathing down our necks, no-one moving the goalposts, taking away our chairs or making us miserable with irrational and whimsical demands. The School becomes a place where it's nice to be and where we can all get on with our jobs."

One of my sixth formers pokes a hopeful head out of our room. I am about to lose them as well as my job.

"I'm sure whenever any Chief Executive is off the premises the mice come out to play."

"Sure. So why don't you take a three month sabbatical? Write a novel. Go to Africa. Just go away and leave us to run the School and settle it down for a while."

"Are you trying to get rid of me?"

"Yes."

The look in his eye tells me that this, my cruellest, most hurtful and unprofessional Scud Missile may have dented his carapace but has, in a spooky parallel with so many of my encounters with Valerie, failed to penetrate it. I seem to have lost the match.

Piers climbs the steps to Admin. He will push open the door and stump in; a frost will fall over the people who work in there, for he is their King and at his approach his vassals must do his bidding without demur. "Piers, just admit it," I call after him, "you wouldn't be without all this argument and rebellion. You love it."

"No, Henry, I don't. There are bigger issues in life and there are some people round here who need to grow up."

The door clicks shut behind him.

35

Jetée à la Russe

Three and a half hours later, a peeping Tom at the uncurtained kitchen window of Number 4 will see me celebrating the fact that there is only a month of school left before the merciful release wrought by the Christmas holidays.

My festivities are somewhat muted, consisting as they do of a repast cobbled together from a stale bun I found in the bread bin, and last Thursday's cold macaroni cheese and broccoli, now rendered pappy and tasteless after an over-cautious session in the microwave. After the washing-up, I tidy the kitchen and hoover through, but despite this frantic domesticity, I am still aware of a feeling in the pit of my stomach (dominating even the leaden bolus of my meal) reminding me that I am not really relishing the idea of a solitary Yuletide; when those three weeks of holiday come, they will stretch dismally away before me and I will be left all alone and forlorn, a sad old adulterer wondering what to do with his life. My aged parents have ruled themselves out of the running by selfishly deciding to go on a whale-watching cruise off Alaska. Maybe I should go down to Exmouth again and be nice to Pauline and Len, or perhaps I should volunteer to serve soup to the homeless in London; that would show everyone what a worthwhile chap I am. For the rest of the time I can go for bracing walks in the forest where maybe I'll meet a nymph or a dryad and be seduced into oblivion.

There has been a blessed silence between Valerie and me for a while now and once again, like a hunted man trapped up a tree, I am beginning to allow myself to hope that the wolf has tired of circling the trunk below me and gone away for good. Time, I think to myself, for a little celebratory Rachmaninov. Plenty of dark moments and not too triumphalist.

I am kneeling reverently at the CD player when I hear a footfall outside the front door. Someone lifts the knocker and raps loudly. I pause the CD before Ashkenazy gets into full swing. Certain that it's only Jo wanting to expropriate some tea bags or suggest a late-night trip to Ikea, I haul myself to my feet and throw the door open in a manner befitting the anticipation of pre-Christmas Good Cheer. However, it is not my neighbour; framed by the darkness is a dreadful and familiar figure dressed in her grey woollen coat, green scarf and high-heeled leather boots. Her eyes are narrow slits of fury. Oh Christ.

"Can I come in?"

"No."

She steps in, closes the door and pushes past me towards the sanctuary of my kitchen. I block her path.

"Valerie, I have had a vile and very possibly terminal day at school," I growl, "and I cannot be doing with your control-freakery now. We are history. Please leave." I open the door again.

"I'm not having this," she snaps. "We're not finished." She closes the door.

"We are," I say. "I just want you out of my head and out of this house. Leave me alone." There's going to be shouting; my voice is already tightening at the certainty of horrors to come. "You just don't get it, do you? You don't understand what I feel about you and what you've done to me. Time after time I've tried to explain, but you refuse to understand." I find myself by the piano vigorously tidying the piles of paper littering the top. "I even wrote you a letter explaining everything. I sat there while you read the bloody thing a month ago, but still you don't understand. What am I to do? You have rejected me! You admit you have withdrawn from me! There is no future for us, no communication between us! It's over. Get out!" I am now screeching hysterically at her, my voice rasping in my throat. Even *in extremis* the actor in me is taking notes from an invisible voice coach.

"I'm staying," she says quietly. "I'm staying the night. We can make love if you like, Henry. I'm not going away."

I stare at her, searching in vain for some tic, some external sign which might betray the cold calculations whirring inside her head.

"Valerie," I say, "I don't want any more sympathy shags from you. No more forgiveness, no more manipulation. I'm asking you very nicely to go home, so please go."

"What's all this about, Henry?" she asks, her face a mask of hurt bewilderment. "Are you seeing somebody else?"

"Of course I'm not." *If only.*

"Well that's something. Let's have a cup of tea to celebrate, and you can rub my feet." She takes another pace towards the kitchen, but her advance is short-lived. I grab her by the shoulders, spin her round and propel her to the door. With one hand on her back and the other tugging at the door handle I hear a voice screaming: "Get out of my house or I'll call the police!" With one final shove she is out into the cold and dark. I seize the door with both hands and fling it shut with such force that the frame comes away from the bricks. Shaking with rage,

I scream a final "Fuck *YOU!*" at the door and tug it back into place before turning the key. This is it, she has finally driven me insane; I want to kill her, wring her neck and stamp on her face until it's flat. One more act of defiance, one more sexual taunt from her might have been her last.

I throw myself panting onto the sofa. Which of the villagers will have heard our little melodrama and actually called the police? I can imagine those net curtains twitching gleefully as all the local do-gooders, the Barbaras, the Daphnes and the Mr Brackenburys watch me being escorted from the cottage and shoved unceremoniously into the back of a squad car. They love this sort of thing in the Village of the Damned.

36

A Flounce à la Tolkien

In the teeth of a horizontal and glacial North Easterly I accompany my latest Visiting Examiner past the Junior Library to my new drama room.

I am a boy brought up by a mother who erred on the side of caution when it came to the vagaries of the English autumn. Today, therefore, I am sporting my provincial drama teacher's green anorak, a Doctor Who scarf and my favourite grey Fedora. VE's mother is evidently no such stickler, and has dressed him in a natty lightweight grey suit, now pock-marked with the rain that beats against us, stinging our faces like splinters of glass from a window after an incident involving bagpipes. I have found my coatless young visitor a long red curtain (tossed inexplicably onto a chair in the Girls' Sitting Room) but it only partially shields him from the onslaught of the elements; despite startled glances from pupils scurrying past, he has chosen to wear it as a cape over his head like Gandalf braving the Misty Mountains.

I scrabble for my room key, force it into the lock and inwardly beg it to turn. It requires all my skill as a seasoned burglar to break into my own classroom each day; the cracked and crazed glass in the door bears witness to much frustrated shoving and heaving in the past. The key refuses to budge. I glance anxiously at Gandalf but his Training has paid off: his expression is inscrutable.

"It's no use," I yell into the wind, spotting a band of Orcs circling in the trees near the café. "It's jammed! I'll have to get in through the window."

Tucking his leather briefcase under an arm, Gandalf nods his assent and pulls the curtain more tightly about his head. One of the Orcs is wearing a bear-skin hat; he creeps nearer. It is Piers doing his morning rounds. I can see droplets of rain on his spectacles and in his goatee. "What are you doing, you madman?" he mouths, uncertain of how to behave in front of a non-employee clad in a curtain. An extra strong blast of wind flicks a damp brown leaf into my face.

"I'm going in through the window!" I scream. "The bloody lock's jammed again." Stepping up into the raised border which disguises the garage-like aspect of my room, I struggle through prickly decorative foliage and begin to wrestle with a loose window catch. "I can't do it. My hand's too big."

"I'll get something, you moron," hisses Piers. "Who is that man in my curtain?"

"He's a Visiting Examiner."

"Is he a lesbian? I bet he won't forget *us* in a hurry."

"No," I screech, "I don't suppose he will!"

A minute later, with the aid of a mop-handle, I force the window catch and allow ingress for the examiner and the first candidates.

And then, just as we are ready to begin, Piers turns up again, brandishing the same mop and grinning from ear to ear under his hat.

"Ah, Headmaster," I whisper, so as not to disturb VE who is arranging his little bell and papers on the table next door, "the mop again. For me?"

"If that ponce can go on stage dressed in my bloody curtain, then I'm allowed to come on with a mop. Here you are," he adds, bowing slightly and presenting me with the pestilent item, "use it wisely. A mop, a mop! My Kingdom for a mop!" We exchange a Renaissance flourish of obeisance and he retreats outside to harangue a Russian girl for wearing non-school uniform Uggs. He has evidently forgiven me again.

It is a mop dripping with poignant connotations.

Four days previously I had completed the transformation of my new drama room. As soon as the testosterone-stained body-building equipment had been removed, Piers had donned his wellies and personally hosed it down to remove all vestiges of masculine bodily excretions before handing the space over to me for "sexing up", as he put it. As a result, it is now hung with strips of multicoloured cloth upon which I have staple-gunned a series of posters, mostly advertising obscure foreign films. Others, supplied by Piers for the benefit of visiting parents, extol the virtues of "Getting the most out of Key Stage 3 Drama": box-ticking and drearily patronising publications aimed at depressing both teacher and pupil alike and absolutely guaranteed to stultify any creativity. But don't start me.

This is the fifth drama room I have decorated during my stay at the Madhouse, yet I am peculiarly possessive about it; I feel it has potential. One of the few warm rooms in the School, it boasts neither toppling chair units nor dead rats, benefits from the merest whiff of damp and, most importantly, doesn't come with built-in noise pollution from below. Indeed I am so pleased with it that I asked a carpet supplier chum of mine to deliver a brand new end-of-roll entirely free of charge so that I could spend a sweaty couple of hours squishing and snipping it into position over the gentle incline of the old garage floor.

The room immediately lost its echo and became warm and cosy; off I went home for the weekend with an unusual feeling of benign optimism wherein seemed to lurk the nascent possibilities of contentment and fulfilment. Out of chaos I had created an oasis of peace and calm, somewhere I can lurk and work without thinking about Valerie.

So when, two days before the arrival of my examiner, I do battle with the lock and saunter smugly into my room, I am not a little discombobulated by the insistent and all-pervasive stink of old trainer that assails my olfactory senses. Closer examination of my cosy new kingdom reveals the full extent of the latest unforeseen obstacle to job satisfaction.

Water.

The weather has intervened in my plans for survival, and much of my beloved carpet is floating in half an inch of muddy rainwater. When I tentatively place a foot onto the affected area, a cold brown liquid squelches up over the soles of my black leather brogues. Infrastructure and insulation not being, as I have said before, amongst Piers' strongest suits, the rain is seeping efficiently through the topsoil of the raised border outside; it passes easily under the original wooden garage wall and then continues its inexorable progress diagonally across my floor to exit under the vast (now sealed) double doors at the far end. Secondly, and more dramatically, water is cascading down the blue cloth I have put up around the alcove where I have positioned my desk. I say 'my' desk advisedly because I was the one who bought it from a charity shop and installed it myself, aware that asking Piers for such a rudimentary piece of lockable teaching equipment was plainly naïve.

I stand, appalled, gazing at a mini Niagara Falls splashing onto the desk top, pouring onto the carpet and eventually joining Lake Titicaca on the far side of the room via a series of meandering tributaries under and over my nice new carpet.

Like Mr Jeremy Fisher on his Lakeland lily-pad I stand marooned on a sopping green circular rug at the centre of the

271

pond. My feet feel distinctly clammy, moisture seeping into my socks. Then, with incredulous cries of "Cor, what's that bloody stink, sir?" the first class of the day arrives.

I have known these young people for some time now. We have passed through four of my five drama rooms together and we understand the stresses of being the victims of low prioritisation, aware of Piers' refusal to build anything lasting or watertight.

"Morning, sir."

"Good morning, Jess. How are you?" I mutter distractedly. Jess is rummaging in her coat pocket and I know what's coming. She is a girl of seemingly restricted diet.

"Do you want a Haribo, sir?"

"No, I'm fine, Jess. It's a bit early for me."

"Sir?" It's Hamish. "What does it feel like to be moved into a garage that leaks?"

"Sir, didn't you buy this carpet yourself?" ventures George, tossing his prefect's gown onto a chair above high water mark. "I bet you wonder why you bothered now." He laughs a little too loudly and I look out of the window at the rain pouring down.

"It was quite nice in here on Friday, sir, wasn't it?" says Katie, adopting a conciliatory tone.

"What are you going to do now, sir?" asks Oliver, with a mischievous and hopeful glint in his eye.

"I don't know, Ollie."

"Sir, this room is fucking crap."

"Thank you, Chris, that'll do. We'll have none of that language." Chris grins at my rampant hypocrisy. "Here's a question, guys: do you ever tell your parents what goes on here? Do they know about this?"

"Course, sir."

"Well, in that case they know what they're getting for their money."

They stand expectantly, waiting for something interesting

to happen, something they hope won't be a drama lesson. And yes, they know me too well for, bang on cue, the purple chemicals of self-pity surge up my legs; the recent and unresolved shenanigans with Valerie have left the vats only precariously balanced. I am beset with the irresistible notion to storm out and run away. To flounce out of this class in particular would be effective, perhaps even politically canny, for Piers would be forced to take notice of their parents' opinion.

"You know what, lads and lasses, this *is* a dump. You're right, George, why do I fucking bother? Help me with this." I bend down and grab the edge of the saturated rug. "D'you know where I found this rug last term? In a skip. Well, it can go back into the skip right now. Let's get it outside." We drag it out and toss it into the middle of the pathway; Piers is bound to spot it there sooner or later. I am shouting now, scarcely able to hold back my tears. "Why did I spend all that time making this room nice? He only had to tell me that it was a flood plain in here and I wouldn't have bothered putting down the sodding carpet. I'd have dug an irrigation ditch first. I'm out of here." I grab my anorak, bag and umbrella. Jess is on the verge of tears as well.

"But, sir, don't go. The examiner's coming on Thursday."

"Listen, people, run your scenes through and you'll be fine. You know what to do. I'm sorry, but I've got to go."

I lurch outside and head towards the car park. As planned, Piers has spotted the rug and is issuing commands for it to be disposed of. I slap him on the shoulder as I stalk past:

"See you later, Piers."

"What's the matter with you *now*?" His eyes are not smiling.

"Take a look in my room."

Once out on the main road I pull into a lay-by and phone the 'Academic Director', she who must take the flak for my sudden exodus and find cover teachers for the remainder of my classes.

"I'm sorry, Sally," I say. "I'm being a bit of a wanker, but I can't cope any more. I've had enough. I'll be back later."

"Don't you dare come back today," she commands. "Stand up for your principles. I'll see you tomorrow."

And with that, the floodgates burst. Thank god I'm off School property; histrionics in a middle-aged teacher look so unprofessional and are very bad for marketing. What would Piers say to a visiting parent?

"Oh, not to worry, Mrs Vassilyev, it's just our drama teacher showing the children how not to face up to life's little challenges. He's a failed actOR, you know. I indulge him until he becomes dangerous."

"But, Meester hHeadmaster, why he how-you-say bash out hees brains on wall like zees?"

"Well, he may have gone a little too far today. He takes Method Acting to extremes. Bloody luvvie."

"But now, please, he cut his throat with cook knife, yes?"

"All part of the Gussage Court Difference, Mrs – um, Vassiloff. Sisyphus! Disarm Mr Robson, would you, and escort him off the premises. Now, Mrs Vaseline, please step this way and I'll show you the new gym."

This is the text I type for Piers:

For Christ's sake,
why can't you just build
something properly
for once?

But I delete it and send this instead:

Dear Piers, I'll
send an email later
explaining myself,
All got too much. Henry

He replies by return:

> Dear Henry, I was as
> upset as u were about ur
> room but within
> 30 mins of the crisis
> I had a professional
> carpet cleaner in
> and the builders
> had fixed where
> the water was
> coming in. Am putting
> in a proper floor.

My heartbeat subsides a little. Is this what happens if you behave like a grown-up and don't shout at people? Is this how you deal with manipulating madmen? It's taken me all this time to work it out. Perhaps I should try it with Valerie.

So Piers' formal presentation to me of a mop is a gesture laden with irony. I have felt it only polite to brief Gandalf on the state of his examination room, and as he ventures into it and shakes off his cloak, the atmosphere is still humid and redolent of athlete's foot. I have folded back the damp half of the carpet to keep it out of the trickle of water still meandering across the acting space, but I am not much concerned with this, because we actors work anywhere and under any conditions.

By the time I arrive the following morning for the second of my examination days, two tattooed builders have already taken possession of my room and have filled it with a lorry-load of flooring materials. They have taken the precaution of tossing my precious carpet outside, but I am just in time to move my desk to safety and tie up my wall hangings. I venture to suggest a plastic sheet to protect the new floor from the effects of the underground stream, but the builders assure me that Piers won't hear of it, saying that we won't be here in ten years' time, so what's the point?

Gandalf is due in five minutes and I have nowhere for him to examine. Piers tells me to find somewhere else, but the only other space large enough would be my previous room, now occupied intermittently by squadrons of lumpish ballerinas under the tutelage of their succulent instructor. "Well, tell the dancers to fuck off," he suggests.

Four minutes later I greet Gandalf by the front door and my eye alights upon the Girl's Quiet Room where I'd found the curtain the day before. Presumably it had once been the drawing room, a peaceful place with intricate plaster coving and an enormous marble fireplace. It now contains a subtle mix of reproduction and Ikea furniture, the intended effect of which is to bamboozle the paying punter into mistaking the property for a World Heritage Site.

While my examiner sets up shop behind an oak-effect dining table at one end, I create a performance area at the other. I up-end three black sofas and wobble them out of harm's way against the walls; I heave three golden baroque armchairs out into the hallway, shove a coffee table and a piano into a corner and, despite wearing my only suit, kneel Cinderella-like in the filth I have revealed to pick up a waste-paper-basketful of empty coke cans, sweet papers, chair stuffing material and assorted school-girl detritus. The good-natured Gandalf declares that he is more than satisfied with the arrangements and, with his paperwork spread before him, he sits poised with a hand on his little bell and awaits my departure. I have triumphed: the first candidates are able to start five minutes early.

Under the guilt-inducing gaze of Horatio (since Lincoln, I despise all dogs and their unspoken demands for love and attention), I flop into one of the ornate thrones, take a deep breath and close my eyes. These examinations will succeed despite the obstacles strewn in their path by the Headmaster. It's certainly one way of earning a crust. But then I remember that it's Friday and, as such, my unpaid day off.

37

E'en so here below below

HENRY'S CHRISTMAS LIST

Please Santa, could you

a) Expunge Valerie from the face of the Earth?
b) Send Piers on a three-year Sabbatical?
c) Abolish Christmas?
d) Fulfil all the above whilst at the same time securing me a REAL acting job? Thanks.

I've posted the letter up the chimney and am now terminally bad-tempered.

Hurrah for Christmas! The season devoted to loving one another when actually I despise nearly the whole of humanity; when the Western World is engaged in its annual binge of enforced jollity, superficial family harmony and alcohol-fuelled bonhomie; when we are assailed by the cynical consumerist riot of chintzy marketing, muzak, coloured lights and tinsel; when, because we have sent no Christmas cards this year, even the arrival of the lunchtime postie triggers a gloomy anticipation of guilt as we open yet another glitter-spangled image of a teddy in a Santa hat from a distant relative or ex-friend saying "We really must meet up in the New Year".

Have Valerie and Piers done this to me? I used to be such a happy-go-lucky chap in the old days, a positively chirpy Christmas Elf.

I am more resentful even than usual because I have abandoned the womb-like comfort of my cottage and dragged myself into downtown Bridlington on a dark grey Sunday afternoon. It has somehow come to light that I am (or was in my heyday) a Grade 8 French Horn player and I have been obliged to root under my desk and pull out the dusty urinal-shaped case containing my old instrument of torture. For the benefit of the specialists amongst us, the horn is a British-built Paxman Series 2 endowed with the Mereweather System, about which there is little to say except that after a decade of neglect it needs oiling. I have already worn out my lip warming the damned thing up and have received impassioned phone calls from neighbours begging me to desist.

But why do I have the bitter taste of brass in my mouth? Because I am to perform at Piers' second most important marketing and self-aggrandisement event of the School year, the Christmas Carol Concert. Like Speech day, this is a three-line whip event and one's absence would jeopardise the receipt of Piers' Christmas Gift to the staff: a Harrods Limited Edition Christmas Pudding with Brandy Butter. Last year two of my colleagues failed to materialise in the church and were deprived of a lavish Marks and Spencers presentation bottle of champagne nestling in a blue silk-lined box.

I shell out vast amounts of cash to park the car, grab my horn and head for the Church of St Bartholomew, surprised that our empire-building Headmaster hasn't already had it reconsecrated as St Piers-over-the-Hill. I can just make out the silhouette of the tower two hundred yards away when a distant but horribly familiar screech reaches my ears. Heard but unseen in the gloaming, members of the bagpipe band are warming up amongst the tombstones. Momentarily unhinged by the noise, a suicidal seagull plummets earthwards and is impaled upon the iron railings of a family tomb. Monica, the local bag-lady is dislodged from her roost in the south porch and skitters screaming through the lych-gate before throwing herself fatally under oncoming traffic. Shouts of bewilderment and horror, lights flicking on in tall Georgian houses overlooking the churchyard, doors opening a crack, sawn-off shotgun barrels pointed out, volleys of bullets fired wildly and indiscriminately into the night. At the West Door, drummers beat a tattoo as I join members of the congregation and enter the church.

We are ceremonially greeted by a daunting double phalanx of gowned prefects all desperate to show deference to Piers by fervently shaking our hands. And there he is at the top of the stairs in his full regalia: double ermine hooded gown flowing down his back over what look like vicar's robes. He lifts the latter a few enticing inches:

"Wouldn't you like to know what I'm wearing underneath this lot, Mr Robson?" he smirks conspiratorially.

"My curiosity knows *almost* no bounds, Headmaster."

"I see you've come to play with your horn."

"Yes, I was up polishing it all night. You'll be able to see it gleaming at the back of the nave."

"Oh, matron!" he giggles. I lean towards him and whisper:

"Just a question of finding an appreciative knave, eh, headmaster?"

Our puerile repartee is brought to a timely close by the arrival of a bouffonned caricature European parent clad in a voluminous fur-collared red coat, shiny green high heels and black leather trousers.

"Good evenink, Hetmaaster," she drawls, pulling off her gloves.

"Ah, Mrs Van ... erm ... Roibotsch, how nice to see you." He bows slightly, twisting his body in awkward and unctuous obsequiousness. "Mr Robson, show the lady to her seat."

"Sank, you, Hetmaaster, I ken mennitch," she simpers; and as she sweeps up the transept Piers murmurs into my ear his stock judgement about her sexual orientation.

The orchestra is a motley collection of local instrumentalists who are paid a small stipend to turn out unrehearsed each year to pay homage to Piers and witness this peculiar event. Our job is to play the nine carols louder than the organ, a role that we relish but one at which we fail. My playing is not as accurate or conscientious as it once was and I am giggled at by the nearest pupils as I fart and grimace from the back row of the band. The service begins with the guttural roar of "School!" from the Bulgarian head boy. At this signal the bagpipers let loose, and Piers, the star of the show, processes up the aisle behind his staff and prefects. He moves slowly in what he supposes to be the regal and stately style of an Archbishop of Canterbury, but the effect is actually more late Jurassic; for the fake ermine hood squats on his back like the hump of an ageing iguanodon.

The first verse of *Once in Royal* is sung by an obese Spanish pupil of mine whose voice reminds me of Alessandro Moreschi, the last castrato whose 1902 recordings cause grown men to cross their legs and think of England. However, he is more endurable than the girl whose trendily crooned version of *Away in a Manger* is a satanical semi-tone flat.

We all know that Piers has hired this lofty church in order to pretend that he is the Master of Eton College and to pay lip service to the English traditions he craves. But Gussage Court music is a hit and miss affair, sometimes reaching a high point when a particularly talented pupil is allowed behind the microphone (O where is the art of vocal projection? *Gone, Philomel!*) but more often degenerating into a rowdy cross between African street singing and a disconsolate primary school choir. The orchestra soon loses heart, discouraged by the volume of Mr Evans' organ, and the lesson readers are querulous and, in the case of many international recruits, unintelligible. During the fifth lesson, read by a tiny angelic Italian boy (whose alleged late-night forays into internet porn have earned him an unenviable reputation), I rotate my horn and, to the evident disgust of Archie in the front pew, pull out its two main slides and watch the excess oily spittle splatter onto the flagstones. I wonder, especially after *Unto us a Child is born*, what the foreign students make of all this. Although all religions are represented here, what does this ersatz Carols from King's College Cambridge mean to them? And what can the average second or third language English learner make of lines such as 'King of squires supernal' or 'O and A and A and O/Cum cantibus in choro'? Guillaume, a diminutive French lad at my elbow mouths "what ze foeck?", and as a canny explanation I point to the line "This did Herod sore affray/and grievously bewilder". He treats me to his speciality *va te faire foutre* look to which I respond with a Gallic shrug, lose count of my bars rest and miss my next entry. I see other international pupils gazing round the packed church in the vain hope that the torture will soon be over, allowing the boarders' Christmas trip to McDonalds to become a reality.

Not long now. Piers is up in the pulpit giving it large and sonorous with the 'In the beginning was the Word' number, always a favourite with headmasters because it reinforces their own god-like self-image. Then we decimate *Hark the Herald* before Piers announces that it had indeed been his intention to "get through it all within an hour" and, at precisely fifty-six minutes, he is delighted to be able to invite parents back to the School to "sample Matron's world-famous titbits", mince pies and mulled wine by the Christmas tree, this year sponsored by Harrods.

We are allowed out again as Mr Evans launches into a

massacred medley of *Ding Dong Merrily, 633 Squadron* and the Widor *Toccata*. Frankly, I am 'sore affray' at the thought of the combination of Matron's wares and polite conversation with the likes of Mrs Van Roibotsch; after due reflection I plump for going home to hone the script for my school pantomime and draw up a costume and props list for the show.

38

Complete Humiliation

The Medusa Effect is an uncanny phenomenon and something to which I still can't become accustomed. It occurs relatively rarely but involves a classroom of children being suddenly turned to stone. Without warning, a mob of unruly teenagers ceases to roll noisily about on the floor and becomes silent. I will watch entranced as they scrabble to the vertical and then stand perfectly still, eyes downcast. The Medusa Effect is precursor to only one thing: Piers.

"Headmaster," I say without looking round as I perceive the Effect three days after the Carol Service. "Greetings and all manner of hallucinations." Piers has sneaked in (or 'snuck' as the Scooby Doo advocates of American Postmodernism would have it) through my antechamber and is wearing a pirate hat he has picked up from my costume box.

"Ha-harrr!" he rasps, removing the headgear and tossing it onto a small Iranian. "Might I have a word, Mr Robson? I'm sure 2B will be good for a minute, won't you, 2B?" To a mendacious chant of "Yes, sir" we step out onto the cold. I hear the class burst into laughter.

"I want you to schmooze a parent for me," he says. (So, one mega-flounce and I'm immediately promoted to Chosen One.) Piers ushers me into the café and introduces me to a neat and handsome man in a red scarf and a camel-hair coat standing by a steamed-up window. He is almost a head shorter than me but compensates for his lack of stature with expensive Cologne, a glint of diamond cufflinks and a handshake of ferrous intent.

"Mr Robson, this is Mr Kozhevnikov, Yuri and Irakli's father. You're looking after him today – he asked for you specially. He's heard all about your drama lessons." The man actually bows at me; in return, I incline my head with what I hope appears to the foreign dignitary to be true British reserve. I'm mystified. I had assumed that Piers wished me to entertain this bloke on behalf of his deputy; parental flesh-squeezing is Dr Thorpe's domain, but he is away in distant climes at the moment doing his Christmas shopping and selling the concept of Gussage Court to the naïve foreigner. Why have I been specially requested? I'm not in Marketing. I can make polite enquiries into how many more small Kozhevnikovs there are in the Russian pipeline, but after that, what? I'm just a drama teacher.

"Pleased to make your acquaintance, Mr Robson," says Mr Kozhevnikov with a smile of icy politesse and a rich Russian accent. "We take lunch, I believe?"

"I'd be delighted to. But Mr Halliday, who will look after my classes?"

"All covered, Mr Robson, all covered," improvises the Headmaster, turning back to our guest. "As you know, Mr ... erm ... Kojnikova, Mr Robson is our resident Drama Queen and luvvie. To tell you the truth, I don't even know why I still employ him." The gentleman has assumed an expression wherein I detect an internal struggle about whether he should pull out a Luger or run for the Urals. "He storms out of my School now and again, but he always comes back. Can't get rid of him." He opens the door. "Mr Robson, I've asked Ron to bring the Rolls round in ten minutes. He'll take you both down to the Queen's Head."

As our guest turns to gather up his hat and briefcase, Piers leans towards me. "Keep any receipts," he whispers. "Accounts will reimburse you later. This is a VIP, Henry, and I'm relying on you to keep him sweet." He turns to Mr Kozhevnikov. "I'll leave you with this madman, Mr ... erm ... Kojnova ... so, enjoy!"

Grinning inanely, Piers attempts a flamboyant bow in the style of Sir Walter Raleigh but, colliding with a broken sofa behind him, succeeds in only genuflecting like an embarrassed employee during the visit of a minor Royal to an organic ostrich farm. He bustles away to supervise the unloading of our Christmas gifts from the back of a Harrods van.

"A true English eccentric," declares Mr Kozhevnikov.

"I couldn't agree more," I reply as we move towards the door. "But you get used to him in the end."

"I'm sure you do," he growls, pulling on a pair of brown leather gloves.

The bell rings for the end of the lesson and we step out of the café just in time to see 2B erupting from my room and scampering away. I notice with resignation that Lev is myopically daubing ruby gloss onto my classroom door-frame. It's already too late for 2B, but now somebody (and evidently it won't be me) will have to spend the afternoon standing guard at the door and screaming warnings; and despite all efforts, dozens of bespoke School blazers will be smeared irreparably. Why does Piers do this? Why can't he wait another day or two until the holidays begin?

Time for small talk. "Do you approve of Mr Halliday's choice of colour?" I enquire.

"I have never been keen on lime green, Mr Robson. It is a known psychological depressant. But the dark red he has selected to set it off is slightly more to my taste. To be honest with you, it has a dried blood quality that reminds me of deeds of great courage, honour and revenge. We value that sort of thing most highly in my country." *This lunch date is going to be a hoot.* "But this is the Rolls, is it not? I have never been in such a splendid old car."

"Nor have I," I own. "It will be a treat and an honour for the both of us."

"Exactly, Mr Robson. An honour."

Ron, one of Piers' long-suffering coach-drivers and *ad hoc* chauffeur, draws up beside us and I open the back door of the Rolls for my companion. Having carefully placed his attaché case on the carpeted floor, Mr Kozhevnikov climbs in and arranges himself upon the plush beige leather upholstery. He puts me in mind of an elderly dowager; his fur hat perched like a cat on his knees and his shiny brown shoes clicked tightly together. He is a curious cross between Hercule Poirot and Miss Marple. As I climb in, I nod to Ron and raise my downstage eyebrow.

"Queen's Head, driver, and don't spare the 'orses!"

"Very good, m'lady." Judging from Ron's Parker impression, I am willing to bet that he is an aficionado of *Thunderbirds*.

Dornford Yates' heroes such as Jonathan Mansel and Richard Chandos regularly hurtle through Europe in Rolls Royces just like this one. Their chauffeurs-cum-batmen are ex-infantrymen called Carson and Bell respectively, and are such splendid chaps (considering their lowly social class) that they can be relied upon not only to buff up the coachwork of their masters' Rollers but also to sling a gun or a punch should either of said deities be in mortal danger. Briefly I allow myself to imagine that I am Jonathan Mansel on my way to face down some unutterable villain in the Pyrenees, but a gentle kozhevnicough reminds me that I must try to concentrate on fulfilling my role as Piers' Ambassador on Earth and entertain my Russian friend. I say Russian, but now I come to think of it, I'm sure Irakli was fiercely Chechen. And then, as we turn into the pub car park, it occurs to me that this little man must therefore be the Chechen Chief of Police. Mr K is the father of Irakli, the under-age driver with the house in the mountains and the car wrapped around a 'street-lump'. Irakli's older brother is none other than Yuri, last year's diminutive Head Boy. Oh my Lord, Piers is making me lunch one of the most powerful and dangerous men ever to send a child to an English boarding school.

Once ensconced near the log fire, Mr K opens up by extolling the virtues of the English countryside. He pauses after ten minutes and I feel obliged to move my schmooze machine into top gear and drain my sump of thespian anecdotes. Mr K becomes somewhat taciturn as I describe the Camden anti-canine campaign and I have the feeling that he does not quite approve of my puerile lack of gravitas. We then clarify that he has only two sons and that his wife and he are separated. Having nearly drained a pint of English beer each, we sit silently for a moment considering the remains of his Stilton Ploughmans and my more effeminate Prawn Cocktail. I am just beginning to formulate the precise wording for some quip about never having dined with a Chief of Police before when he startles me into rapt and egotistical attention with some praise for my teaching methods.

"So, Mr Robson, Irakli has been telling me about your drama lessons. They sound very lively. In fact, both my boys have very much enjoyed your company and guidance."

I can't resist a verbal nod towards Oscar Wilde: "'I do my best to give satisfaction, sir'," I say, "and I have always enjoyed working with your sons. They are most enthusiastic and polite young gentlemen. But thank you, anyway, Mr Kozhevnikov." This would be the moment for him to say "Call me Sergei, Henry."

"Mr Robson, you may now be reduced to teaching drama but at heart I detect you are still an actor."

Self pity wells up. "Shall we say *failed* actor?" I murmur.

"I wonder then whether you would like an opportunity to do some real acting once more, Mr Robson? I know how frustrating it must be for you to be working here for your Mr Halliday when in fact ideally you would like to be on location somewhere with Steven Spielberg. Am I right?"

"Well, I do still have an agent and very occasionally I find some acting work. But Spielberg may indeed have overlooked both my potential and my existence."

My companion smiles. "Show me that you are an actor of courage and personality and I will be – we will all be – in your debt." He pauses and leans closer to me. "Yuri told me how grateful he was for your concern after Speech Day." He now has my full attention, but I have no idea precisely what he wants from me. I wonder whether the local beer may have been too much for such a small man. Also, he has failed to utter that keenly anticipated cliché, "and I'll make it worth your while".

"I'm sure I'd love to help," I say, still quasi-marine (by which I mean 'somewhat at sea'). "But for whom would I be working?"

"For me and my sons, Mr Robson, and also for one or two other people."

"Ah."

"Yes. It is work in what I understand to be your own area of expertise: the English pantomime tradition. I am aware that you are rehearsing such a thing for the end of term and I need you to participate in it yourself to – how would you say? – create a fitting climax to the proceedings." The bloke knows how to work my actorish ego; I already feel a buzz of excitement at the thought of showing off in front of the baying punters. "And furthermore, Mr Robson," he continues, pulling a sheet of paper out of his attaché case, "I shall need you to write in a short scene for me as well. At the end of the show would be ideal, I think. What I have in mind, and of which I have penned a short précis here, will not be an easy act to follow, if you take my meaning, Mr Robson."

I certainly do not, but feel somehow that clarification is in the offing. He hands me the piece of paper which I read with a heady mix of thespian excitement, disbelief and finally, alarm.

"Mr Kozhevnikov," I splutter, fiddling with my spoon, "I really don't think that I can be involved in this sort of caper." I hold out the paper for him but he makes no move to take it from me.

"This 'caper', do you call it? – I have not come across the word – has your name written all over it. I have taken the liberty of speaking to your Agent, (Agent P, don't you affectionately call him?) and he is perfectly willing to accept a bankers draft from me to cover any expenses you might incur in costume hire and so on. It's up to you to let him know. A fee I am not in a position to offer, morally speaking, but Agent P is perfectly willing to waive this little matter in exchange for any contacts in film production I might be able to put his way – and, by definition, *your* way – in the future. I was able to persuade him that I could be very useful to him. We all do what we can to help each other during these difficult times."

"You have *contacts*?" I gasp.

"Of course. In my line of work, Mr Robson, I meet very many interesting and influential people. Your Headmaster is wise enough to recognise the advantages of my, shall we say? – gregarious nature in the world of big business."

The obnoxious little man is surely bullshitting me, so I decide to ignore his boasting. "I can't believe you've actually spoken to Agent P? He never told me."

"It was only an hour or so ago and he was just rushing out to catch a plane. Maybe he has already sent you an encouraging text?"

I pull out my phone but there are no messages; confirmation that the man is a fantasist.

"If there's no fee, then what's in it for me, Mr Kozhevnikov?"

"You will do this partly out of the goodness of your heart and partly because I'm sure you can't resist dressing up as a woman again and showing off! I've read your CV, Mr Robson. Ugly Sisters seem to be your forte. Also, I know what you feel about Mr Halliday, professional discretion not being your strongest suit." I feel myself blushing and notice that my right forefinger is moving a beer mat around the table. "It might be a good time to get a move on with organising the requisite costumes and wigs, don't you think? May I suggest we draw this charming meeting to a close in order for you to make some phone calls?"

"I have not yet agreed to this absurd plan," I say, a sudden sweatiness breaking out in my armpits and crutch. "And I'm not sure Mr Halliday would agree to participate."

"Mr Halliday is not and will *never be* in a position to disagree with anything I suggest, Mr Robson. Since the unfortunate conflagration of his admin block, he and I understand each other absolutely. And you will remember what happened to RJ, that busybody American who thought he could get the better of me. How wrong he was." Mr Kozhevnikov leans towards me and places a perfectly manicured hand on my sleeve. "Mr Halliday knows where he stands, Mr Robson. As, I suspect, do you." He smiles thinly and gestures to the barman to make up our bill. "So, we are all agreed? You'll do it?"

"Much as I would like to help you out, Mr Kozhevnikov, I think I am going to have to say No this time. I have my job to consider." This is sounding like Custer's last stand. "And what would the pupils think? What you're asking me to do is neither honourable nor a good example to young people."

He smiles broadly this time. I am transfixed by a small dark red spot in the white of his right eye.

"Aha," he chuckles. "You speak again of honour? Yes, of course, the Englishman and his moral code. In my country, we too set great store by such things. Allow me to play something for you, my dear Mr Robson. I think it will amuse you immensely. It certainly amuses me."

Mr Kozhevnikov reaches down and produces the most slimline laptop I have ever seen. It makes Apple's latest offerings look like chunks of Stonehenge. He opens it, whispers something Russian into its electronic ear and then turns the screen towards me.

"Do you care for the art of ornithology, Mr Robson?" A cold breeze drifts through my abdomen and ruffles the feathers of a profound and as yet unacknowledged malaise.

"I don't know whether I would have called ornithology an art, Mr Kozhevnikov."

"I'm sure that – if I may coin a phrase – a *cunning linguist* such as yourself will appreciate the art of knowing just where and when to be hiding to be able to catch the two birds in the one bush, if I may abuse that most poetic of your English metaphors." Something between a snigger and a belch emits from deep in his thorax as a still photograph flips onto the screen; with a jolt of nausea I realise that he or his birdwatching spies have captured Valerie and me walking down a lane towards an isolated cemetery. Kozhevnikov dabs at a button which starts a video, the camera following us into the supposed privacy of a secluded field with a Norman church behind. I sit as if petrified as the opening of Beethoven's Pastoral Symphony seeps from hidden speakers in the infernal machine.

"My intrepid cameraman shot some admirable footage," smirks Mr Kozhevnikov, "which bears witness to the entire gamut of your sexual frolics that day. I won't play it all now; we haven't time. I'm only sorry you were put off your stride by a tickle in his throat. He sends his apologies, by the way. He was so hoping to catch 'the sun on your bum', as he put it. Let me cut to the end." He flicks a button and there is Valerie propped up on one elbow and I can almost hear her saying "Well, hurry up and sort yourself out." As I remember only too well, success is not destined to crown my supreme efforts that afternoon.

My double humiliation almost complete, I reach out to stop the performance before we reach the moment when Valerie gives up watching me and starts to get dressed; but the iron grip of my torturer stops my interference.

"You have an unorthodox sexual relationship with Valerie," he persists, still smiling. *How does he know her name?* "I enjoyed some very funny moments when you became artistic with Nutella. You English, you make me laugh. I should have used caviar – more spreadable!" He gives a Chechen chortle. "But I will admit, she is a very beautiful woman indeed. Congratulations on your catch. I'm only sorry you don't seem to be able to keep up with her, Mr Robson." He gestures towards the screen as the final images show my ultimate failure amidst heart-rendingly comic scenes of terminal flaccidity and wilt. "What value do we men place upon 'the bird in the hand'? – if I may once again desecrate your delicious language."

Unable to speak and suddenly regretting the prawn cocktail, I am remembering how, during the love-making débâcle that day, I was sure that we were being watched. As if able to read my thoughts, the Chief of Police, well practised presumably in this sort of interview, goes on: "It must be a great disadvantage to be quite so short-sighted. I am sorry for you," he says and squeezes my arm. "I'm not so sure, however, that Mr Halliday or his senior management would be so sympathetic when I email this fly-on-the-wall docu-soap material to their personal computers. I know your employer likes to be entertained late at night, but I think even he would draw the line here." He fixes me with a stare. "However, I wouldn't be so cruel as to send hard copies to her estranged husband. I wouldn't want to rub salt into his wounds. Frankly, it would have been better if he had gone to Kuwait with only the one shoe-lace, would it not?"

He pauses and finishes his beer. "I also have a charming photographic sequence taken at an hotel in Lincoln. Such a bad dog, Christine's dog, wasn't it? The pictures are rather grainy, but my ornithologist was working in conditions far from ideal. From the cathedral roof, as it happens. I'm sure though that Christine's current husband – not to mention Valerie herself –

would be most intrigued to see them." He pauses again. "It is fortunate that the daughter Millie is at an age too tender legally to appreciate such adult material." He smiles. "Do you not agree, Mr Robson?"

A torrent of fear floods my body. He knows everything about me. I am awash with terror and impotence in the face of overwhelming odds stacked in favour of my complete vilification and annihilation. I am nothing more than an insignificant failure of a man pitted against an international machine whose tentacles have explored every part of my vulnerable underbelly.

"I see," I whisper.

"I knew you would understand, Mr Robson. An actor cannot resist a good plot, can he?"

"What do you want me to do?"

"Simply to arrange the scene in your pantomime, as described on this sheet."

"And if I do?"

"Then I shall delete the video like this, and then delete it permanently from my hard drive like this." Shivering, I watch as he causes the file to vanish from his screen. "And then," he says, pulling a tiny silver USB stick from his breast pocket, "I shall send your Agent this. He will post it on to you thinking it is a copy of your showreel I have seen. Quite a performance, eh?" He laughs aloud. "That way, no direct contact is required. I don't imagine Agent P will take the trouble to watch it though, do you? After all, you're not one of his, shall we say? – significant clients. You will retrieve this stick if you're shrewd and cunning enough, and we both know that cunning and deception are two of your greatest strengths. My instinct is never to trust an actor, but on this occasion, I think I can trust you to give the performance of your life. We do not take kindly to humiliation in my country either. It is a matter of honour for us."

I fold his sheet of paper up and stuff it into my pocket as the barman takes his gold credit card. I have nothing to say and can no longer look at him.

"I can promise you, Mr Robson," he says confidentially as we go back out to the Rolls (Ron's fast asleep), "I am a man of my word. Do my little job next week and you will hear no more from me. And I have kept only the one copy of the film, I promise you. I shall have no further need of it after the pantomime."

We arrive back at school towards the end of lesson seven.

"You're a bit quiet, Mr Robson," says Ron as I climb out of the car. "Good lunch, was it?"

"Most entertaining," my guest replies for me. "But I think the thrust of my conversation may have been too much for our Actor-in-Residence! Goodbye and thank you, Mr Robson. I'll see you before curtain-up! Make those phone calls now!" He shakes my hand and bows. "I'm a 42 chest, by the way!"

As I watch him disappear round the corner of the building, my phone burps and there is a message from Agent P.

> Gd luck with show.
> Ur perfect casting!
> Hell of a guy, yr
> friend. Thx for the
> contact. Send pix.

39

R.S.V.P.

On the table in front of me is the opened Harrods package from Piers; will I really be able to manage a whole Christmas pudding by myself or should I be charitable and give it to Daphne and Barbara to squabble over at the sheltered housing development down the lane? My landline rings.

"Hi. It's me."

"Oh." *Christ.*

"I'm fine, thanks for asking."

My hackles rise. What can she possibly want? "Look, I'm sorry about what happened that time. I shouldn't have come round."

"Forget it, Valerie," I say, as evenly as possible. "How can I help?"

"I want to invite you for an early Christmas." *What?* "It'll be a good opportunity to start afresh. It's not been an easy few weeks for either of us." *She's certifiable.* "My parents are going away for Christmas itself," she informs me irrelevantly, "and

I've invited them down next weekend for a celebration before they go." Would I be justified in pulling the phone cable out of the wall? "I've never cooked them a meal by myself before. Not since leaving my husband. It's a big thing for me, Henry, and I need you there for moral support."

"The answer's no, Valerie. Don't be absurd."

"My mother doesn't think I should have anything more to do with you, Henry, but I've told her it's my life and I'm inviting you. You have to prove her wrong for me."

"Oh. Good plan, Valerie. That's really tempting." I have never managed quite to reel in the fierce matriarch; unusual for me because I'm normally pretty good with the older lady, but despite my best efforts at tactical flirtatiousness, I have been unable to dent her intuitively maintained carapace of mistrust. The tool-kit incident had done nothing to improve the situation. "You're mad. Of course I'm not coming – or were you planning to allow me to meet Millie at this late stage?"

"Don't be silly, Henry. That would be really awkward for everyone."

"You don't say."

"I have invited my sister though, so you definitely need to come too."

"What, the dreaded socio-feministopath sister who hates me? *That* sister?"

"Yes, she's coming down specially on Sunday morning. And she doesn't hate you. She's never said she hated you. She just doesn't trust public schoolboys. Please say Yes, Henry."

"No."

"Henry, please. For me."

"No, Valerie, it's an awful idea. Thanks anyway."

"Alright," she wheedles, "not for the whole weekend. Just for a nice meal on Saturday night. You, me and my parents." Grown-up and civilised like a happily married couple. "You must come, Henry. You must."

Is she crying? I would rather have my testicles impaled on red-hot kebab skewers than accept such an invitation. "Please, Henry. You can stay over. My parents are heavy sleepers."

40

Rank Humiliation

True to form, I cave in and accept Valerie's invitation. I justify my cowardice by telling myself that I am simply being kind and charitable, that I have no ulterior sexual motive born of screaming desperation, and after what we have been through, an evening of best behaviour with overtly polite but subtextually hostile parents might not *necessarily* turn nasty. An actor with his balls on the bacon slicer might be able to survive and triumph by treating the ordeal as performance art. I shall rise to the occasion into which I have been thrust, acting myself into a veritable lather in the rôle of Good Chap to putative parents-in-law. God, imagine being *married* to Valerie.

Under the watchful eye of the mother, a burly blonde Hausfrau whose vast presence dominates the house, Valerie is perhaps slightly more aloof even than usual. I am careful not to incur her wrath by invading her space, but it is particularly hard tonight because she is dressed to kill, playing her Tantalising Bottom card by wearing her tightest pair of green trousers, the sight of which makes my fingers tingle; I long to kneel down before her, cup her buttocks with both hands, and soothe my addled brow between those firm thighs. She is also modelling a new black silk chemise, open at the neck to show off an intoxicating cleavage and a triangle of smooth pale chest, adorned in my honour with the necklace I bought her in Earlham Street. Her scent is everywhere and, powerless against such artistry, I feast my eyes. There is nothing Valerie-lite about her this evening; she is purring with an unusual erotic energy and I know I'm in trouble.

She needs no help from me to prepare the meal; my job is to buttle, keep the dining-room fire alight and entertain her parents with actorish anecdotes, avoiding any mention of future plans. We sit like early Victorians in the echoing and candlelit dining room, eating delicately and appreciatively, complimenting the cook and making the smallest of talk. And after the meal, as if by some pre-arranged signal, the female ancestor looks at her husband and they rise in unison from the table.

"Valerie, darling," she intones, "it's been really lovely, hasn't it, John?" Her diminutive spouse nods and grunts. "But we've had a long drive and need our beauty sleep."

"Long day," agrees John, expansively.

"It's been so nice to meet you, Henry," adds the mother in a manner which by no means convinces me. "We'll see you in the morning, shall we?"

"Bright and early," I reply. "Will Modom be taking breakfast in bed?"

Valerie gives me a look which says 'Don't over-egg it, love' and kisses her parents goodnight. I incline my head formally, as befits a butler.

"Let me do the washing up," I say, as soon as the door closes.

"No, don't be silly. Come and sit down here by the fire."

I join her on the tiny sheepskin rug and put the last log into the flames. Many is the time we have squatted here like Bedouins (but without the benefit of cushions), and I know the drill; I am aware that I shouldn't, but in a spirit of seasonal forgiveness and slightly muzzy after too much venison, red cabbage and potato *au gratin* (not to mention nearly two glasses of some rather acrid red wine courtesy of the parentals), I engage in my well-practised, slow-motion foreplay. I rub her feet, pushing my fingers between her toes to splay and stretch them. I caress her legs, pushing a hand up inside her trousers and squeezing her calves. She then turns, settles her head into my lap and closes her eyes so that I can massage her scalp by entwining my fingers in her hair and pulling it gently but firmly in the way she loves. We talk of this and that – the latest divorce, her holiday plans – but I do not regale her with what (apart from the obvious) is foremost in my mind: any mention of Mr Kozhevnikov and his ornithological studies is bound to unnerve even the most resilient of hostesses. Valerie and I will be finished sooner or later and I will keep those horrors to myself.

Just when I think she'll never suggest bed, Valerie gets up and stretches. Unobserved, I breathe in the exquisite scent of her hair on my fingers. I am lost.

"I need you to rub my back too," she says. "I've been cooking all day. Come upstairs."

Suffused with a familiar and dangerous excitement, I obediently follow that delicious bottom up the stairs, my heart – despite my best and earlier intentions – bubbling once more with longing and anticipation. A low murmur of voices ceases as we creep past Valerie's own bedroom door. The parents are bitching about me in the only double bed in the house. And then suddenly, I begin to feel sick: I know what Valerie is going to say next.

She closes the spare bedroom door quietly behind us.

"Henry, I feel a bit awkward saying this after you've been so fab this evening, but the thing is that I don't have any room for you tonight." She pauses to look at herself in a mirror. I notice her mobile phone on a chest of drawers, its little blue light flashing. She picks it up and reads the message. "My sister'll be here at about ten tomorrow," she says, after a pause. "Do you mind very much going home, Henry? I'm so tired."

"So, why am I in your bedroom?" I start. "Why am I here at all? I thought we were doing the Happy-Ever-After routine for your parents. You absolutely bloody insisted I came tonight as a favour to you. They're even expecting me to take them breakfast in bed, for Christ's sake!"

"Don't raise your voice, you'll wake them up," she hisses. "I never promised anything, Henry. And please don't start all this needy stuff again, I can't bear it. You're the one who's always wanting us to break up. You can't have it both ways. Just be nice and undo me please and then you can rub my back." She turns away and lifts her hair for me to fiddle with the miniature clasp on the necklace. My fingers brush her skin, a tiny contact which nevertheless shoots an electric charge through me. I lean forward to kiss the nape of her neck, but she spins away and begins to undo the buttons of her shirt. This is soon tossed to the floor and then she is on the edge of the bed slipping off her trousers. She allows me the briefest of tantalising glimpses of the body I have worshipped and known so well; one moment she is poised there in her black underwear (which, come to think of it, I don't recognise) and the next, the bra and knickers are off and, like that bloody Waterhouse mermaid diving back into the foam, she has slithered out of sight under the duvet. I carefully lay out the necklace along the mantlepiece.

"Rub my back, I said, Henry. Please."

With a buzzing in my ears far beyond my usual tinnitus, I remove my glasses and kneel by the bed. If I were a child, I would say my prayers now. God Bless Mummy, God Bless Daddy, God make her be kind to me. I slip my hands gingerly under the duvet. She is lying on her front, facing away from me, waiting for my touch. I run both hands up and down the smooth warm curve of her spine and when I have re-familiarised myself with the beloved contours, I set to work kneading the muscles until I find the knots. She moans quietly with pleasure. My fingers and thumbs know what to do and I press firmly into the moist satin of her skin, just hard enough to release the tension, just softly enough not to hurt her. The tips of my fingers slide down below her hips, smoothing their way into the soft flesh of her buttocks. I am leaning forward now, my face resting on the duvet, on her back, my eyes closed. I can hear the rhythmical beating of her heart. My own crashes and jolts as I suppress an urge to scream, to throw myself upon her, against her, inside her. My hands move ever downwards, squeezing the buttocks, rubbing the backs of her thighs as far as I can reach, and then up again between her legs and gently, oh so gently around those delicious curves which so tenderly guide a man onwards. My fingertips brush against the first of those tiny moist hairs, guardians of her inner temple across whose warm threshold I so long to pass.

Suddenly she squirms onto her side away from me. "Henry, stop it, what the hell are you doing?" I begin to loosen my belt, tugging at the buckle and undoing the waist button of my chinos. "What is the matter with you?" she snaps. "Don't you dare get undressed! Kiss me goodnight and let me get some sleep."

"Please, Valerie," I mutter, "please. I'm begging you. Just let me give you a cuddle. I won't stay the night, I promise. Come on, it's Christmas." I pull my shirt over my head and try to take her in my arms. The touch of her bare shoulders against my skin is more than I can bear.

And then, to my amazement, she flashes me a wonderful smile. I am not dreaming this.

"Alright, you win. As it's Christmas." She reaches out and deftly unzips my flies. "Come on then, my naughty schoolboy, let's see what you're made of."

Within seconds, I am standing naked beside her. She reaches out and taps the end of my penis. "Mmm, what have we here, then?"

I have no words.

"So you still think I'm a beautiful woman, do you, big man?" She reaches up and strokes the hairs below my tummy button with a crooked index finger. "Yes, I think you still find me sexy. Do you want to check, just to make sure?" And with a sudden flick of her wrist she folds the duvet back and stretches out like a goddess, displaying for me her whole body, writhing almost imperceptibly and gleaming golden in the light of the bedside lamp.

She wants me at last; she is offering herself to me to kiss, to stroke, to explore, to lick, to make love with. I am stunned by this action – so unlike the Valerie I know – frozen with fascination, transfixed by the glory of her form. The warm smell of her assails my nostrils and I gulp down the saliva pouring into my mouth.

"My god, Valerie," I swallow. "I want you so much."

"Then I'm all yours, Henry," she giggles. "I want you to explode for me."

'Penetration' now being only moments away, I begin to sob, my breath coming in spasms. "Thank you, thank you."

"Worship me, Henry," she smiles. "*Watch* me and show me your desire. Stand over there by the door and have the orgasm of your life. And I shall lie here, watching you and knowing how much you love me." *What had she said?* With the buzzing now so intense, my heart pounding, my whole body pulsating with exquisite pain, I must have misheard her. "Go on, then," she urges, "or I shall get cold." Her own left hand moves between her legs and I can just make out her middle finger beginning to flex up and down amongst the tangle of dark hair. With her free hand she pushes a box of tissues across the bedside table. "Use these when you've sorted yourself out. Try not to drip on the carpet. The landlord will be cross."

And then suddenly she reaches out again and clasps me firmly in her hand. I cry out "Don't, Valerie! Don't touch me there – not *now*!" She quickly withdraws her hand but it is too late. I see her smile as, with a moan of pain and joy, I erupt. In an effort not to sully her, I fall back against the wall, slide to the floor weeping uncontrollably, sobbing with animal release and humiliation and the realisation of what has happened, of the depths to which I have sunk in my obsession with this viper.

I feel for my glasses and with everything back in focus, reach for the tissue box and wipe up as best I can. There are blobs of semen on the carpet, on my trousers, on her bra. She has snuggled back under the duvet and is peering at me, the remains of a triumphant smile still playing about her lips. Short of choking the life out of her, all I desire now is to gather up my clothes and leave her presence for ever.

I hear a little voice say, "Better now?"

I remain silent.

"Don't sulk, Henry," she taunts. "Talk to me."

"I have nothing to say."

"What, the great Henry Robson, actor and Lothario at a loss for words? This can't be right. What were you saying before that unfortunate occurrence, that *premature* exhibition of virility? Were you going to say how beautiful I am, how much you adore me, how much you want sex with me and – blah blah blah." She pulls the duvet tighter around her shoulders.

I find my voice. "I see it all clearly now, my *love*. I didn't just want sex, and you know it. That's the whole point. I wanted to make love with you, not to end up wanking over you like that poor sod your ex-husband. I didn't want *this*." I throw the wad of sodden tissues across the room. "Can't you understand?"

"Oh, I understand everything about you." She is up on one elbow now, her eyes flashing with fury. "Poor ickle Henry never had a proper Mummy, did he?" she sneers, "and he's spent his whole life looking for a replacement. Well, guess what, I'm no longer in the market. I've had enough of your pathetic neediness, your obsessions and your whining. If you don't want love on my terms, then you can fuck off out of my house."

I am standing naked, my clothes clasped to my chest. Not the moment to share Happy Thoughts about my First Mother. "Your ex-husband was right about one thing, though."

"What?"

"About you being a frigid fucking weirdo, that's what. I expect he rejoiced when I came and released him from his marriage vows."

"You bastard."

"And good luck to any other man who follows in our misguided footsteps."

I open the door. "One other thing, Henry," she whispers, with the faintest hint of a smile, a surreal touch under the circumstances. "Have fun with your pantomime next week."

I shiver as I feel my way down the stairs. Through my tinnitus I hear a voice murmuring "It's ok, he's just leaving". Have the ancestors overheard the whole episode?

I creep away from that house for another last time, leaving the front door unlocked for once. With a bit of luck, a band of masked marauders will break in and slay them all in their beds.

As I drive out of the village, I notice a long black limousine parked in the lay-by opposite the Post Office. Another rich teenager being collected from some drunken Christmas party. How lovely to be so cherished.

41

Enquire Within

The following Thursday evening finds me sitting in the gloaming, hunched before my computer and chewing disconsolately on some rubbery peanut-butter-and-honey toast. In a vain attempt to blot out memories of the cataclysmic last scene of my liaison with Valerie, I have already phoned my First Mother (who blames the inclement weather for not feeling 'a hundred percent, darling') and have now reverted to fretting darkly about Mr Kozhevnikov. His extra scene is causing me a good deal of trouble not only because it is in danger of turning my fluffy pantomime into a Five Act Tragedy, but also because I don't know whether either of my unrehearsable Guest Stars can act. I suppose this is the price of adultery and blackmail. I have ordered the costumes as commanded and am reading the script through aloud to make sure there are no glaring missed opportunities for ribaldry, satire, bitterness or bile. Periodically, I leap to my feet and conduct choice passages from my favourite CD, currently *French Overtures* conducted by Ernest Ansermet.

In short, I am mouldering.

It is then particularly disconcerting to hear a knock at the door just as Ernest and I are about to embark upon that boisterous finale to *Orphée aux Enfers*. Who could it be at this time of the evening? Please let it not be Valerie riding on a high moral wave of magnanimity to forgive me my trespasses and corner me into negotiating the parameters of a renewed relationship. Anything but that.

I fight off the temptation to hide, pause the CD and, steeling myself to receive either absolution or a flood of invective from an incandescent apparition in a grey coat and red scarf, I cautiously open the door. However, silhouetted against the light of the pub car park is a tall lady whose presence on my threshold sparks a positive flurry of Dornford Yates relief and excitement in my diaphragm. Thank god I'm not already in my Noel Coward dressing gown.

> *I cannot believe that any man, high or low, that ever met her, will ever forget the first time she crossed his path. For myself, my whole being thrilled, just as a bowl will quiver to some particular chord – not because she was so good-looking or because her air was so proud, but because her charm was compelling and had ridden over my spirit before I knew where I was. Though her manner was careless, vitality burned in her eyes, and I never saw on a woman a keener, more resolute face. Her head was well set on, and her features were fine and clean-cut: she was tall and slim and well-made.*

Pausing only to recite the above passage to myself, I stand back and invite her in. *Did I not once see her on a train?*

"Hi. Sorry to disturb so late," begins my visitor, slightly flustered, "but I was passing on my way to the pub and saw your light on. I wondered whether I had the right door. Are you Henry Robson, perchance?" *Perchance? Who, apart from me, employs such archaic vocables?*

"Undeniably," I reply, feasting my eyes upon her as far as I can without actually dribbling. "Come in, come in."

"I'm Matilda Lattimer," she declares, glancing round at my bachelor squalor. "I live just over the Green. We moved down a few months ago. My husband's in London most of the time, though."

She is a remarkably beautiful woman, tall and blonde, wearing a beige puffer jacket, an Indian scarf and black suede boots with alarmingly pointy toes. Although they must be torture to wear, they make her so tall that, as she shakes my hand (*Yes! I recognise the rings!*) I find I can look her straight in the eye. Which I do, causing something inside me to melt.

"Haven't I seen you walking a Dalmatian?" I begin, trying to quash a flash of disappointment that Matilda must be another doggie person like a soprano I once knew.

"I sometimes walk Lottie, the neighbour's dog," she parries, as if reading my innermost thoughts. "It gets me out of the house."

Relieved, I offer my guest a cup of tea to encourage her to come clean about her presence in my front room.

"Tea?" she says with what seems to be almost a sigh as she takes off her jacket and scarf. "Yes, please."

"Mind your head," I say, as I duck through into the kitchen and fill the kettle. "I'm afraid I've only got Lapsang or Earl Grey. I can do you a mixture if you prefer but I'm clean out of builders'."

"Lappers for me, please," she says, evidently the sort of properly educated girl with whom I can do business. "Thing is, a woman in the butchers said you gave French lessons."

"*C'est vrai, Madame,*" I reply pretentiously, shrugging and splaying my hands in the Gallic manner. "I have been known in my time to oblige would-be French house-purchasers with conversational practice." (It is a talent I have and one which has spun me a little money in times of trial and desperation. I keep quiet about it for fear of being asked to teach French at Gussage Court, something which would only lead to daily *contretemps* with the defenders of the National Curriculum.) "Do you need lessons?"

"Well, actually I do," she goes on, "but not until January. My husband's in air-conditioning and he's coerced me into spending Christmas in Dubai. His chosen contribution to global warming is to keep the world's richest golfers cool in some god-awful new hotel complex." She pauses, absent-mindedly running her finger along Cecil's set of Dornford Yates. She doesn't seem, even at this early stage of our acquaintance, to be a girl likely to relish life as a golf widow.

"*Pas de problème, Madame,*" I simper, emptying my teapot into the compost bowl. I must take on this Matilda at whatever the cost to my school work. "I don't have much free time either at the moment. I've a lot on at School – pantos and things – you know how it is."

"Yes, I'm a teacher as well," she definitely sighs this time. "Spanish and French. Started in September at St Anthony's up the road. My Spanish is fine, but now they tell me I need to brush up on my spoken French to do their bloody immersion teaching. It's a stupid idea because essentially none of the pupils ever understand a word the teacher says; call me old-fashioned."

"In which case," I say, turning my back on her for a second, partly to conceal a smile and partly to make the tea, "I shall restrict my activities henceforth to gazing forlornly out of the window pending your return from foreign climes. At which point I shall be up for a trial lesson any time you fancy. Just to make sure everything is absolutely *ça va* and tickety-boo between us."

She says nothing to this and when I set the teapot down in front of her, I notice a faint flush of colour on her cheeks.

"I'm sorry," I murmur, "I've embarrassed you. *Mille excuses*, it's the flirtatious old luvvie in me."

"No need to apologise to me, Mr Robson," she smiles. "It takes one to know one."

"Call me Henry. Please."

When Matilda has drunk her tea and eaten one solitary custard cream biscuit from my antiquarian collection of two, we arrange a couple of tentative dates in the New Year and I let her out into the night again.

"Thanks for the *bonne bouche*," she says as she tucks her scarf into her collar. "I'll check those dates are alright with my husband, but otherwise I'll see you then. Wish me luck in Dubai."

"I think the phrase is 'Happy Christmas', actually."

"*Vous aussi, Monsieur.*"

I close the door quietly and listen until the clack of those torture boots fades away along the pavement. She has evidently thought better of going to the pub.

With unwonted lightness of spirit, I shimmy (or is the word sashay?) over to the stereo and press 'Play'. Ansermet and I, let loose with Offenbach's *Can-Can*, shake the cottage to its very foundations.

42

Utter Humiliation

Show time. The last day of term. My mobile rings five minutes from the School. Illegally I answer it.

"Sir?"

"Yes, Harry?"

"It's Chris, sir. Where are you, sir?"

"I'm nearly there, Chris. Two minutes. What's up?"

"We have a bit of problem, sir."

The only problems I can see concern the staging of a relatively (some of it entirely) unrehearsed pantomime at half past ten in front of three hundred and fifty pupils and staff. Nonetheless, my heart sinks. Instinct tells me that the Bad Fairy has been at it again. What has Piers been up to this time?

"I thought I'd better warn you, sir, before you go ape."

Chris is one of the many cross-dressing boys in this production (I like to see boys in touch with their feminine side) and his story is likely to be riddled with hyperbole. "I'll be there soon. Don't panic, Mr Mainwaring."

I enter my room on Red Alert with my powers of observation as honed and sharp as a coiled Cumberland sausage. What has the bloody little man thrown in my path this time? He knows there's a show in an hour and half and, according to Mr Kozhevnikov, he knows he's in it. I detect an unfamiliar breeze blowing through my normally cosy room; Chris has not been exaggerating. His 'bit of a problem' takes the shape of a burly builder in a red T-shirt. To the accompaniment of Radio 1 emitting from a plaster-spattered ghetto-blaster squatting on my desk, he has taken the liberty of tearing down a number of my expensive cinema posters, ripping off a vast swathe of my wall hangings and is now, with the aid of a heavy club-hammer, in the process of punching a man-sized hole through the outside wall.

Up to and including today, we have entered my room through two low doors and a damp antechamber. Piers had once mentioned a plan which involved sealing this off and installing a main entrance door at the far end, thereby releasing the potential of the antechamber to be turned into a wardrobe and props store. He had been characteristically specific in his requirements. "Get some costumes in there so I'll be able to come in at weekends and dress up as a woman". And who am I to deny him such innocent pleasures? But why has Piers chosen this precise moment on the last morning of term, show day, to nuke my room? I can't even be bothered to find him and make enquiries; the man does what he wants, how-when-and-where-and-to-whom he wants and without reference to anyone else. He is the outright owner of Gussage Court and therefore feels he has a right to rule his Kingdom with recourse to neither governing body nor Parent-Teachers' Association. Ofsted would find no record of any committee in Piers' realm because His word is law and committees imply democracy. The random upheaval in my room is just another straw on the camel's back.

Oddly, I am not even cross at seeing the recently sorted piles of costume scattered around the room amongst the building materials, and merely suggest to my nervous cast that we go and prepare elsewhere. I know they fear another sudden exodus on my part but they nod philosophically as I remind them that we are all inmates of The Madhouse and that we must focus up and drive the show through to the end, at which point the audience will have been:

a) given a good soaking with water guns.
b) sprayed with shaving foam and orange paint
c) dusted with flour
d) rendered delirious with mirth.

It's how it has to be.

"Sir?"

"Yes, Hamish?"

"Will it matter if we've never rehearsed in the Hall before?"

"No, Hamish. Actors can work anywhere, remember? Even in this corridor. I'm going to leave you to rehearse now – Smith's in charge. I'm busy. You've got an hour and twenty."

I remain sanguine even when I behold the Wasteland that is the Sports Hall (or Theatre) after last night's Christmas banquet. Most of the round hired tables have been folded up and Sisyphus is – rather prematurely, I feel, given my plans – hosing down the floor. Using slave labour drawn from the bands of marauding boys skiving lessons, I soon have the stage cleared of torn crackers, piles of holly and broken plastic glasses.

After forty minutes, the chairs are reset in Sisyphus's puddles for the beginning of the show and when we have nearly finished, Piers turns up clad in his absurd bearskin hat and starts barking orders. The sight of him makes my stomach flip. Pre-show adrenalin is pumping.

"Sam! Go and fetch a dustpan and brush! Aitor and Vadym, take that throne back to the Quiet Room, it cost me a fortune.

Don't drop it, you idiots!" He turns to me, beaming his naughty schoolboy smile. "Bloody children. Who'd have 'em? Masturbate and adopt, that's what I say."

"Absolutely, Headmaster."

Piers bends down to pick up a half-chewed turkey thigh and I glimpse the full glory of his bald patch under its lid. "Well, look, Mr Robson, if you've nothing to do, will you organise some of your actors to get shot of these tables?"

"Piers, I'm in the middle of setting up for a show and I have a final rehearsal running as we speak. So, er no, not really."

"Oh? Whatever."

"And don't be late for your cue, Headmaster," I add. "You'll be on at about eleven forty-five. You know what to wear, yes?"

He turns and climbs the steps to the stage. "I can't promise anything, Mr Robson. I've three boarders with visa problems to sort out. I'll be there as soon as I can." *Yes, Piers, I'm sure Mr Kozhevnikov will see to that.* "Christ knows what you said to that bloody Russian, but he's been a pain in the arse ever since. It's the last time I trust you to entertain a parent."

He wiggles his bum at me and disappears out of sight behind the curtain.

As promised, by eleven-forty, the soaked audience is hysterical and ripe for anarchy. The pandemonium only increases when Abanazar strides on stage decked out in a monstrous seven foot-six gold costume with long black beard and wig; with flagrant disregard for thematic authenticity, our baddie is accompanied by three rat-like creatures who drag their tails through the remnants of the slosh scene.

"Ladies and Gentlemen," crows Abanazar in an unmistakably Chechen accent, "I am Abanazar, the Wicked Wizard of the East!" (Boos and hisses from all). "Pray silence for our first special guest, all the way from the magic Kingdom of Gussage: Baron Hardup!"

There are shouts of glee as, mercifully bang on cue, Piers

minces onstage. He is sporting a curly white wig, but I'm a little disappointed to notice that the baronial outfit I'd hired for him from London makes hardly any difference to him at all: he looks just the same as he does when presiding over any grand School occasion – like an anachronistic twat. A large sign marked 'Barbara's Barbershop' is wheeled on behind him; one of the rats supplies a chair.

"I say, I say, tall gold person, do you know a cheap barber?" recites Piers, reading his lines from inside his three-cornered hat. "I'm in need of a shave but have not a penny on me."

"Take a seat, Baron," booms Abanazar. "Ladies and Gentlemen, I'm sorry to hear that Baron Hardup finds himself in financial difficulties. Look," he shouts, grabbing an empty leather purse from the Baron's belt and waving it at the audience, "the poor old boy cannot even afford a shave."

"Aaaaaaahhhh," encourage the rats.

"Shall we shave him for free today, Ladies and Gentlemen? Shall we?"

From my position at the back of the Sports Hall (or Theatre), I would hazard a guess that the audience thinks they should. A rat brings on an enormous plastic basin of shaving foam, adds a few squirts of orange paint I've stolen from the art room and positions himself with a large paintbrush beside the Baron. The audience is going mad and I fear for the radio-mikes.

"First, we must foam him up properly," roars Abanazar. "You, Ratty One, apply the shaving cream!"

Piers is beginning to look uncomfortable, but one of the rats leans over his shoulder and whispers something reassuring in his ear. The School roar delightedly as their headmaster's physiognomy disappears behind a cloud of orange foam.

Someone jogs my elbow. It is Matron.

"Mr Robson, is that you under that wig? What the bloody hell's going on? I can hear this din in my office." The penny drops. "Oh Christ, is that Piers up there?"

"'Fraid so, Matron. Aren't you proud of him?"

"Well, I'll be buggered."

"Shush now, Matron, I'm nearly on. Is my wig straight?"

"Very sexy, Mr Robson, very sexy." She squeezes my right boob and sees what I'm holding. "What the hell are you doing with that, Mr Robson? You can't use that! Piers'll kill you."

"Not if I kill him first."

Abanazar strides downstage; for a Chief of Police, Mr K is splendidly camp.

"Ladies and Gentlemen," he bellows, "now is time to welcome today's second special guest. All the way from the backstreets of Bridlington, please welcome Barbara, the Buxom Blonde Barber of Balaclava!" (My geography becomes a little unsteady when being blackmailed into writing cheap alliteration).

I storm forward, brandishing Matron's treasured samurai sword aloft, my enormous bosom gyrating before me. The crowd cheers and yells. Riding on this wave of adulation and with my pink flowery dress billowing behind me, I leap onto the stage and skid to a halt beside Piers.

"Oo, 'ullo, is this the one, Mr Ave-a-banana?" I squawk.

"Indeed it is, dear lady," he replies, squeezing my left breast. I slap his hand away.

"A freebee for you, is it, love?" I pout at my employer. "A quick shave and a short back-and-sides for the noble Baron?"

"Just get on with it, you bloody luvvie," Piers spits gobs of foam into the audience. "I've just about had enough of this nonsense." I'm not sure the Baron is entirely in character; it's a mercy we haven't miked him up. I appeal to the audience.

"Shall I shave him? Shall I?"

Their response being volubly in the affirmative, I pull the samurai from its scabbard and brandish its gleaming blade in front of Piers' face. The audience is baying for stage blood and Piers is sitting very still indeed, leagues out of his comfort zone, staring at the weapon. Although I feel Mr Kozhevnikov's eyes boring into me, I reckon it would be counter-productive to maim or slay a Headmaster in front of so many witnesses; I settle instead for gingerly pretending to shave him with the four foot blade. Piers trembles as the steel passes up and down his cheeks. Large blobs of orange foam plop onto the floor. Two rats close in behind him.

"All done!" I whoop as I flick a spotty handkerchief from my bosom and wipe the remains of the foam from Piers' chin. I hand the sword to the nearest rat. "And now for a haircut, Baron! Off with his wig, Ratty!"

The left hand rat grabs the Baron's powdered wig. As anticipated, the comb-over pings up into a manic cockatoo quiff, and the School erupts. Piers screams inaudibly, struggles to get up, but is pinned into his seat by the rats. Abanazar steps forward once again and holds up his hand for quiet.

"Baron Hardup, or should I say? – Mr Halliday," he begins in a dreadful voice, "the time has come to show you how we do things in my country, in Chechnya. Public humiliation is not something we encourage, but when people go too far, as you have done on so many occasions, Mr Halliday, they must be taught a lesson. It is a matter of honour."

Ratty Three brings Piers' heaving and twisting under control by holding the sword to his throat.

"You went too far," the Chief of Police goes on, "when you made my son stand on that box at Speech Day last summer. He was humiliated and ashamed." The first rat removes his headgear to reveal Yuri, our diminutive erstwhile Head of School. A half-hearted cheer goes up. "You went too far again when on the same occasion you declared Johannes to be the fattest boy in the School." To another demi-ovation, the second, more portly rat removes his disguise. "Gunter, whom you humiliated as being the only gay in the School is unable to be here because, guess what? – he is opening his very own wine bar in Hamburg this evening. But he sends his best wishes. However, Wolfhart, whom you so roughly pulled to the ground and dragged out of the church last year is here to say hullo as well."

"Hullo, Sir," says Wolfhart in his high German voice. "How are you feeling *now*?"

"You're all traitors," mouths Piers, his eyes blazing. "I'll pay you back, every one of you. Can no-one take a bloody *joke*?"

"Silence, Mr Halliday," commands Mr Kozhevnikov. "It is time to show you how we respond to public humiliation in our countries. You will perhaps now think twice before you dishonour your pupils in front of their friends, their teachers and even their parents." My blackmailer turns to me and I register that dark spot in his eye again. My moment has come. "Barbara! To work!" he intones. I obey, reaching into my cleavage and pulling out a large pair of fluorescent green plastic scissors. I hold them aloft for all to see. "Snip, snip, woman!"

I pass behind Piers and his ratty oppressors and grab the trademark hank of lacquered hair between my left thumb and index finger. With flamboyant exaggeration I make much of snipping it off. The crowd is still cheering, but with a little less enthusiasm. Squawking like a fish-wife and snipping away with my harmless shears, I am now so involved in my Commedia dell'Arte version of Sweeney Todd that I am not on the ball enough to stop Wolfhart shooting a hand under my left arm, and with the deft application of an enormous pair of steel carpet cutters, snipping through the hank of hair that I am holding. Abanazar immediately grabs my left arm and we jointly brandish the wodge of now ownerless hair. With an inward shriek of horror, I wrench my arm from the Police Chief's grip, stunned and powerless in the face of the act to which I have been party. This wasn't in my script. This hasn't happened, can't be happening. I'm not this vindictive and cruel. I'm just a failed actor and drama teacher. And here's the proof: I had insisted on all four of us rehearsing the barbershop scene together with the current Head of School sitting in for Piers; it was never in the plan to go the whole way. Plastic scissors were

Kozhevnikov's idea, a jolly jape, a joke, a parable for Piers. I had been used as a pawn in someone else's petty melodrama and we had all gone too far. This was supposed to be a British public school panto, for god's sake, not *The Revenger's Tragedy*. I look down at the pale shining pate open to the elements for the first time.

"Piers!" I yell, "I'm sorry, this wasn't meant to happen!"

"Fuck off, you treacherous cunt!" he hisses. Released by the rats, he stumbles towards the stage door. Is he crying? A few younger members of the audience begin to applaud and are shushed by their form-teachers. Still holding the hank of hair, I turn to follow Piers. But Kozhevnikov and a gaggle of hefty Chechens, Kazakhs and Georgians (who have appeared seemingly from nowhere) block my way.

"Move, you bastards," I bark, "let me through!" My wig has fallen off, taking the radio mike with it. I feel it crunch under my high heel. My assailants move in and I am grabbed by a dozen arms and pinioned against the back wall. Laughing, one of the boys pummels my boobs like a punch-bag.

"Mr Robson," says Mr Kozhevnikov, smiling calmly and steering me downstage, "we have something for you." The audience is silent now and I sense hostility. "Ladies and Gentlemen," smirks my tormentor, "if I may quote for you the legend of this samurai sword: *In the battles of old, leaders were given swords representing the passing of a war.* Today, in witnessing the restitution of our honour, we have, in our own small way, seen the passing of just such a war. Mr Robson, you have been our inspiration." *Oh please!* "To you therefore shall pass the sword. Irakli and Yuri, my dear sons, please do Mr Robson the honour." The two lads come forward holding the sword between them. Absurdly, they kneel before me and proffer the ridiculous weapon. I look beyond its blade and lock eyes with Smith, one of my best and most stalwart actors, now sitting slumped with his feet dangling over the edge of the stage. He is staring at me in appalled disbelief; almost imperceptibly he shakes his head. I have always respected Smith's steady influence and, now that I am on my way out, I will do *him* the honour of not disappointing him further. I accept the sword and drop it over the edge of the stage onto the concrete floor below where its blade shatters into three pieces. Cheap reproduction shit, typical of Piers. I chuck the flap of hair down onto it, nod curtly to the silent School and walk back upstage. This time, the cast stand aside to let me through.

"Are you satisfied now, Mr Kozhevnikov?" I ask quietly. "If I missed anything out, I'll just have to risk your displeasure and take whatever's coming to me. I've deserved it."

"Mr Robson," he smiles, "you have given me more than you know. Honour is satisfied. And, by the way, I sent your agent the package yesterday. You didn't let us down. I knew you wouldn't. Actors can be so cruel, can they not? Happy Christmas." He reaches out his hand. It seems best to shake it, under the circumstances.

In the unearthly silence that now hangs about the Sports Hall (or Theatre), I grab the bag of my belongings I'd left with rare prescience behind the stage door and walk to my car as swiftly as I can in boobs and high heels. Pupils and staff look away as I drive for the last time round the cedar tree and back towards the Village of the Damned.

43

Additional Humiliation

 Pauline, my First Mother, dies in Exmouth Hospital on Boxing Day. I spend the last six shopping days before Christmas either keeping Len company in the flat or at Pauline's bedside where, in moments of consciousness, she holds my hand and repeatedly apologises for having 'caught this bloody liver cancer' which would, she said, if the docs were to be believed, severely curtail our acquaintance. I am transfixed by how her wasted body hardly makes an indentation in the hospital mattress; she had been all skin and bones five months ago when I first set eyes on her, but now she is almost translucent: not translucent enough for me to glean many last-minute details from her about the soldier-boy who had done so much to beget me on the top deck of that double-decker bus, but enough for her to be able to murmur "Darling, I know what you want me to talk about, but we're not going to go into that now, I'm too tired. His name was David, I think. Will that do? I'm sorry. Oh – *bottoms!*" she adds as a

spasm of pain shoots through her distended abdomen. "But tell me about you, dear heart. Are you still being Mummy's naughty schoolboy?"

"I don't think Mummy's going to be too pleased with my end-of term report," I say, stroking her arm. "I've been having adventures," and during her more lucid moments, I entertain her with epic tales of honour and revenge and of my subsequent plummet from Grace.

Len and I miss her last breath, of course, because at about the time of her passing I am pleading for clemency and ingress with the disembodied voice of the hospital authorities at a non-functioning car-park barrier. By the time I have clambered out of the car and persuaded everyone queuing behind me to reverse so that we can all make use of an adjacent and less temperamental entrance, the moment has passed and all that is left of my First Mother when we arrive on the ward is a scurrying of nurses, the rattle of trolley wheels and the squeak of the sponge as her name is rubbed off the whiteboard.

The funeral is delayed for three weeks for reasons beyond both my comprehension and control. Paperwork, Bank Holidays and a backlog of Christmas cadavers are cited, but finally, towards the middle of January, I find myself sitting in a gloomy church behind Len, Ken and Beryl. To my left is Pauline's sister June and beyond her an older brother called Derek who declines to acknowledge me, despite our obvious physical similarities. Up in the pulpit, a tubby little vicar haltingly improvises a eulogy based upon a sheet of notes supplied, so Ken tells me, by Derek. I listen attentively to see how the family will deal with the Bogey in the Woodpile sitting in the second row.

According to the vicar, Pauline met Len in July 1958 and began a whirlwind romance with him which culminated in their marriage a mere two months later. I switch off as he witters on about their long, happy and childless married life together because I am considering whether now would be the moment to stand up on the pew and denounce the idiot for misleading the congregation. "Dearly beloved," I would declare, bounding forward, grabbing Christ's unfortunate little jobsworth by the cassock and lobbing the sack of guts into the choir stalls. "Dearly beloved, how differently would you all feel about Pauline were I to tell you that the most important moment in her life occurred not in September 1958 but eight months before when she gave birth to a baby boy called Keith?" With manly cries of 'Who is this impostor?' and 'Shame on you!' a gaggle of the good burghers of Exmouth gather up their swooning womenfolk and herd them outside. "Ladies and gentlemen," I boom, bringing to bear all the under-used acting skills at my disposal, "despite the fact that I sport no moustache and have been living all my life under an assumed identity, I am here to tell you that I am that baby boy, Keith. Also –" I raise my clenched fist and bring it down with a dusty thud on the bible before me, "I refuse to be airbrushed out of history by those amongst you, Derek Davies, who are too ashamed to forgive my mother her one mistake, to acknowledge her immense courage. Ladies and Gentlemen, compare my face to my two uncles' if you don't believe me!"

A babble of eager conversation breaks out at this point and the uncles are forcibly turned about so that the curiosity of the congregation, voracious for fresh gossip, can be sated. And then, Len makes his move. Now doubly distraught with grief and repentance, he rises unsteadily to his feet. "We should have raised the lad together, Pauline," he sobs, prostrating himself upon his wife's coffin. "Forgive me, my darling! Forgive me, Henry!"

In reality, when I see how the cookie is crumbling, I resort to being stiff-upper-lip British and a moral coward, merely pulling up my coat collar and slumping lower into my pew. For once, I am electing to remain stoic; surely on such an occasion, it's all right to allow the truth to be suppressed out of sympathy for grieving family members? After all, the preposterous misinformation being pedalled from the pulpit is painful only to me, and I'm sure I'll be able to man up and absorb what is only another low blow in a series of recent realignments to my ego.

Ken grips my shoulder as we follow the coffin out into the cold winter light. "Don't let it worry you, Henry," he says. "It's not worth upsetting the chicken coop."

44

Total Humiliation

I see Valerie approaching before she sees me. My guts immediately twist and grind as the not too distant memories of love and hurt, frustration and sorrow, mingle and meld deep inside me, but short of throwing myself under a parked car or burying myself crab-like in a skip, there is nowhere to hide.

When I had apprised my neighbour Jo of the news that Valerie and I were no longer an item, she took the opportunity of speaking frankly to me: "Darling Henry," she announced, "Val was nothing but an ugly little troll. Have a cup of tea and give me a hug, you stupid great wanker."

Having not seen my ex-lover for a month, I am surprised at how short she is, but I find her neither ugly nor troll-like. To what I had hoped by now would be an almost objective eye, she is still lovely, albeit not quite as lovely as I had remembered. She wears achingly familiar clothes and is carrying the wicker basket I used to carry; it is full of organic goodies from the church where they hold the farmers' market we used to visit together. In my refusal to change my routines to avoid her, I am on my way to the same market. It's Thursday and buggered if I'm going to give up for her my source of local veg and those delicious little French tartlets.

"So," she smiles, "how are you? You're looking really – so much older."

"Thanks," I say. "I'm fine." I'll not be giving her the opportunity to crow over Pauline's demise.

"Are you happy?"

"Yeah, how about you?"

"I'm good."

"Excellent."

"I'm over you, Henry," she smirks tightly. "I've got a new lover now. He's a keen yachtsman. I met him quite by chance right here in the market. He bought me a coffee just before Christmas. He has children at a school nearby."

"Oh." My heart lurches. She really has moved on.

The church clock lugubriously bongs the half hour. A kernel of immense sadness stubbornly takes shape in my middle, making it hard to acknowledge that I am witnessing both the death and burial of our liaison. But even at the point of its demise, my obsession aches to tell her that despite all the misery and pain, despite all the misunderstandings, I will always love her. I despise myself for being so deeply pathetic and hope I can avoid crying before we part.

"You've been wanting to get rid of me for months, and now you're free," she says, apparently enjoying herself. "Are you happy now or will you remain guilty to the end of your days?"

"I'm happy for *you*," I lie. I feel as if someone has pulled the plug out of my bath. My grip on the enamel is slipping and I am about to be sucked down into a void of indefinite and hopeless misery, solitude and joblessness. Tussling with an overwhelming sense of pathos, I attempt a rally: "Does this sailor-boy of yours own a yacht, then?"

"Actually, he has two. I've just spent a week with him on the Black Sea." Yes, I can see him now, standing proudly on his poop deck with an arm around his prize, a rich city slicker running to fat in his spotty sailor's cravat, checked Viyella shirt, pink mariner's trousers and deck shoes. He looks a bit like Piers, come to think of it, but without the comb-over. (But wait – Piers no longer has one of those, does he?) What the hell does Valerie see in *him*?

"Two yachts?" I consider how to respond and choose the vindictive route: "You *have* done well."

A familiar little ice cloud forms between us.

"It's not a question of doing well, Henry. It's a question of trying to be happy with someone."

"And are you? With him? Happy?"

"Yes." She shakes her hair ecstatically and smiles up at me. "I even like penetration with him."

I pause and blink twice as her comment thumps me in the side of the head like an organic marrow thrown at high velocity during a Harvest Festival brawl. I nod to an old lady I recognise as she potters by with her tartan shopping trolley and try to eradicate a couple of images which flash into my mind from Mr Kozhevnikov's video.

"My heart rejoices for you," I declare breezily. "I'm sure one day I too will have a normal and sexually fulfilling relationship just like yours."

She pauses to digest any possible latex-laden subtext I may have laid here. "You'll soon find someone else to shag," she comments airily, putting her basket down on the verge. "You should market yourself around the village:

Ladies, the Panto's over … !
But call Henry Robson
any time for a private audience.

See how many more marriages you can destroy with your rampant need for sex and intrigue."

I take a breath; there mustn't be shouting. "I've had enough lonely nights to work us out, Valerie. I realise that you and I have absolutely no affinity. Donal and I were talking about it."

"Oh, so you 'asked a friend'? How brave." She glances at her watch. "You're just a failed specialist in the art of melodrama," she sneers, "you don't actually want a stable relationship at all. You thrive on all this nonsense. Don't let your next conquest get her hopes up or make any plans. You know what you're like." She flicks her hair back again. "I loved you, Henry, but you weren't interested."

"If I thought it would do any good I'd suggest you go home and re-read my letter – if you didn't burn it."

"Actually, Mister Little-Boy-Lost, I tore it up and flushed it down the toilet." She sighs and plucks absently at my sleeve, just as she used to. "I heard you lost your job. I'm sorry."

"I didn't lose it. I left it. I felt it was the only honourable thing to do."

"Very noble, Henry. Noble and honourable." She places a particular emphasis on this last word and I am reminded of someone. Who is it?

"Did you hear about Piers?" I plough on, having no time to think right now. "He sold up and bought a beef farm in southern Africa. He emailed me to say that my appalling conduct gave him just the impetus he'd been waiting for. Also, he says, foreign cows don't answer back."

Valerie seems suddenly not to be listening; she looks at her watch again and glances almost nervously up and down the street.

"Going somewhere?" I enquire. "Got a yacht to catch?" She flashes me one of her speciality withering looks that I know so well; things are about to turn nasty again. Time to draw the encounter to a close. "Well, it's been a joy. Must be off or I'll miss all the homemade cakes."

"Oh, Henry, don't be like that. Give me a hug. Just for old times' sake."

I put my arms about her and give her a token squeeze – the same scent, the same slim waist and unyielding shoulders – and then, on a sudden impulse to say farewell properly, I lift her off her feet as I used to in the old days; I don't think she ever found it patronising, but who can say? Having put her down, I look into her eyes, searching in vain for some sign of fondness or regret. I try to control my breathing as we kiss each other chastely on the cheek.

"Goodbye, Henry. You'll never see me again. I'm moving away next week. My lover wants me – me and Millie – to get to know his two sons and – ,"

"– *Great!*" I interrupt. "That makes me feel a million times better about myself. How lovely for you all. One big happy step-family. Another sailing holiday?"

"Actually, if you want me to spell it out, I'm going to live with him. During term-time at least. He has a villa outside Grozny. He's quite high up in the Chechen security services." She picks up her basket. "Goodbye, Henry."

My world stands still as the rouble drops through the hole in the bottom of my life. A familiar long black limo sweeps slowly by and stops beside her. A chauffeur opens the back door and a young girl jumps out and flings her arms around her mother. A suave and equally familiar figure in a camel coat emerges, kisses Valerie's hand and fondly strokes Millie's cheek. After a short conference, they all turn to face me; Valerie smiles and waves, Millie adopts that 'what-the-hell?' face that teenagers do so effortlessly, and Mr Kozhevnikov inclines his smug little head. A moment later, the chauffeur steps round the back of the car, pauses to let a motorbike go past and looks across at me. With a triumphant smirk, the man lifts an imaginary camera to his eye, mimes taking my picture, and gives me the thumbs up.

"You know what, Henry," I hear myself croak as I turn and

head for the church, "you've been royally fucked over here." I quicken my pace. "But I really wish you luck with her, Mr Kozhevnikov. All strength to your elbow, old boy. You'll be needing it."

At the church porch, I know for certain that I won't be able to cope just now with the jolly banter of the organic meat woman whose stall will be just inside the door. My eyes are stinging and something terrible is welling up inside me. I turn instead to the left and stumble round to a secluded spot under the east window and flop down on the damp grass between a gravestone and a flint buttress. I lean back and close my eyes. Has the naughty schoolboy been punished enough yet for his self-centred and rampant behaviour? Are my buttocks sore enough from the slippering meted out, and if so, would this be a good moment to stop flailing about and start behaving instead more like a grown-up? Perhaps now I should try for a better end-of-term report, one of which everyone – even my lost Mummy – can be proud.

My lips begin to tremble and I allow myself at last to fall into the waiting pit of despair, engulfed by a crescendo of grief and self-pity wrought by loss, humiliations and disappointments both public and private. Startled by a sound somewhere between a sob and a howl, a thrush interrupts the rhythmical smashing of a snail against a rock and flies off, the remains of its victim curling and twisting in its shattered shell.

45

To Affinity and Beyond

The following Monday morning I am wondering whether to invite Barbara and Daphne in for tea or not when the phone rings. I am not in the bath because daytime ablutions, together with many other tendencies pertaining to fretful middle age, have been banned.

"*Bonjour, Henri, c'est moi.* Matilda."

Unaccountably, my spirits lift. "Why, *bonjour* to you, Madame. I'm sorry about the hiatus in my curriculum planning, but I have become more than usually the victim of circumstance since your departure for Dubai."

"I got your messages and yup, your Christmas sounds almost as jolly as mine. I'm sorry to hear about your Mamma."

"Don't worry, I've still got a spare one in reserve."

She pauses for a second. "Though I cudgel my brains, Henry, witty response comes there none." I love the way she talks.

"Remind me to bore you to death sometime about my interesting origins," I reply, "and on behalf of the Village of the Damned, allow me to welcome you back to beleaguered old Blighty. How is life in the hot-*air* business or are you in no *condition* to tell me? How was Christmas? A *breeze*?" I have been working on these gems for weeks.

"Hot air is endemic in you men, Henry," she laughs. "My husband's certainly full of it. *And* hot air. Is Thursday still okay?"

"I'll have the kettle on."

"Earl Grey this time, please."

That Matilda is *très snob* about tea is a source of great joy to me. I know she adores Bach too. Lapsang souchong, Earl Grey and the Mass in B Minor are absolute necessities in her life whilst Rock Music, Modern Jazz and pretty much anything plinkety-plonk or crunchy composed since 1880, she tells me, is anathema.

During the following two weeks, Matilda comes for three hour-long French lessons, behaving like a model student and beavering away in a manner calculated to impress any Head of Department with an eye to productivity and top grades. She sits attentively with her long legs crossed under the table and hangs on my every word as I meander through my checklist of *avoir* and *être*, the *passé composé* and *l'imparfait*, linguistic hurdles to be jumped before any self-respecting GCSE can be attained. Matilda writes down all my pearls in green ink on a large pad of yellow A4 paper. I have never seen such a thing before and am fascinated that she should take such notice of my wafflings. Half way through lesson three, I feel she is sufficiently confident to be able to broach the occasionally tricksy areas of Need and Necessity in French.

Example numéro 1

Il faut prendre une tasse de thé:
I/you/they/we all must have a cup of tea.

Example numéro 2

Il lui faut une conversation importante:
He/she needs an important conversation.

Example numéro 3

Il me faut de la passion dans la vie:
I need passion in my life.

Also, in the case of a satisfactory and adoring lover, *il m'en faut une* eftsoons and right speedily. You understand the basics.

My pupil seems to be absolutely *dans le marché* for discussing Life and its disappointments with me (especially in French, the traditional language of love) and I positively bound around my tiny kitchen in my enthusiasm for the topic, having found, or so it seems, an equally unhappy, like-minded and similarly dissatisfied person with whom to discuss the topic of misery in another tongue. I deluge her with details about my own terminally tempestuous non-relationship with Valerie, and in return she tells me how her single-mindedly dreary husband has made a mockery of her maternal instincts by refusing to abandon the prophylactic, prioritising instead his dogged ambition to build and maintain a splendidly isolationist 'his and hers' career structure; his, as has already been revealed, in the supply and maintenance of air conditioning units in far-flung places, and hers in the British Council.

Her speciality had been to organise visits to Spain by world-class artistes and to produce colourful educational packs about them for local children: industrial-scale patronisation of the under-privileged native with the wonders of late Beethoven string quartets. However, having taken the rap for having supposedly mislaid an eminent young conductor for a whole night in the back streets of Sevilla, she had finally thrown in the cultural sponge and taken up a post as a Modern Languages teacher at the *combien prestigieuse* St Antony's School on the outskirts of our very own Village of the Damned. In her excellent-if-rusty French, Matilda leaves me in no doubt that the current twin marital bed arrangements (her husband's in

Clapham, hers in darkest Wessex) are conducive neither to making babies nor to marital harmony. I try suggesting that living alone *dans le Village des Condamnés* is *quand même* better than sleeping alone in Madrid, but she is not convinced.

In my turn, I feel able to reveal to her why my not entirely dissimilar relationship with Lucy came unstuck a lifetime ago. What I begin to understand is that Matilda and I both crave affection and companionship and both suffer from the onset of spiritual desiccation; but whereas I am becoming mildewed at the soft centre of a chocolate box village, she fears becoming stranded in the midst of an air-conditioned desert of hot sand, concrete, glass and steel.

Now and again, in an attempt to lower the emotional temperature of the lesson, I feel it professionally prudent to try to regain a certain level of banality:

"*Alors, Madame, qu'est-ce que vous avez reçu comme cadeau de Noël de votre mari?*"

"*Normalement* il me donne un ..." She stops and gazes wistfully towards the church. "Normally he gives me a winter woollie. He rolls into the first shop he comes across on his way back to the station late on Christmas Eve. And because he's invariably drunk by then, he panics and buys the brightest one he can find." She looks suddenly very bleak. "This year, however, his present came as a real surprise."

"Ah," I mouth, "congratulations on your new camel." I am jumping to a defeatist conclusion and resorting to stock racism in an effort to disguise a sudden and absurd stab of jealousy tinged with regret.

"You're on the right lines," she says. "We were sitting in the hotel bar and he gave me an enormous fruit cocktail and an envelope containing the lease for a bloody apartment on the twenty-second floor of his new complex. An executive suite with double water bed and *en suite* bar plus his and hers jacuzzis."

I feel sick. "That sounds lovely." I try an encouraging smile but my cheek muscles have atrophied.

"He's decided to rent out the house in the village, but the London flat's sold and the furniture's being shipped out next week. They told him they were closing the London office and if he wanted to keep his job he'd have to up sticks to Dubai. Chance of a lifetime thing. 'And don't worry about what you'll do all day,' he said to me, 'there's plenty of tennis and bridge parties to keep the little memsahib occupied.'"

I am numb. "When are you leaving?"

"There's something else, Henry," she goes on quietly. "I was at a New Year's drinks party and guess what happened."

"You have me at a disadvantage, Madame."

"I overheard one of the company *grands fromages* begging him to reconsider his decision to move to Dubai. 'Sure we can't persuade you to stay in London?' the guy said. 'The office really needs you'."

"Ah."

"The spineless little tosser had made the whole thing up just to get his own way. He knew I'd never agree to it."

"*Je vois,*" I transliterate.

She pours herself another cup of Earl Grey. "It was his turn to be surprised when I wished him all the best for the future and packed my bag. 'Just as well you didn't sell the country cottage too,' I said. "Your ex-wife will be needing somewhere to live.'"

I get up ostensibly to refill the teapot but mostly because if I sit stupidly opposite her, Matilda will notice tell-tale flutterings above my left temple.

As Garrison Keillor might put it, 'It has been a quiet week in the Village of the Damned'. A dusting of snow lies upon the Green and I have lit a fire to keep me company as I scan through the 'Situations Vacant' columns in the *Wessex Week*. The phone rings and makes me jump. Matilda is due after lunch: don't say she's cancelling.

"*Bonjour, Monsieur le professeur!*" she bubbles. "Listen,

the fact is that I may have been less than discreet in the staff room and I'm afraid word has got out about your plight."

"Oh god, you've not booked me a session in the village stocks, have you?"

"D'you feel you deserve it?" I can *hear* her arching an eyebrow. "No, the Deputy Head says she wants to see you about a new Initiative the school governors are brewing. Something to do with recruiting an Actor in Residence. The job has your name on it."

My heart leaps. "But St Antony's has an actual functioning drama department with a real theatre, doesn't it, with lights and curtains and dressing rooms and *everything*?" *What a woman.* "I can't tell you how grateful I am."

"I've told them I'm sure you'll be able to rise above the dysfunctional challenges of Gussage Court to the world of high-pressure professional education."

"Ma chère Madame Mathilde, I'm sure I can manage something! Bring me the details later and we can discuss everything."

"Everything, Henry. I can't wait."

"*Vous vous moquez de moi, Madame?*"

"*Pas du tout, Monsieur.* I'll see you later."

I have hoovered, plumped the cushions and wiped the table down. The sun is shining and the snow is melting. My pen, pad of paper and Collins-Robert English-French/French-English Dictionary for Big Learners are poised ready for action, as are the kettle and the loose leaf Earl Grey. According to the church clock at the top of the Green, it is two twenty-one. I consider opening the front door and leaning nonchalantly against the frame in anticipation of Matilda's arrival, but she might think it *de trop* and passers-by would talk. I stand instead at the window admiring the endlessly pleasing chocolate-box view. The phone rings.

"Hello?" I chirrup.

"Henry, darling, it's Kate," screams the over-projected vocal training of an outraged actress. "For Christ's sake, where are you?"

"Hi, Kate," I quip, "I'm right here at home. You rang my number, old girl. What's the problem? Are we still meeting tomorrow?"

"*Fuck!* Henry! It's now! Didn't you get my email? You were supposed to be at the Charing Cross Hotel an hour ago. What are you playing at?"

I am still an inept amateur when it comes to electronic mail. Perhaps I had just not opened, or sent to 'Junk', or maybe simply forgotten the content of an email from Kate confirming the date for a Murder Mystery in London due to start not tomorrow as I had thought but in forty-three minutes time, at least three hours away.

"Oh my god, Kate, I'm sorry," I moan.

Someone knocks at the door and, still on the phone, I open it to let Matilda in. Today she is wearing a creamy silk scarf and a black leather jacket and looks fabulous. Her smile fades as she sees my face.

"Don't worry your little head about it, Henry," snaps Kate, seeing that I have completely screwed up by being a luddite wanker. "We'll cover your part somehow. It'll be fine. Gotta go."

"I'm so sorry –" I begin, but the line is dead.

I look at Matilda and usher her through the low door and into the kitchen.

"Mind your head," I whisper, leaning against the counter, not daring to meet her gaze. I feel sick and foolish; I have never before messed up so spectacularly on one of my increasingly rare acting engagements; Kate will never employ me again and Agent P will take a dim view, despite the fact that my BBC jam-acting piece is to be aired at the end of the month. I go through the motions of making tea and describe to Matilda what has happened; I speak in English, because I shall never charge her for this lesson. Carefully, I put the tea-cosy over the pot and when I turn round, she is looking at me with an expression in her eyes which tells me that I have no need to explain myself any more. She puts down her yellow pad on top of my Collins and takes a step towards me, her leather jacket creaking slightly as she breathes.

My heart is suddenly quiet. "I need a hug," I say.

I wonder whether it is in the remit of Benign Destiny to allow everyone at some point in their lives to find themselves in the happy position of becoming entwined with the right person. Clues to affinity between you and your partner of choice can be found in various felicitous manifestations: your respective heights seem to be in the right proportion, any cultural divide you may have been used to in the past is non-existent, and your pheromones seem to bond and chatter affectionately with each other like long-lost friends at a school reunion. When spotted in the wild, an affinity like this is so astoundingly refreshing and easy to appreciate that you can't imagine how or why you felt the need to pretend you were happy with anyone else ever before.

I wax lyrical merely to prepare you for the news that Matilda omits to say, as I take her in my arms, "Don't, Henry, you're in my space". Instead, we cling to each other for a long while before our lips find their soul-mates and our bodies meld into a liquid embrace.

As we come up for breath, Matilda smiles and looks into my eyes and my world becomes warmer and softer and quieter.

"I hope this means you're going to take me to bed," she says.

Acknowledgements

There are a number of people who, in an ideal world, would be paid vast amounts of money for the time, care and expertise they have put into this book on my behalf. The cheaper option, however, is to mention them **in bold** in a roll of honour and to assure them of my gratitude for their unstinting friendship, encouragement and support.

Roll of Honour

Donal Walsh, as may have been gleaned from a perusal of the preceding pages, is an old friend of mine. He it was who, in a restaurant in Pimlico five years ago, made the gentle enquiry: "And what do you hope to achieve with this writing, Tim?" He does indeed possess a colossal brain, and is someone whose opinion I value so highly that I willingly sat at his feet three years later whilst he painstakingly slashed at an early draft with an HB pencil. Amidst scenes of Irish ribaldry at my expense, whole chapters were lost that evening.

Although not in my presence, **Charlie Hartley** did the same thing and made some outstandingly useful suggestions, all of which I followed.

Crispin Caldicott, sitting and scratching himself thoughtfully somewhere in New Zealand, penned a two thousand-word critique of an early-to-middle draft. I realise, having just glanced through his words again, that he was uncannily prescient in all he said.

Katrina Lesaux read it, giggled, and rightly took issue with (amongst other things) the excessive use of the word 'discombobulate'.

Jo Thompson, **Kate Plantin** and **Roger Williams** suffered even earlier versions but came through the experience with nothing but cheerful and constructive comments.

Pascale Hugues, Miranda McIntyre, **Pauline Asper**, **Luke Smith** and **Vicki Ireland** have also made more than enthusiastic noises.

The Prize for Extreme Excitability, however, is awarded to the voracious **Mel Bourne** who insisted on reading a recent draft on her iPhone during a two-day bath.

Thanks too must go to **Jennifer Camilleri,** the whirlwind Picture Librarian at the Royal Academy in London who arranged permissions for the reproduction of my favourite picture, the Waterhouse Mermaid.

This roll of honour would not be complete without mentioning **Amy Statham, Aimee Bell**, **Rachel Gregory** and **Rosie Grindrod**, the admirable ladies at Matador who have patiently withstood and occasionally realigned some of my more unreasonable demands. Without their calm enthusiasm, this project would never have been realised.

It may have come to the attention of the reader that the book is affectionately dedicated to my wife **Julie**. She has endured years of authorial rantings, crises of confidence, mood-swings and the general bad temper of a husband at war with his computer. She it was who, at Dolphin Dave's (a lonely clifftop cabin in Cornwall), and in the teeth of a husband's outraged ego, sensitively steered plot and character, removed myriad inconsistencies and soothed the addled brow. It is to her that I owe the deepest debt of gratitude – for being kind enough to laugh at stories she has heard so many times before.